Topography of Terror

Topography of Terror

Gestapo, SS and
Reichssicherheitshauptamt
on the
»Prinz-Albrecht-Terrain«
A Documentation

Edited by Reinhard Rürup

Translated from the German edition
by Werner T. Angress

Verlag Willmuth Arenhövel

Organizer: Berliner Festspiele GmbH
Intendant Dr. Ulrich Eckhardt
Deputy Manager: Andreas Nachama
Commissioned by the Berlin Senate
for the 750 Year Celebration 1987

Direction:
Reinhard Rürup

Academic Collaborators:
Frank Dingel, Thomas Friedrich, Klaus Hesse

Academic Advisors:
Wolfgang Scheffler, Gerhard Schoenberner

Topography of Terror:
Gestapo, SS and Reichssicherheitshauptamt on the "Prinz-Albrecht-Terrain" — A Documentation

Provisional Building adjacent to the Martin-Gropius-Bau, Stresemannstrasse 110, 1000 Berlin 61
The Documentation was put together as part of the exhibition "Berlin, Berlin — The Exhibition about the History of the City" in the Martin-Gropius-Bau, and opened on July 4th, 1987.

Design of the Exhibition:
Claus-Peter Gross, Margret Schmitt

Exhibition Hall: Jürg Steiner
Mounting of the Exhibition: Museumstechnik GmbH

Photo Reproduction:
Wolfgang Krolow, Margret Nissen et al.

Arrangement of the Descriptive Plates of the Documentation:
Studio für Grossfotos Wolfgang Schackla
Gleissberg und Wittstock (typesetting)

The authors thank the following persons and institutions for their assistance and advice:
Archiv der sozialen Demokratie, Bonn; Hannah Arenhövel; Christian Axt; Joachim Baumann; Bodo-Michael Baumunk; Berlin Document Center, Berlin; Bezirksamt Kreuzberg, Stadtplanungsamt, Berlin; Hendrik Biermann; Bildarchiv Preussischer Kulturbesitz, Berlin; Bildarchiv Süddeutscher Verlag, München; Jochen Boberg; Karsten Bremer; Bundesarchiv Koblenz; Jan Foitzik; Willi Gleitze; Michael Grüttner; Falk Harnack; Brunhild Hesse; Ursula Hinkelmann; Bernhard Horstmann; Wolfgang Kaiser; Gottfried Korff; Guttaborg Kreissl; KZ-Gedenkstätte Dachau, Dachau; Landesarchiv Berlin, Berlin; Stephan Maetzel; Karen Meyer; Nordrhein-Westfälisches Hauptstaatsarchiv Düsseldorf; Marie-Louise von Plessen; Albrecht Pünder; Marianne Reiff-Hundt; Katharina Rürup; Reinold Schattenfroh; Bernhard Schneider; Heinz Schröder; Pamela Selwyn; Arnim Sürder; Hans Christian Täubrich; Johannes Tuchel; Ullstein Bilderdienst, Berlin; Marie Louise Waga; Edith Walz; Wolfgang E. Weick; Sabine Weissler; Rudi Wunderlich; Willi Zahlbaum; Zentralrat deutscher Sinti und Roma, Heidelberg

Lectorship:
Alfons Arenhövel, Michael Bollé, Jutta Kindel

Cover Arrangement:
Margret Schmitt

Production: Reiter-Druck

Typesetting: Mega-Satz-Service

Bookbinding:
Bruno Helm

All in Berlin

The cover arrangement is based on an aerial photograph of southern Friedrichstadt, taken in 1947.

Table of Contents

TRANSLATOR'S NOTE

Anybody reading the documents in this catalogue will be struck by their frequently convoluted, pedantic and otherwise graceless language. I could have tried to render the contents of the documents in a smoother, perhaps more elegant translation. This I have intentially not done. The *Schreibtischmörder* (lit. murderers sitting behind their desk, or armchair killers) from Himmler and Heydrich on down to the local Security Police or Security Service officials wrote letters and memoranda marked by bureaucratic punctiliousness, long-windedness, vicious invective, and often seemingly innocent terms that camouflaged their real meaning – extermination, murder, death. This tenor of brutality and terror which the language of these documents reflects I wanted to preserve, having tried at the same time to convey their contents clearly and unmistakably to English speaking readers.

Introduction

The Documentation "Topography of Terror" developed within the framework of the preparations for the central historical exhibition mounted in the Martin-Gropius-Bau on the occasion of the 750 Year Celebration of the City of Berlin. In conjunction with it, attention was directed to a location which was an important part of Berlin's history between 1933 and 1945. The area had been in oblivion much too long, and only within the last few years was partially restored to public consciousness.

Directly to the east of the Martin-Gropius-Bau, on a terrain bound by Prinz-Albrecht-Strasse (today Niederkirchnerstrasse), Wilhelmstrasse and Anhalter Strasse, was the location of the most dreaded institutions of terror during the "Third Reich": the Secret State Police Office, the *Reichsführer-SS* (Heinrich Himmler), his personal staff and additional prominent SS leadership agencies, the Security Service (SD) of the SS and, from 1939 on, also the headquarters of the Reich Security Main Office. The most important buildings were the former School of Industrial Arts and Crafts at Prinz-Albrecht-Strasse 8, headquarters of the Secret State Police Office, of the *Reichsführer-SS*, and subsequently also of the Reich Security Main Office; the former Hotel Prinz Albrecht at Prinz-Albrecht-Strasse 9 (the "SS-House") and the Prinz-Albrecht-Palais at Wilhelmstrasse 102 into which the Security Service of the SS moved in 1934, and where Reinhard Heydrich and subsequently Ernst Kaltenbrunner resided also as (consecutive) directors of the Reich Security Main Office.

This was an unusual concentration of power and terror most narrowly confined in one spot. But there were, of course, many other places where National Socialist crimes were planned and executed. Important decisions were made outside the jurisdiction of SS and police. Governmental ministries and other administrative agencies, leading echelons of the armed services, business enterprises, academic institutions and many others were active and sometimes even prominent participants in the oppression, persecution, exploitation and extermination of human beings within and outside the German state frontiers. The ever-expanding terror apparatus of the SS soon extended beyond the buildings on Prinz-Albrecht-Strasse and Wilhelmstrasse into other parts of the city. The principal offices of the SS were only to a limited extent located on this terrain; the important Main Economic Administrative Office [*Wirtschafts-Verwaltungshauptamt*] was in Berlin-Lichterfelde; the Inspector of the Concentration Camps had his administrative headquarters beyond the gates of the city in Oranienburg; and the Reich Security Main Office spread likewise with its numerous departments across the entire city — the "Office for Jewish Affairs" ["*Judenreferat*"] run by Adolf Eichmann, who initially had worked in the Prinz-Albrecht-Palais, was at Kurfürstenstrasse 115–116.

Nevertheless, it is justified to call the "Prinz-Albrecht-Terrain" the actual administrative center of the SS-State. Here was Heinrich Himmler's headquarters where he functioned in his capacity as *Reichsführer-SS* and Head of the German Police until his appointment as

Reich Minister of the Interior in 1943. Here the "Special Units" [*Einsatzgruppen*] of the Security Police and the SD (Security Service) were formed, and it was to this part of town that they sent their reports about the mass murders which they had carried out. Here the genocide on the German and European Jews was planned; here the organizational foundations were laid for deportation and extermination; here the "Wannsee-Conference" was prepared. Here it was decided to segregate large numbers of Soviet Russian prisoners of war within the camps and to kill them. Here was the center out of which the *Gestapo* conducted all its activities directed against real and alleged opponents of the NS-System. Here, based on accounts of informants, the SD compiled its "Reports from within the Reich," intended to provide the men in power with as reliable information as possible about the mood of the population. Here was the command center for the system of Higher SS- and Police Leaders, including also the occupied territories.

No doubt, it was a place where terror was planned and administered, a place for armchair killers [*Schreibtischtäter*], men who concentrated upon the "orderly processing" of "occurrences" and who as a rule stayed away from the sites of horror. On the other hand, it should not be overlooked that some of the department heads within the Reich Security Main Office were also commanders of the infamous "Special Units" [*Einsatzgruppen*] in Poland and the Soviet Union, and that other officials attached to the Reich Security Main Office likewise belonged, for shorter or extended periods of time, to these killing squads. Finally, concrete physical violence was practiced also at Prinz-Albrecht-Strasse 8 itself. In the *Gestapo* prison ["*Hausgefängnis*"] (prison within the building) members of the opposition against the NS-System — from the Communists and Social Democrats to the officers and public officials of July 20th (1944) whose interrogation was particularly important to the persecuting administrative agencies, were held there in confinement for days, weeks, months, and some even for years on end. Many were brutally tortured during their interrogations, and some committed suicide while in prison. For these reasons as well Prinz-Albrecht-Strasse 8 was considered by the political opponents of National Socialism as the "most dreaded address" in Berlin. Conversely, the *Gestapo* prison ["*Hausgefängnis*"] with its prominent inmates but numerous unknown persons as well testified to the fact that there were people who refused to bend, who did not take the easy route of accomodation or of closing their eyes but who opted for resistance and did not hesitate to risk their lives in order to prevent, lessen or shorten injustice. To them who became victims and who, through their actions, stood for a different Germany, this place is therefore a memorial.

The Documentation aims first and foremost to inform about the institutions that were operative here between 1933 and 1945, about their organization and structure, their ways of functioning and the effects of their activities. For multiple reasons — the limited space available, the still unsatisfactory scholarly findings in many areas of research, and of course also because of the limited working possibilities of a small group entrusted with the preparations — this can be done only by means of selected examples. Many questions will have to remain open, others will be only partially answered. It is, then, an interim statement which aims, through the presentation of both unknown and familiar pictures and documents, to stimulate further work on the subject. This also holds true for the history of that section of the city and of the individual buildings, but most decidedly so for the decades after 1945 when this historical period was suppressed, rendered invisible, and only later rediscovered. The Documentation therefore goes until 1987. It will have achieved an important objective if it should contribute its share to prevent the discussion about the suitable treatment of this historical site from breaking down again.

Beyond the information offered by pictures and texts, the visitors of the exhibit are given the opportunity to acquaint themselves with the terrain as such. They can walk it, and small explanatory markers will give them the most relevant information about the individual buildings right on the spot.
In addition, a platform situated on one of the remaining hills formed of debris provides an overview of the entire terrain and how it ties in with Berlin's municipal landscape as a whole. In the summer of 1986, in connection with the planned Documentation, some of the terrain was dug up in an effort to search for clues about the still remaining ruins of the former buildings. In the process, parts of foundations, walls and basements were unearthed beneath the deposits of dirt and rubble. Most worth seeing is a part of the prison floor — protected by a weatherproof roof — which still shows traces of the cell walls that were erected in 1933. Finally, as late as March 1987, while the construction work for the temporary hall housing the Documentation was going on, extensive and hitherto unknown basements of an annex of Prinz-Albrecht-Strasse 8 built during the Second World War were discovered; they were accordingly included into the further planning operations in order to emphasize the workshop character of the Documentation.

The fact that the Documentation as well as the work on the terrain were brought to a successful conclusion is due to the strong support from numerous individuals and institutions. Our thanks go first of all to those who commissioned the project, i.e. to the Senator for Cultural Affairs, Dr. Volker Hassemer and to the Commissioner of the Senate for the 750 Year Celebration, Dr. Ulrich Eckhardt, for their personal commitment and their dependable support in all important matters. We also received generous and courteous assistance from the directors and co-workers of many archives, administrative bodies, picture archives, libraries and collections. To numerous private persons, among them a few survivors of the Gestapo prison ["Hausgefängnis"] or their relatives, we are likewise indebted for their readiness to provide information. The discussions and talks we had with the members of the "Citizens Concerned with the History and Future of the Gestapo Terrain" [Initiative für den Umgang mit dem Gestapo-Gelände], with the co-workers of the Senate Administration and the members of the Directorate of the Central Historical Exhibition were important to us. In regard to the initial preparation of the terrain we benefited from the experience and counsel of Dieter Robert Frank, who conducted the excavations; of Hendrik Gottfriedsen, who supervised the work on the terrain; of Dr. Alfred Kernd'l, who advised on how to care for the (excavated) building fragments on the ground; and Peter Hielscher, who handled the various coordinating tasks.

We owe special thanks to Reinold Schattenfroh and Johannes Tuchel, who furnished us with the results of their study on Prinz-Albrecht-Strasse 8 even before its publication. Of decisive importance for the realization of the project was the assistance of Professor Dr. Wolfgang Scheffler and Gerhard Schoenberner, who beyond their function as scholarly advisors became co-authors of the Documentation. That the building that houses the Documentation was erected on time despite difficult conditions we owe to Jürg Steiner's energy and wealth of ideas. In similar ways this holds true for Claus-Peter Gross and Margret Schmitt whose experience and personal commitment were prerequisite for the punctually completed design of the Documentation even under unusual time pressure. Finally, we want to thank Dr. Willmuth Arenhövel for his careful supervision of this publication.

A final comment: Because of its size and the decision to keep the sales price low, the published volume does not contain the entire content of the Documentation. But it presents all significant pictures and documents, at least as far as they could be reduced in size.

1   Aerial photograph of the terrain Prinz-Albrecht-Strasse, Wilhelmstrasse, Anhalter Strasse and Stresemannstrasse around 1934. In the center of the picture is the Europahaus compound, alongside the diagonally running Stresemannstrasse which was renamed Saarlandstrasse in the spring of 1935. Next to it, on the left, at the corner of Prinz-Albrecht-Strasse, is the Museum of Ethnology. Adjacent, on Prinz-Albrecht-Strasse, is the Museum of Prehistory and Early History (formerly the Museum of Industrial Arts and Crafts, today the "Martin-Gropius-Bau"), and opposite the building that housed the Prussian Chamber of Deputies. To the right of the Museum of Prehistory and Early History is the former School of Industrial Arts and Crafts, since spring of 1933 the Secret State Police Office [*Gestapa*]; adjacent to it is the Hotel Prinz Albrecht. Below, at the right edge of the picture, is the main building of the Prinz-Albrecht-Palais, to which the park belongs, which extends to the Europahaus. The buildings opposite the Hotel Prinz Albrecht on Prinz-Albrecht-Strasse, corner Wilhelmstrasse, were torn down in 1935 when the Reich Air Force Ministry [*Reichsluftfahrtministerium*] was built in their place.

1. Administrative Center of the SS-State: Addresses and Institutions

Between 1933 and 1945, some of the most important institutions of NS-terror were located on the terrain bounded by Prinz-Albrecht-Strasse, Wilhelmstrasse and Anhalter Strasse. In closest proximity, in part even in the same buildings, were the headquarters of the Secret State Police, the SS Reich Leadership, the Security Service (SD) of the SS, and the Reich Security Main Office (RSMO).

Already prior to January 30, 1933, and even more so after the "Seizure of Power," the interest of the NS-leadership focused on this terrain which, among others, was marked by its immediate proximity to the government quarter. Within a few years the police, NSDAP and SS occupied virtually the entire terrain.

The decisive first occupancy that took place on the "Prinz-Albrecht-Terrain" came as early as May 1933 when the newly created Secret State Police Office moved into the building Prinz-Albrecht-Strasse 8 where the former School of Industrial Arts and Crafts had been located. When in April 1934 Himmler was appointed "Inspector" — in reality the actual Head — of the *Gestapo*, he transferred as *Reichsführer-SS* (Reich Leader of the SS) both the administrative branch of the SS and the SD (Security Service) from Munich to Berlin and settled them in the immediate proximity of his new headquarters. By the end of 1934, important segments of the SS-leadership moved into the Hotel Prinz Albrecht (Prinz-Albrecht-Strasse 9). The SD, whose Head was Reinhard Heydrich, moved into the Prinz-Albrecht-Palais (Wilhelmstrasse 102).

With the physical proximity of police agencies, SS and SD, the close interconnection between state and party organs of power so characteristic of the National Socialist ruling system became distinctly evident until finally, in 1939, *Gestapo*, Criminal Police and SD were officially merged into one institution, the Reich Security Main Office, which was simultaneously a state agency and part of the SS-Empire. Since the machinery of surveillance and persecution amassed ever increasing additional tasks and employed ever increasing personnel, the buildings on Prinz-Albrecht-Strasse und Wilhelmstrasse soon no longer sufficed. The administrative departments expanded first into the surrounding neighborhoods, then spread across the entire city. The Reich Security Main Office alone had distributed its individual administrative departments by 1943 throughout more than thirty buildings between Weissensee and Wannsee, among them the Bureau Eichmann [*Eichmann-Referat*] at Kurfürstenstrasse 115–116 — and the Reich Security Main Office was only one of twelve main offices [*Hauptämter*] of the SS.

The Terrain Prinz-Albrecht-Strasse/Wilhelmstrasse remained until the end the administrative center of the SS-State ["*Regierungsviertel des SS-Staates*"], the center of the terror apparatus. Here stood the desks of Himmler, Heydrich, Kaltenbrunner and Heinrich Müller ["*Gestapo Müller*"]. Here was the "*Hausgefängnis*" of the *Gestapo*, but also the hub of the network of *Gestapo* Regional and Local Commands [*(Leit)-Stellen*] and administrative offices of the Higher SS- and Police Commanders [*Höhere SS- und Polizeiführer*] that was strung out across Germany and large parts of Europe. From here the genocide of the Jews was prepared, and deportations and extermination were coordinated by the state authorities. The Special Units operating in Poland and the Soviet Union sent their reports here concerning their murderous exploits. From here the persecution of the opponents of the regime in Germany, and subsequently in all occupied territories as well, was organized.

Today none of these buildings exists anymore. In as far as they had more or less survived the war, they were demolished or blown up in the mid-fifties. In the beginning of the nineteen sixties all buildings had been cleared away and the ground leveled. On the vacant terrain nothing was any longer reminiscent of its history.

The NSDAP acquired its first property on the terrain already before January 30, 1933. In October 1932 the editorial office of the party newspaper, "*Der Angriff*" (The Assault), founded 1927 by Goebbels, had moved from Hedemannstrasse 10 situated only a few hundred meters south into the building Wilhelmstrasse 106, not far from the

2   "Angriff-House," Wilhelmstrasse 106, 1933.

3   Layout, October 1932.

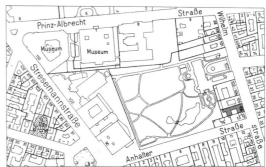

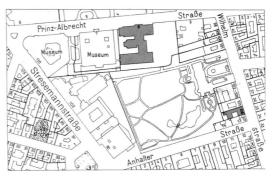

5   Layout, May 1933.

4   Secret State Police Office, Prinz-Albrecht-Strasse 8, about 1934.

In the beginning of May 1933, the Secret State Police Office, established on April 26, 1933, moved into this building. Prinz-Albrecht-Strasse 8 remained the headquarters of the Secret State Police until the end of the war; from 1939 on it was also the central address of the Reich Security Main Office.

Prinz-Albrecht-Palais (No. 102). The building on Wilhelmstrasse was now called "*Angriff-Haus.*" In the spring of 1934 the editorial office of the "*Angriff*" moved into nearby Zimmerstrasse. On July 23, 1934, the adjutancy of the newly appointed SA-Chief of Staff Lutze – successor of the murdered Ernst Röhm – moved temporarily into the building. From the end of 1934 until January 1937 it served as headquarters to the *SA-Gruppenführung* (Stormtrooper Division Command) Berlin-Brandenburg; subsequently it was used by the Security Service (SD) of the SS.

On April 20, 1934, the "*Reichsführer-SS*" Heinrich Himmler was appointed "Inspector" of the Secret State Police in Prussia; his administrative office was located at Prinz-Albrecht-Strasse 8. During the following months the SS leadership commands were moved from Munich to Berlin. In the beginning of November 1934 the adjutancy of the "*Reichsführer-SS*" (subsequently: Personal Staff *Reichsführer-SS*) moved into Prinz-Albrecht-Strasse 9. The Hotel Prinz Albrecht became the "*SS-Haus*" which was also used by the *SS-Hauptamt* (Main Office), the actual central administrative office of the SS. Since the Head of the Security Service (SD) of the SS, Reinhard Heydrich, had been appointed Himmler's deputy in April 1934 to become Head of the Secret State Police Office, the SD also moved from Munich to Berlin with quarters in the Prinz-Albrecht-Palais.

The number of those employed, from 1933 on, in the Secret State Police Office and the various administrative offices of the SS increased continuously. This meant that the demand for space re-

6   Hotel Prinz Albrecht, Prinz-Albrecht-Strasse 9, around 1932.

7   Layout, end of 1934.

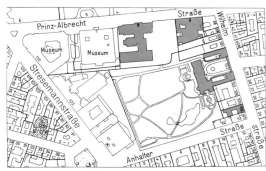

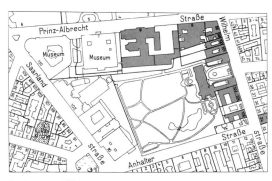

9   Layout, 1938.

8   Prinz-Albrecht-Palais, Wilhelmstrasse 102, around 1930. Since November 1934 the Palais was the seat of the Security Service (SD) of the SS, and since September 1939 headquarters of the Head of the Reich Security Main Office (Heydrich; since 1943 Kaltenbrunner).

quired by personnel, departments and technical equipment grew accordingly. In 1935 the SD moved into Wilhelmstrasse 101 and 103/104, a building directly adjacent to the Prinz-Albrecht-Palais. In 1937, after the Stormtrooper Division

10   The Reich Air Force Ministry on Wilhelmstrasse, between Prinz-Albrecht-Strasse and Leipziger Strasse, around 1937.

11   The former Prussian Chamber of Deputies, Prinz-Albrecht-Strasse 5, 1934. Known as "Preußenhaus" [Prussian House], it was in 1934–35 temporarily the seat of the "Volksgerichtshof" [People's Court]. At the end of 1935, after the People's Court was transferred to Bellevuestrasse, it was renamed by Göring "House of the Flyers."

12   The Europahaus on Askanischer Platz, July, 1943.

Command [SA-Gruppenführung] Berlin-Brandenburg had moved out, Wilhelmstrasse 106 was occupied as well. Other administrative SS offices were housed after 1936 at Wilhelmstrasse 100 (initially the SS Main Office).

In 1935/1936 the Gestapo built a garage at Prinz-Albrecht-Strasse 8 and thereby closed the gap between that building and the former Hotel Prinz Albrecht. Some administrative departments moved into Wilhelmstrasse 98 and 99.

By the end of the thirties, then, all buildings from Prinz-Albrecht-Strasse 8 on to Wilhelmstrasse and the corner of Anhalter Strasse were occupied (with the exception of two houses) by administrative departments of the Gestapo and the SS, aside from additionaly properties in the immediate vicinity (e.g., Wilhelmstrasse 20 and 34).

By the beginning of 1936, within a period of only fifteen months, the Reich Air Force Ministry building compound [Reichsluftfahrtministerium] had been put up along the entire stretch of the Wilhelmstrasse between Leipziger Strasse and Prinz-Albrecht-Strasse. During the Olympic Games in 1936 the building was shown off to visitors from abroad as a symbol of the "new" Berlin. A contemporary guidebook of the city referred to it as a "monument, hewn in stone, to the reawakened fighting spirit and rekindled military preparedness of the new Germany."

The former Prussian chamber of deputies (Prinz-Albrecht-Strasse 5) was likewise taken over by Reich Minister for the Air Force, Göring. It was named "House of the Flyers" [Haus der Flieger] after it had served briefly, in 1934/1935, as the seat of the "People's Court" [Volksgerichtshof]. During the final phase of the Second World War, Himmler used the building for conferences of the leading echelons of the SS and the Reich Security Main Office. Toward the end of the thirties, the Reich Ministry of Labor moved into the Europahaus at Askanischer Platz after the neon lights had been removed from the face of the building. In October 1941, Himmler considered having his personal staff lodged there, but this never materialized.

13   The National Socialist government quarter, 1936.
The layout shows the extent of the NS-Government quarter as it existed essentially until the end of the war. (1938–39 a second large government building, in addition to the Reich Air Force Ministry, was added, the "New Reich Chancellory" on Voßstrasse). The Central Office of the Gestapo on Prinz-Albrecht-Strasse formed the southern limit of the government quarter. That the Gestapo resided here was never concealed; it was listed in travel guides and on city maps as a matter of course.

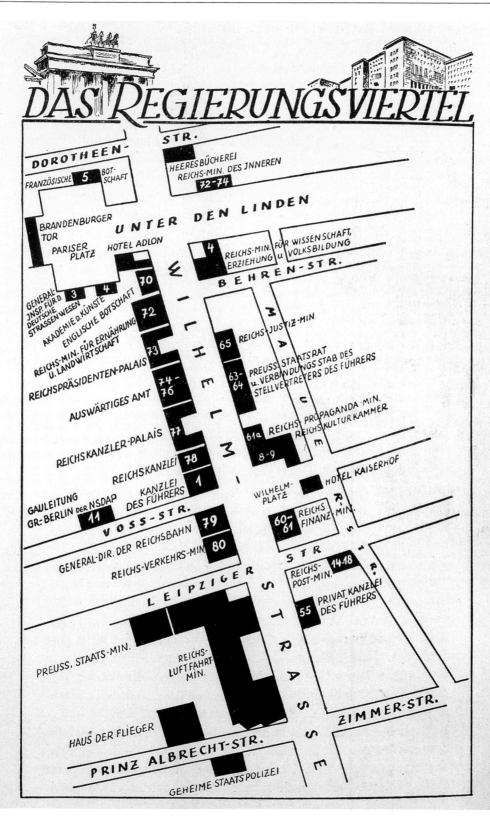

2. History of the City District and its Buildings

2.1. A Quiet Area at the Edge of the City (1732–1880)

Friedrichstadt (lit. Frederick's Town) developed southwest of Berlin and Cölln, beginning in 1688. For a brief period of time it possessed its independent municipal rights but was incorporated into the newly formed royal residency, Berlin, in 1710.

Frederick William I, the "Soldier's King," extended Friedrichstadt from 1732 on toward the south, a project based on plans drafted by his chief building director [Oberbaudirektor], Philipp Gerlach. At that time the street pattern developed which for two and a half centuries remained characteristic of the southern section of Friedrichstadt, whereby the three main arteries – Wilhelmstrasse, Friedrichstrasse and Lindenstrasse – ran from north to south into the "Rondell" (later Belle-Alliance-Platz, today Mehringplatz) at Hallesches Tor, constructed in 1734. While at that time several aristocratic mansions [Palais] were built in the northern section of Friedrichstadt which put their imprint on this part of the city and which, after the empire was founded in 1871, were turned into government buildings and embassies, southern Friedrichstadt initially possessed a plainer, in some places even "shabby," appearance. Essentially, immigrants were settled here – on Wilhelmstrasse predominantly Protestants from Bohemia. An exception was the Palais which Baron Vernezobre de Laurieux built in 1737 on lower Wilhelmstrasse; it was for Berlin at that time an unusually splendid edifice.

After repeated changes of owners and the ways in which it was utilized, the Palais was acquired in 1830 by Prinz Albrecht of Prussia, son of Frederick William III, and was called after him ever since. He had it remodeled between 1830 and 1832 by Karl Friedrich Schinkel. The rearrangement of the park was entrusted to Peter Joseph Lenné. In the process – among others by the acquisition of the neighboring property at Wilhelmstrasse 103–104 – the garden was considerably enlarged. In the western part of the park Schinkel put up royal stables and a riding hall next to several small utility buildings. Aside from the Palais and its adjacent buildings as well as the simply constructed houses two or three stories high and situated north and south of the Palais on Wilhelmstrasse, the neighboring area remained undeveloped until the last quarter of the nineteenth century. The effect of the park was reinforced by the fact that directly to the north of it were the adjoining gardens of the Prussian War Ministry.

The southern limits were formed since 1840 by Anhalter Strasse which constituted a better connection from the inner city to the Anhalter Bahnhof (railway station), opened in 1841. Königgrätzer Strasse (today Stresemannstrasse) on the western side developed in the 1860's from the connection of Hirschelstrasse with the so-called "Communication," and the demolition of the city wall that had separated them. Despite the construction of Anhalter Bahnhof and Potsdamer Bahnhof (1838), and despite the new streets, the southern area of Friedrichstadt still retained its quiet edge-of-the-city atmosphere for decades to come. The Baedecker of 1878 states: "The southern half of Friedrichstadt is considerably more monotonous and quieter than the northern half. It offers little to the foreigner." And yet, in 1875 construction had begun for the new Anhalter Bahnhof, and in 1877 for the Museum of Industrial Arts and Crafts. Within a few years the character of this part of the city was to change fundamentally.

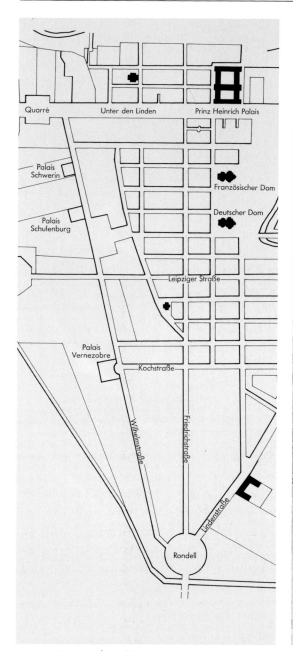

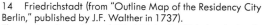

14   Friedrichstadt (from "Outline Map of the Residency City Berlin," published by J.F. Walther in 1737).

The eastern boundary of Friedrichstadt which, beginning in 1732, had been extended up to the "Rondell," was formed by Lindenstaße where the "*Collegiengebäude*" [*Kammergericht*], then supreme court, built in 1734—35 was situated. It is today the Berlin Museum. From the "Rondell" toward the northeast ran the tariff wall [*Akzisemauer*] toward the Potsdamer Tor at the "Octogon" (later Leipziger Platz) and on to the Branden-burger Tor at the "Quarré" (later Pariser Platz). The lot of the Palais Vernezobre is marked opposite the junction Koch-strasse and Wilhelmstrasse. Its construction began in 1737.

15   Friedrichstadt (section from "Map of the City of Berlin" which was published under the guidance of Count von Schmet-tau in 1748); as the map was printed "south-up", the writing here is upside down).

The topographically precise map shows also the outline of the garden arrangement of the Palais Vernezobre. It adjoins in the north the gardens of the Palais Happe which the Prussian War Ministry had acquired at the end of the eigtheenth century. Between Leipziger Strasse in the north and the "Rondell" in the south, no cross streets as yet existed.

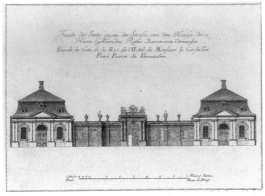

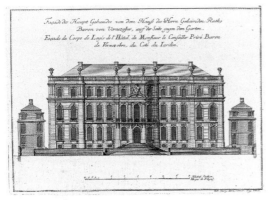

16   Street front of Palais Vernezobre (from an engraving by J.G. Merz, around 1740).

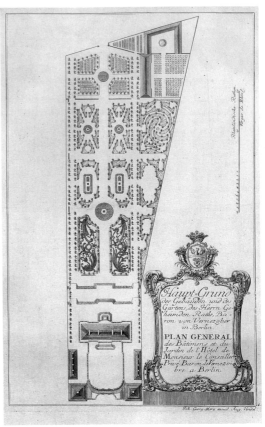

17   Garden front of Palais Vernezobre (from an engraving by J.G. Merz, around 1740).

19   Floor plan of the overall setting of Palais Vernezobre (from an engraving by J.G. Merz, around 1740).

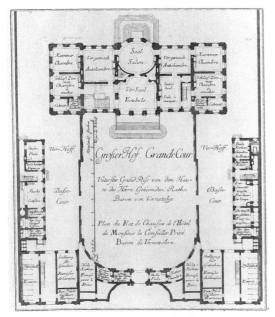

18   18   Floor plan of Palais Vernezobre (from an engraving by J.G. Merz, around 1740).

Chronology of the proprietary and utilization status of the Palais at Wilhelm-Strasse 102

1737–39
Baron Mathieu Vernezobre de Laurieux, on the insistence of Frederick William I, has the Palais built. Together with the large park which belongs to the property it serves him as summer residence ("Palais Vernezobre").

1760
The Palais is purchased by a banker, Werstler.

1763–64
The Prussian court rents the Palais for the stay of the Turkish ambassador.

1769
The Prussian Minister Baron von Hagen acquires the Palais.

1772
The Palais passes into the possession of Princess Amalie, Frederick II's sister, who uses it as her summer residence.

20   Street view of Prinz-Albrecht-Palais after it was renovated by Schinkel between 1830 and 1832 (from a colored
engraving by Lemaitre, around 1837).
The most important alterations were the modification of the
street front by way of colonnades, the two gateways, and the
addition of a second floor to the side wings.

21   View of the main building of Prinz-Albrecht-Palais from
the garden after it had been renovated by Schinkel between
1830 and 1832 (from a colored engraving by Lemaitre,
around 1837).

1790

The Palais becomes the property of the Margrave
of Ansbach-Bayreuth ("Ansbachisches Palais").

1806

The Palais reverts to the possession of the Royal
House of Prussia.

1807

The French use it for their army postal service.

1810

A facility for feeding the poor is being established
in the basement; it continues to operate until the
1830s.

1812

The Louise Endowment [*Luisenstiftung*] receives
permission from Frederick William III to use the
Palais. Wilhelm von Humboldt had temporarily
considered using the Palais as the domicile for
Berlin University, recently founded in 1810.

1826

The restoration studio of the royal collections
moves into the Palais with 1200 pictures. It had
been used already during the preceding years to
house collections of portraits and to establish studios for painting artists.

1830

The Palais passes into the possession of Prince Albrecht who uses it as his domicile until his death
(1872).

1830—32

Prince Albrecht commissions Karl Friedrich
Schinkel to renovate the Palais. The park is being
enlarged and newly arranged by Peter Joseph

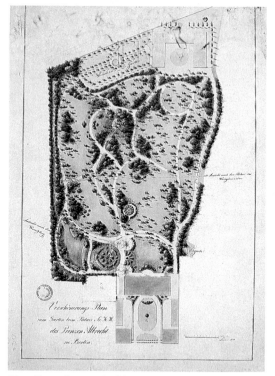

22   „"Beautification Plan" for the park of the Prinz-Albrecht-
Palais by Peter Joseph Lenné, 1830.
By this beautification process, the park area was virtually
doubled in size. "With its variety, neatly differentiated spa-
ciousness and the wealth of trees and flowers, the Prinz-Albrecht-Garden was one of the most beautiful municipal pal-
ace-gardens created by Lenné" (H. Günther, *Peter Joseph
Lenné,* Berlin, 1985).

23   Entrance hall of Prinz-Albrecht-Palais around 1900; it was designed by Schinkel.

Lenné. Henceforth, the Palais bears the name "Prinz-Albrecht-Palais."

1860—62
The inner rooms are being remodeled by Adolph Lohse.

1872
The Palais passes into the possession of Prince Albrecht's son, who bears the same name.

1874
The southern side of the main building is being enlarged by the Master Builder of the royal court [Hofbaumeister] Hauer.

1906
After the death of Prince Albrecht (the younger), the Palais passes into the hands of his three sons.

1918
After the Revolution the Palais still remains property of the Hohenzollern family.

1924
The western part of the park is being sold for building lots.

1926—31
After the royal stables built by Schinkel were torn down, together with other buildings, the Europahaus is built here.

24   The dance hall of Prinz-Albrecht-Palais on the first floor
around 1900, it was designed by Schinkel.
During the renovation of the inner rooms between 1860 and
1862, the entrance hall as well as some banqueting rooms on
the first floor remained unchanged.

1928−31
When the Reich Government rented the Palais as a place to house guests, some of the persons who stayed there were the Kings of Afghanistan (1928) and of Egypt (1929) as well as the British Prime Minister MacDonald and Foreign Minister Henderson (1931).

1934
The SS rents the Palais which becomes headquarters for the "Security Service (SD) of the SS" under the command of Reinhard Heydrich.

1939
The various administrative departments quartered in the Palais become components of the newly created "Reich Security Main Office." The Palais becomes now the central office of the director of the Reich Security Main Office (Heydrich, subsequently Kaltenbrunner).

1941
By order of Heydrich, extensive renovations begin; they are to emphasize the representative function of the Palais.

1944−45
In May 1944 the Palais gets severely damaged during a bombing raid. Prior to the end of the war it was hit again several times.

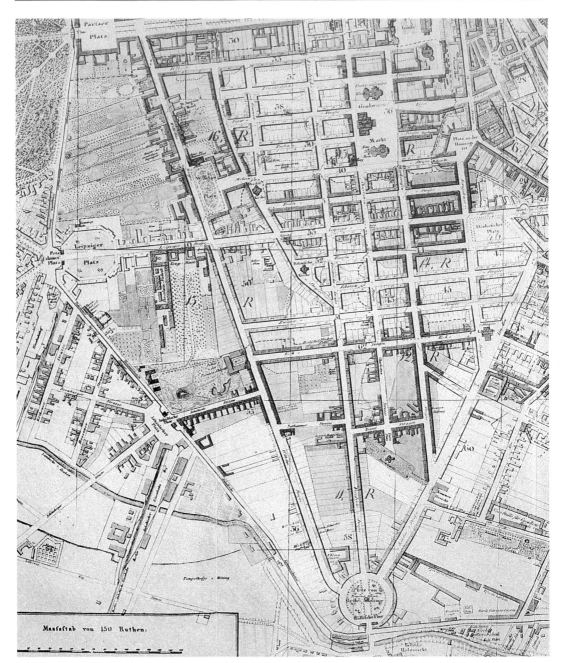

25   Friedrichstadt, a section from the *Grundriß von Berlin* (outline map of Berlin) by J.C. Selter, 1846.
The opening of Potsdamer Bahnhof (1838) and Anhalter Bahnhof (1841) generated a lively building activity. With the "Anhaltische" Strasse a connection between Wilhelmstrasse and Askanischer Platz was created. It now formed the southern boundary of the park of the Palais. At the park's western end, which is the *Akzisemauer* or the "Communication" as the case may be, one can make out the additional buildings placed there by Schinkel (Royal Stables and Riding Hall).

1949
The still standing remains are torn down in April.

1958
The property is being cleared of rubble, and leveled.

1961
The *Land* Berlin becomes the owner of the property.

2.2. Career of a City District (1880–1918)

"Berlin's rise to metropolis" was the catch phrase frequently used; and, indeed, the growth of the city since 1871, when Berlin became the capital of the newly founded German Empire, proceeded at a speed that was breathtaking even for contemporaries. With a sligth delay the terrain west of the Prinz-Albrecht-Palais was also included in this development. The expansion of the public transportation system necessitated the construction of new streets; thus developed, in 1872, Vossstrasse and Hedemannstrasse close to the Palais. The railway stations, no longer suited to cope with the new demands made on them, had to be remodeled. Thus Potsdamer Bahnhof had already received a new entrance hall between 1870 and 1872. The new structure of Anhalter Bahnhof, built between 1875 and 1880, was considered an architectonic marvel with its imposing roof construction. The immediate surroundings of both stations, especially Königgrätzer Strasse, became a tourist center with dozens of small and somewhat larger hotels.

The "invasion of modernism" onto the terrain between the Prinz-Albrecht-Palais in the east and Königgrätzer Strasse in the west was manifested in April 1877 when the cornerstone was laid for the Museum of Industrial Arts and Crafts designed by Martin Gropius and Heino Schmieden; the building was completed in 1881. During the same year, immediately adjacent, began the construction of the Museum for Ethnology; it was inaugurated in 1886. Both museums were a response to the pressure for modernization which the empire faced from the competing European powers. The Museum of Industrial Arts and Crafts for which artisans, industrialists, businessmen, senior officials and artists had clamored ever since 1867 was expected to help raise the quality of German artistic production and the applied arts industry as such to an internationally competitive level. For this reason, exhibits of collections, library and classrooms had been combined within the museum into one cohesive unit. Significantly, the construction of the Museum of Ethnology coincided with the acquisition of the first German colonies.

Soon after the museums had been built, a hotel boom — combining public and private interests — had seized the inner city in consequence of an expanding tourist traffic and spread to the Prinz-Albrecht-Palais terrain. In 1887–1888 the Hotel "*Vier Jahreszeiten*" (originally "*Römer-Bad*" [Roman Bath] and since the turn of the century, "Hotel Prinz Albrecht") had been erected between the museums and the corner house at Wilhelmstrasse 98. The property owners in the Wilhelmstrasse were likewise bent upon expansion: all around the Palais old stately dwellings [*Bürgerhäuser*] had floors added, new houses were built, and in the rear, toward the courtyard, side wings and "garden" houses were put up.

Initially, museums and hotel could only be reached from either the west or the east by way of provisional dead end streets. Not until after the Prussian Chamber of Deputies had been built between 1893 and 1898 opposite the Museum of Industrial Arts and Crafts did the Ministry of War relinquish its resistance to a breakthrough for a street (which became the western extension of Zimmerstrasse). Now Prinz-Albrecht-Strasse could be constructed. Shortly after the turn of the century the gap between museums and hotel was likewise closed. As the Museum of Industrial Arts and Crafts suffered from increasing lack of space, it was resolved to house classrooms and library in a new building on a neighboring lot. Thus was created, between 1901 and 1905, the building of the School for Industrial Arts and Crafts. With this in addition to the "Museum Island," a "second museum district" had developed in Berlin.

Within a few decades the terrain at Prinz-Albrecht-Palais had not only taken on a new appearance, the social significance of the district had likewise undergone profound changes. It was now embedded within the functional network of the inner city, consisting of the government district (which by this time began at the Prussian Chamber of Deputies on Prinz-Albrecht-Strasse), the business district (along Leipziger Strasse, with the "showpiece" of Wertheim's Department Store), the traffic center (between Potsdamer Bahnhof and Anhalter Bahnhof) and the newspaper district (between Zimmerstrasse and Kochstrasse, seat of the publishing combines of Mosse, Ullstein and Scherl). From an edge-of-the-city district a part of the inner city had developed.

26   The northern face of the Museum of Industrial Arts and Crafts, with main portal; wood engraving, 1881.
The building, constructed between 1877 and 1881 from designs by Martin Gropius and Heino Schmieden (today: "Martin-Gropius-Bau"), is the most important and last remaining building in Berlin of the younger Schinkel School. The paper of the construction trade [*Baugewerkszeitung*]," wrote at its inauguration in 1881: "With this building our construction trade and our arts and crafts trade have shown that they are completely up-to-date."

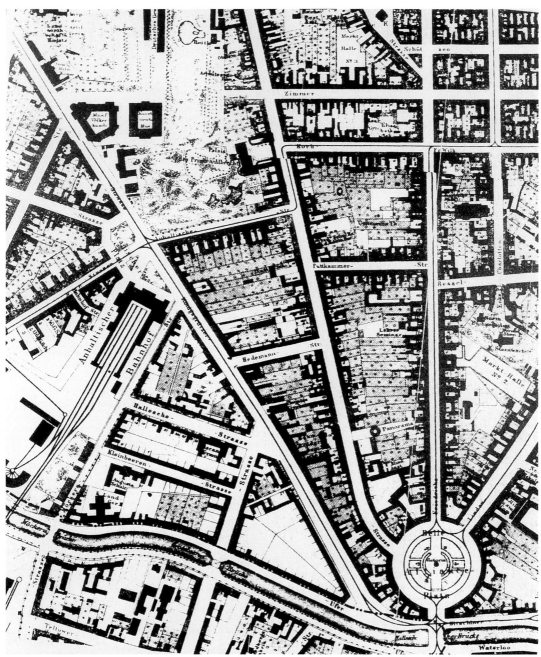

27   A section of the "Site Plan of the Capital and Residency, Berlin and Environs" ["Situations-Plan von der Haupt- und Residenzstadt Berlin und Umgebung"], ed. by W. Liebenow, 1888.

The terrain west of the Prinz-Albrecht-Palais is at this time nearly entirely surrounded by streets. The newly constructed museums at the northwestern boundary and the Hotel "Vier Jahreszeiten" (on the map still indicated as "Römer Bad") at the northeastern boundary are all accessible through dead end streets [Stichstrassen]. The gardens of the War Ministry, however, which in the south extended to the park of the Prinz-Albrecht-Palais prevented the construction of through-streets, very much to the ennoyance of contemporaries who complained about traffic impediments and the thereby resulting detours.

28   The dead-end street in front of the Museum of Industrial Arts and Crafts, around 1890.
The main portal with the sandstone statues of Hans Holbein (front) and Peter Vischer. Behind the blocking wall lies the southern part of the garden of the Prussian War Ministry which refused for years to permit a breakthrough on its property for construction of a street.

30   Hotel Prinz Albrecht, Prinz-Albrecht-Strasse 9, around
1905.
The hotel, built between 1887 and 1888 from designs drawn
by Wesenberg (until the turn of the century, the name of the
hotel was "*Vier Jahreszeiten*"), was described in a contemporary city guide book as "a splendid edifice constructed in Re-
naissance style." With its 120 beds it did not belong to the
great hotels of "superior rank" such as "Adlon" or "Kaiserhof,"
but it counted well into the period of the Weimar Republik as a
"first-class hotel."

29   The Museum of Ethnology on Königgrätzer Strasse,
corner Prinz-Albrecht-Strasse, 1887.
The floor plan of the building constructed between 1881 and
1886 from the designs by Hermann Ende and Wilhelm Böck-
mann corresponded with the lot that ran in an acute angel toward the street corner. To the left, the Museum of Industrial Arts
and Crafts; Prinz-Albrecht-Strasse has not yet been connected.

32   The School of Industrial Arts and Crafts at Prinz-Al-brecht-Strasse 8, around 1910.
In this building, designed by the Ministry of Public Works and constructed between 1901 and 1905, the classrooms and the library of the Museum of Industrial Arts and Crafts were housed, including the Lipperheide costume library; the library could be reached through the side entrance No. 7 a.

31   The entrance hall of Prinz Albrecht Hotel in 1909 after its renovation by Bruno Möhring.

33   View onto Prinz-Albrecht-Strasse from the west, 1905.
To the right, the Museum of Ethnology, to the left, the building of the Prussian Chamber of Deputies. In the foreground to the left a concert hall, built in 1904–05, the first building in Berlin to be constructed entirely of reinforced concrete. Prinz-Albrecht-Strasse, as the western extension of Zimmerstrasse to which it was connected by a breakthrough, has now become an important west-east connection within the inner city.

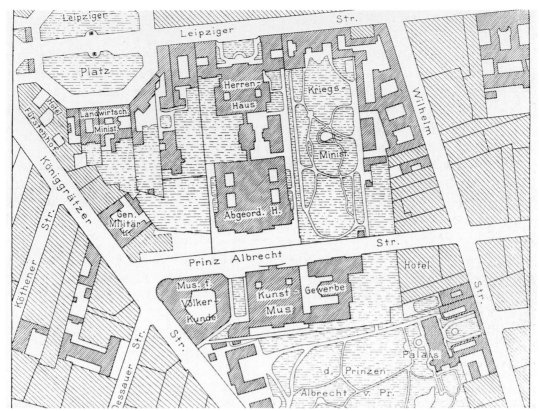

34   Map of Prinz-Albrecht-Strasse and surroundings, 1913. Prinz-Albrecht-Strasse connects the tourist center on Königgrätzer Strasse with the eastern part of the inner city. The three buildings on the southern side of the street form the new — second — museum district. Including the Prussian Chamber of Deputies, the government quarter now extends to the northern side of the street.

35   Wilhelmstrasse looking north, with Prinz-Albrecht-Palais, around 1910. The house at No. 100, only three floors high and two houses beyond the Palais, constitutes a last remainder of Wilhelmstrasse's original building pattern.

2.3. Changes and Crisis (1918–33)

During the winter of 1918–19, Berlin was the scene of revolutionary conflicts and far-reaching political decisions. The struggle for a new democratic order in Germany did not only take place in government buildings and parliaments, but also on the streets and public squares of Berlin. The picture of the city was marked by huge demonstrations and rallies, but soon by clashes and street fighting as well.

The buildings on Prinz-Albrecht-Strasse stood during these months repeatedly in the center of events. From December 16th to the 21st, 1918, the Reich Congress of Germany's Workers and Soldiers Councils met in the Prussian House of Deputies at Prinz-Albrecht-Strasse; there it was decided to hold elections for the German National Assembly on January 19, 1919. During these days notably Prinz-Albrecht-Strasse became the place where large political demonstrations were held. By the turn of the year 1918–1919, the German Communist Party was founded in the [Prussian] House of Deputies. A few days later heavy and bloody fighting broke out in the neighboring newspaper district, in the course of which government troops were quartered in the Prinz-Albrecht-Palais.

Because the revolution was arrested and the newly created parliamentary democracy rested on a compromise with the conservative forces, the property of the ousted dynasties was barely touched. The Prinz-Albrecht-Palais remained the private property of the Hohenzollerns. During the mid-twenties they sold the western part of the park to a construction company which, between 1926 and 1931, built the Europahaus on this property. Further municipal building projects for the entire property came to naught, as also happened to the plan of the Hohenzollerns to build on the remaining park plot – not accessible to the public – a high-rise hotel.

During the nineteen-twenties, important changes took place regarding the utilization of the buildings on Prinz-Albrecht-Strasse. The Museum of Industrial Arts and Crafts was transferred to the vacant city palace [*Schloss*]. Into the now unoccupied building moved the prehistorical division of the Museum of Ethnology; out of it developed very soon the independent Museum of Prehistory and Early History. The State School of Industrial Arts and Crafts fused in 1924 with the Academy of Fine Arts and was moved to Charlottenburg. Only the State Library for the Arts, independent since 1924, remained in a side wing of the building. Likewise, the studios on the top floor continued to be rented out to artists until February 1933. The better part of the building was entrusted to a private firm whose lease expired on March 31st, 1933.

Since February 1932, the Hotel Prinz Albrecht was used repeatedly by Hitler and Goebbels as well as by National Socialist delegates of the Prussian Diet [*Landtag*] for rallies and meetings.

36   Rally in front of the Prussian Chamber of Deputies, Prinz-Albrecht-Strasse 5, on December 16, 1918.
From December 16 to 21, 1918, the "General Congress of Germany's Workers and Soldiers Councils" met in the Prussian Chamber of Deputies. For the opening day of the congress, the Spartacist League [*Spartakusbund*], subsequently the German Communist Party, and the Group of Revolutionary Shop Stewards ["*Revolutionäre Obleute*"] had called for a rally in front of the building. Karl Liebknecht (on the balcony, center) is speaking to the demonstrators.

37   Demonstrators in front of the Prussian Chamber of Deputies on December 16, 1918.
In the background, the Museum and the School of Industrial Arts and Crafts.

38   The former School of Industrial Arts and Crafts on Prinz-Albrecht-Strasse 8, around 1932.

In February 1924, in order to attain "significant savings," the Prussian Ministry of Culture combined the School of Industrial Arts and Crafts with the Academy of Fine Arts and moved the former to Hardenbergstrasse where the latter was located. The library remained at Prinz-Albrecht-Strasse 7a and became the "State Library for the Arts."

The now vacant rooms were rented out by the Prussian Building and Finance Directory to a private holding company, Richard Kahn, Inc., for the period from June 1, 1925 until March 31, 1933. In a special clause it was agreed upon to allow artists the continued use of the 42 studios on the top floor. Among the students who worked there was the sculptor Kurt Schumacher

– he was imprisoned here in 1942 in the "*Hausgefängnis*" of the *Gestapo* – and the future writer Peter Weiss. The remaining rooms the firm Kahn rented out to administrative agencies, e.g. in November 1925, to the Revenue Office Friedrichstadt. In the beginning of the twenties, the contents of the Museum of Industrial Arts and Crafts were transferred to the Berlin Palace where they were combined with the art objects there and have henceforth formed the "Palace Museum." The vacated rooms were then occupied by the East Asian Art Division (ground floor) and the Prehistorical Division of the Museum of Ethnology (first floor); the arch well [*Lichthof*] was utilized for varying exhibits. The building was first called "Museum on Prinz-Albrecht-Strasse," later on "Museum of Prehistory and Early History."

The "Large-Scale Construction Company for Building Commercial and Industrial Structures" ["*Großbauten-Aktien-Gesellschaft für die Errichtung von Geschäfts- und Industriehäusern*"] that had purchased one third of the property (west, toward Königgrätzer Strasse) from Prince Friedrich Heinrich (heir to the Prinz-Albrecht-Palais and its parks) invited in 1924 a "contest of ideas on what to construct on the grounds of the Prinz-Albrecht-Gardens." Most of the participants in the contest suggested a high-rise structure which would have exceeded by far the legal height (15 meters) stipulated by the building police. Prince Friedrich Heinrich was himself a stockholder in the "Large-

Scale Construction Company". The design displayed here belonged to the purchases by the jury for the competition.

The architect and writer Werner Hegemann lamented in connection with the designs submitted: "It's so boring to have to repeat the obvious over and over again, but the menacing 'lung tuberculosis' of Berlin forces one to do so. Thus, it must be said today once more: Of course it is high time to stop building houses on garden plots in Berlin ... All open spaces within a big city should of course be kept inviolable ..." The most favorable outcome one could hope for was to limit construction along the borders of the Prinz-Albrecht-Gardens as

39   Bruno Möhring's draft proposal for a hotel on Askanischer Platz, viewed in 1920 from Königgrätzer Strasse.
The architect Bruno Möhring, who in 1908–09 had renovated
the interior of the Hotel Prinz Albrecht, suggested in a series of
articles written in 1919–1920 the "alteration and opening up
of the Prinz-Albrecht-Garden." The park was to be made accessible to the public, the horse stable [Marstall] Schinkel had
built was to be transformed into workshops for industrial arts
and crafts, and a "skyscraper hotel" was to be erected on Askanischer Platz.

40   Otto Firle's draft proposal for a high-rise building on Askanischer Platz, viewed in 1924 from Anhalter Bahnhof.

41   The Europahaus Compound on Askanischer Platz, 1931.
The Compound developed in two building stages. The first, in
the foreground, was constructed between 1926 and 1928
after designs by Bielenberg and Moser; the second one –
1928–1931 – after designs by Otto Firle. It was initially conceived as a hotel. Work on the neon light advertisement on top
of the eleven story building is here still in progress.

much as possible, and that it would allow for as pleasingly effective a view upon the greeneries as had Schinkel's colonnades on Wilhelmstrasse.

What in 1920 had been the sketchy idea of a plan which remained a mere project in 1924 was in part realized at the beginning of 1926, during the brief period of the republic's economic prosperity. With the "rape" [*Verbauung*] of the Prinz-Albrecht-Gardens" (W. Hegemann), private business interests were now able to assert themselves ruthlessly. The "Large-Scale Construction Company, Inc." erected between 1926 and 1931 — "by a thorough utilization of the property" — the

Europahaus Compound along the western edge of the park. Schinkel's riding hall and horse stables were torn down. Prinz-Albrecht-Palais and its park remained the private property of the Hohenzollerns and were therefore not open to the public. But as the heirs were troubled by the high costs of maintenance they intended to build a giant hotel on the remaining part of the property. However, these plans (1928 and 1930) were not realized. The public use of the Palais around 1930 was indirect, so to speak: the Reich Government rented it repeatedly to high ranking official visitors as a guesthouse.

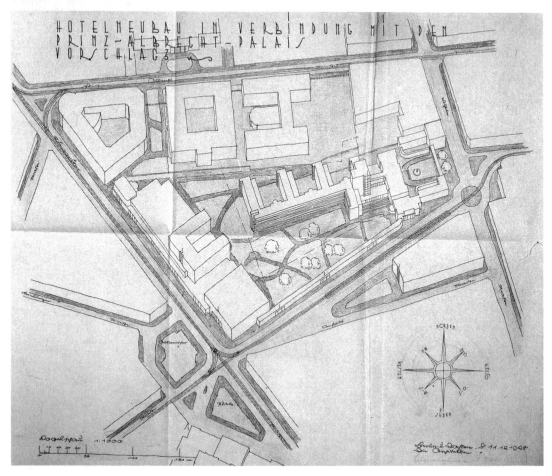

42   Draft design for the planned hotel construction, viewed from Anhalter Strasse, 1928.

43   Sketch map for the hotel construction "in connection with the Prinz-Albrecht-Palais," 1928.

44   Hitler and Goebbels are leaving the Hotel Prinz Albrecht after a meeting of the NSDAP delegation in the Prussian Diet on May 19, 1932.

45   National Socialist delegates to the Prussian Diet in front of the Hotel Prinz Albrecht on May 19, 1932.

3. Institutions of Terror

3.1. The Reichsführer-SS and his Empire

The most important tasks of *Reichsführer-SS* Heinrich Himmler and his SS were:
- surveillance, persecution and elimination of all political forces which the state considered its enemies,
- preservation and advancement of the Aryan "race" and the creation of a "racially pure" Germany, especially through the systematic persecution and expulsion of the Jews,
- conquest of "living space" [*Lebensraum*] and the "national and racial reorganization" [*volkstumspolitische Neuordnung*] of Europe.

The Secret State Police [*Gestapo*] and the Security Service (SD) had the task in their respective spheres of police work and intelligence gathering to guarantee the security of the NS State. Himmler's appointment as "*Reichsführer-SS* and Head of the German Police" (1936) served the long-range objective of severing the connections of all police forces (in Germany) from the state, and fusing their personnel with that of the SS.

Security of the state meant for Himmler: "To safeguard the German people and its organic entity, its vital energies and its institutions against destruction and disintegration." To attain this "safeguard" and as a supplement to police work, Himmler created a concentration camp system. Such a system made it possible to isolate and exclude all persons declared "enemies of the state or the people." Alonside political opponents of National Socialism, "enemies" included a multitude of minority social groups. For the purpose of murdering the "racial-political chief enemy" – the Jewish people – special extermination camps were created. To the *Schutzstaffel* (SS) [literary: "protection squadron"] of the Nazi party were alotted certain elite functions in forming the National Socialist Empire. As an ostensibly "racially pure order" the SS furnished the personnel for the realization of the NS system's key objective, the "racial-political purification" of initially the Aryan people in Germany, and after the outbreak of war, of the populations in the countries conquered by Germany.

What had begun as a system designed to secure political power inside Germany expanded from 1939 on across all of Europe. The persecution and elimination of alleged and actual political enemies was ruthlessly carried out. *Waffen-SS*, or Combat SS, units participated in the campaigns of conquest. The SS, in cooperation with all police units and participating state institutions, played a decisive role in the planning and execution of the racial-political concept of subjugation and extermination. Particularly in Eastern Europe the SS was the driving force behind the ethno-political "reorganization" that was carried out rapidly and with all available means. The program of the SS led to the following results:
- A campaign against the "Jewish-Bolshevik System" and the systematic murder of the Jewish populations in all German-ruled territories.
- Murder of the Gypsies and of other human beings termed "unworthy of life" such as the inmates of mental asylums and other institutions caring for the physically disabled in Germany, Poland, and the Soviet Union.

46   Hotel Prinz Albrecht, since 1934 Headquarters of the "*Reichsführung-SS*" [lit.:
SS Reich leadership]

- Persecution of all political enemies and all "unwanted" social groups, ranging from homosexuals to religious minorities.
- Exploitation and enslavement of millions of people who, next to the Jews, were likewise considered "racially inferior," predominantly the Polish and Soviet Russian populations. This was connected with the attempt to exclude or murder the intellectuals among these people.

What began in 1933 as a presumed restoration of national strength ended with millions of dead, immeasurable suffering, and a devastated Europe. In the center of this development stood Heinrich Himmler and his SS State.

47   The leader corps of the SS prior to the "Seizure of
Power," probably in 1932 in the "Brown House," Munich.
In the first row, third from the right, Himmler. Left, next to him,
Daluege. In the third row from below, second from the right,
Heydrich.

48   Adolf Hitler, guarded by the *SS-Leibstandarte* (approx.:
SS-bodyguard), in 1934.

50   The SS organizations in the "Great German" Reich, 1939.
The legend on the right refers to the main structure of the various SS organizations. These were:
1) The General SS [*Allgemeine SS*],
2) SS Death's Head units [*SS-Totenkopfverbände*] (including concentration camp guards)
3) SS Reserve units [*SS-Verfügungstruppen*]
4) SS Economic Enterprises [*SS-Unternehmen*]

49   Reich Party Rally in Nuremberg — SS units lined up in marching order.

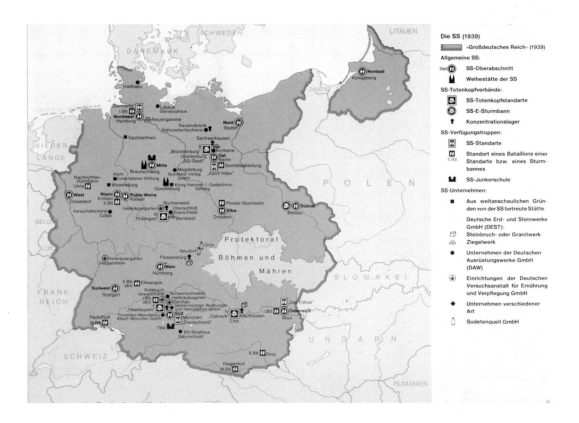

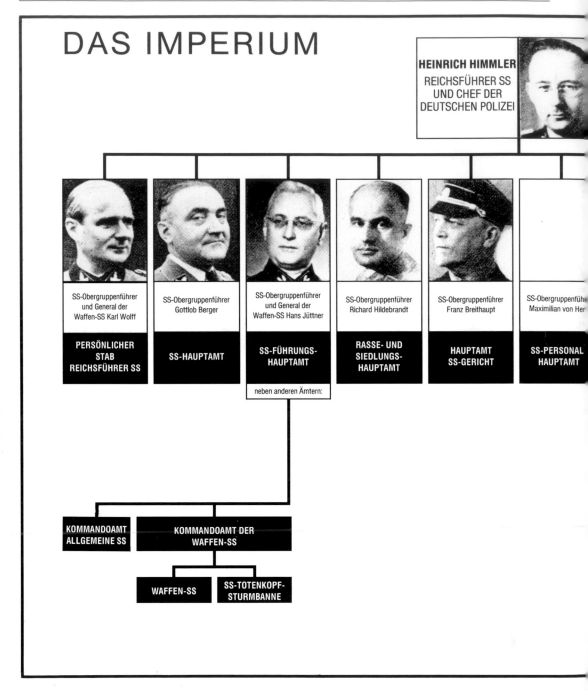

DAS IMPERIUM

HEINRICH HIMMLER
REICHSFÜHRER SS
UND CHEF DER
DEUTSCHEN POLIZEI

SS-Obergruppenführer und General der Waffen-SS Karl Wolff

PERSÖNLICHER STAB REICHSFÜHRER SS

SS-Obergruppenführer Gottlob Berger

SS-HAUPTAMT

SS-Obergruppenführer und General der Waffen-SS Hans Jüttner

SS-FÜHRUNGS-HAUPTAMT

neben anderen Ämtern:

SS-Obergruppenführer Richard Hildebrandt

RASSE- UND SIEDLUNGS-HAUPTAMT

SS-Obergruppenführer Franz Breithaupt

HAUPTAMT SS-GERICHT

SS-Obergruppenführer Maximilian von Her[ff]

SS-PERSONAL HAUPTAMT

KOMMANDOAMT ALLGEMEINE SS

KOMMANDOAMT DER WAFFEN-SS

WAFFEN-SS

SS-TOTENKOPF-STURMBANNE

51   The 12 SS Main Offices in 1944.

THE EMPIRE OF THE SS [SCHUTZSTAFFEL] IN 1944
(The Chiefs of the 12 SS Main Offices and their appellations.)
Top: Heinrich Himmler, *Reichsführer-SS* and Head of German Police.
Below Himmler, from left to right:
Karl Wolff. Office: Personal Staff of the *Reichsführer-SS*. Since September 23rd, 1943, Karl Wolff was the Highest SS- and Police Leader in Italy (HöSSPF). His functions in the Main Office Personal Staff were taken over by his former deputy, Dr. Rudolf Brandt.
Gottlob Berger. Office: SS Main Office [*Hauptamt*], the chief administrative office of the SS.
Hans Jüttner. Office: Main SS Leadership Office: Administrative Headquarters of the General SS and Administrative Headquarters of the *Waffen-SS* (plus Death's Head units).
Richard Hildebrandt. Office: Main Office for matters concerning Race and Settlement.
Franz Breithaupt. Office: Main Office of the SS Tribunal.
Maximilian von Herff. Office: SS Personnel Main Office.

DER SCHUTZSTAFFEL STAND 1944

ergruppenführer
hard Heydrich
olger seit 1943
ergruppenführer
nbrunner (rechts)

SS-Oberstgruppenführer
Kurt Daluege

SS-Obergruppenführer
Oswald Pohl

SS-Obergruppenführer
Dr. August Heißmeyer

SS-Obergruppenführer
Werner Lorenz

SS-Obergruppenführer
Ulrich Greifelt

**REICHS-
HERHEITS-
AUPTAMT**

**HAUPTAMT
ORDNUNGSPOLIZEI**
Uniformierte Polizei

**WIRTSCHAFTS- UND
VERWALTUNGS-
HAUPTAMT**

**DIENSTSTELLE
SS-OBERGRUPPEN-
FÜHRER
HEISSMEYER**

**HAUPTAMT
VOLKSDEUTSCHE
MITTELSTELLE**

**HAUPTAMT REICHS-
KOMMISSAR FÜR DIE
FESTIGUNG DEUT-
SCHEN VOLKSTUMS**

neben anderen Ämtern:

neben anderen Ämtern:

**KONZENTRATIONS-
LAGER**
(einschließlich der SS-
Totenkopf-Sturmbanne, die
aber truppendienstlich
dem Führungshauptamt
unterstellt waren)

BAUWESEN:

**WIRTSCHAFTS-
UNTERNEHMUNGEN**
u. a. 296 Ziegeleien, Porzel-
lanmanufakturen und 75
Prozent der nichtalkoholi-
schen Getränkeindustrie
(z. B. Apollinaris)

KOMMANDOAMT
der uniformierten
Polizei

TRUPPENVERWALTUNG

**TRUPPEN-
WIRTSCHAFT**
(Wirtschaftliche Versorgung
der Waffen-SS)

DER SPIEGEL

Reinhard Heydrich and, since 1943, his successor, Ernst Kaltenbrunner (right). Office: Reich Security Main Office.
Kurt Daluege. Office(s): Main Office of the Uniformed Regular Police and Command Post [*Kommandoamt*] of the Uniformed Police.
Oswald Pohl. Office(s): Main Office for Economic and Administrative Matters. Also: Concentration Camps (incl. the Death's Head units, although these stood, as far as their personnel records were concerned, under the jurisdiction of Jüttner's Main SS Leadership Office). Construction and Economic Enterprises of the SS, i.e., brickyards, manufacture of chinaware, and control over 75% of the non-alcoholic beverages industry (e.g. Apollinaris). Administration of troops, including provisioning the *Waffen-SS*.
Dr. August Heißmeyer. Office: Command [*Dienststelle*] SS-*Obergruppenführer* Heißmeyer.
Werner Lorenz. Office: Main Office for Ethnic Germans [*Volksdeutsche Mittelstelle*].
Ulrich Greifelt. Office: Main Office of the Reich Commissioner for Strengthening Germanism [*Deutsches Volkstum*]. (This pertained to the conquered Eastern territories.)

52   Meeting of "Himmler's circle of friends" (*"Freundeskreis Himmler"*) in the Prinz-Albrecht-Palais in 1937. In the front row, from the right: Former Reich Minister Dr. Kurt Schmitt (Chairman of the Board of the Rückversicherungs-Gesellschaft in Munich), Carl Vincent Krogmann (Lord Mayor of the Free and Hanseatic City of Hamburg), Ewald Hecker (President of the Industrie- und Handelskammer at Hanover), Reinhard Heydrich, Dr. Karl Rasche (Member of the Board of the Dresdner Bank), Heinrich Himmler, August Rosterg (General Manager of Wintershall, Inc.).

DOKUMENT 453-EC
SCHREIBEN DES BANKIERS · VON SCHRÖDER IN KÖLN AN HIMMLER VOM 21. SEPTEMBER 1943 ZUR ÜBERSENDUNG EINER LISTE VON BETRÄGEN, DIE IHM (HIMMLER) AUS WIRTSCHAFTSKREISEN IN DER GESAMTHÖHE VON 1 100 000.— RM ZUR VERFÜGUNG GESTELLT WURDEN (BEWEISSTÜCK US-322)

BESCHREIBUNG:
zweiteilig I Phot

Erstes S:

, den 21.9.1943.
Wiener Platz 5.

Reichsführer-SS Heinrich H i m m l e r ,

B e r l i n .

Sehr verehrter Reichsführer !
Für Ihren liebenswürdigen Brief vom 14.ds.Mts., mit dem Sie mir eine grosse Freude gemacht haben, danke ich Ihnen bestens.
Gleichzeitig übersende ich Ihnen anbei eine Liste mit dem Gesamtergebnis der Ihnen in diesem Jahre zur Verfügung gestellten Beträge Ihres Freundeskreises, abschliessend mit einer Summe von RM 1.100.000.—. Wir freuen uns aufrichtig, Ihnen damit bei Ihren besonderen Aufgaben eine gewisse Hilfsstellung leisten und Ihnen bei Ihrem wieder vergrösserten Aufgabenkreis eine kleine Entlastung zuteil werden lassen zu können.
Indem ich Ihnen, mein sehr verehrter Reichsführer, weiter alles Beste wünsche, verbleibe ich in alter Treue und Verehrung mit

H e i l H i t l e r !
Ihr sehr ergebener
v. S.
SS-Brigadeführer.

Z w e i t e s S: alle Posten außer zweimal „Hermann Göring-Werke" und außer dem letzten Posten r angehakt

A n B e i t r ä g e n g i n g e n a u f S o n d e r - K o n t o „ S" i m J a h r e 1943 ein:

durch Herrn Dr.R.Bingel
v/Siemens-Schuckertwerke A.G. .... 100.000.—
„   Herrn Dr.Bütefisch u.Herrn Geh.Rat Schmitz
v/J.G.Farbenindustrie A.G. .... 100.000.—

532

453-EC

durch Herrn Dr.Friedr.Flick
v/Mitteldeutsche Stahlwerke GMBH .... 100.000.—
„   Herrn Ritter vom Halt
v/Deutsche Bank, Berlin .... 75.000.—
„   Herrn Ewald Hecker
v/Ilseder Hütte .... 25.000.—
„   Herrn Staatsrat Helfferich
v/Deutsch-Amerikanische Petroleum-Ges. .... 10.000.—
„   Herrn Staatsrat Lindemann
v/Deutsch-Amerikanische Petroleum-Ges. .... 10 000.—
u.persönlich .... 4.000.—
„   Herrn Dr. Kaselowsky
v/Fa.Dr.August Oetker, Bilefeld. .... 40.000.—
„   Herrn Dr.Alfred Olscher
v/Reichs-Kredit-Gesellschaft A.G. .... 30.000.—
„   Herrn Prof.Dr. Meyer u.Herrn Dr.Rasche
v/Dresdner Bank, Berlin, ... 50.000.—
„   Herrn Staatsrat Reinhart
v/Commerz- und Privatbank A.G., Berlin, ... 50.000.—
„   Herrn Gen.Dir.Roehnert
v/Rheinmetall Borsig A.G. .... 50.000.—
„   „ Hermann Göring-Werke .... 30.000.—
„   Herrn Dr.Voss
v/Hermann Göring-Werke .... 30.000.—
„   Herrn Gen.Dir.Rosterg
v/Wintershall Akt.Ges....................... 100.000.—
„   Herrn Fregattenkapitän Otto Steinbrinck
v/Vereinigte Stahlwerke A.G. .... 100.000.—
„   Herrn Kurt Frhr.v.Schröder
v/Braunkohle-Benzin A.G. .... 100.000.—
„   Felten & Guilleaume Carlswerk A.G. .... 25.000.—
„   Mix & Genest A.G. .... 5.000.—
„   C.Lorenz A.G. .... 20.000.—
„   Gewerkschaft Preussen .... 30.000.—
„   Zinsen u.selber .... 16.000.—

RM 1.100.000.—

533

---

53   Letter from the banker Baron Kurt Schröder to the *Reichsführer-SS* (Heinrich Himmler) of September 21, 1943. It pertains to the financial contributions of the *"Freundeskreis Himmler"* [lit.: Himmler's circle of friends], a group of wealthy businessmen, industrialists, and economists whose financial contributions Himmler used for his various pet enterprises. This document (453-EC) was submitted in evidence during the Nuremberg Trials of the Major War Criminals. The letter pertains to contributions made in 1943.

54   Himmler, as Commander of the *Waffen-SS*, accompanied (from the left) by Wilhelm Keitel (Army), Karl Dönitz (Navy) and Erhard Milch (Air Force), congratulates Hitler on his birthday, the 20th of April, 1944.

55   A conference at Prinz-Albrecht-Strasse 8 on the first floor. From the left: Head of the SS Main Office for Ethnic Germans, Werner Lorenz; Head of the Security Police and the Security Service (SD), Reinhard Heydrich; the *Reichsführer-SS* and Head of the German Police, Heinrich Himmler; and the Head of Himmler's "Personal Staff," Karl Wolff.

3.2. Assumption of Power and Early Terror

Hitler's appointment as Reich Chancellor on January 30, 1933 was followed by the systematic destruction of the democratic state — a state based upon due process of law. Since the means of power were now at the disposal of the state, the National Socialists were able to eliminate systematically every possible form of opposition. This they accomplished in part through the formation of an auxiliary police force in Prussia consisting of both Stormtroopers (SA) and members of the SS. They also used the notorious Reichstag fire as an excuse to proclaim a state of emergency "for the protection of people and state." Mass arrests took place of Communist and Social Democratic party members, as well as of other individual critics of the NSDAP, calling a halt to their activities. The important stages of the so-called "*nationale Erhebung*" (the rise of the nation) consisted of the elimination of power of the Reichstag and of the various state diets. It was followed by the "Boycott of the Jews" (April 1, 1933) and the introduction of the first antisemitic laws and decrees, and furthered even more by the *Gleichschaltung* (or nazification) of all autonomous and semi-autonomous institutions including the labor unions whose functionaries were often arrested. The Communist Party was virtually destroyed and the SPD and all other remaining parties banned until ultimately the Nazi one-party state emerged.

The terror and the legal vacuum within which the SA and SS were able to operate undisturbedly during these months added to the desired atmosphere of fear and intimidation necessary for the political and ideological nazification of the German people. This reign of terror took place not only in the torture basements of the SA and in the "wild concentration camps," but also at the workplace and in public, causing thousands of people to flee Germany.

56   The first Head of the Prussian Secret State Police, *Regierungsrat* (approx. administrative councillor) Rudolf Diels (fourth from the left, partly concealed) presents to the foreign press in March, 1933 the journalist and writer Carl von Ossietzky, the Chairman of the Communist *Reichstag* delegation, Ernst Torgler (fourth from the right), and the writer Ludwig Renn (second from the right); they had been arrested on the basis of the Decree of February 28th, 1933 (Decree for the Protection of People and State).

Reichsgesetzblatt

Teil I

83

| 1933 | Ausgegeben zu Berlin, den 28. Februar 1933 | Nr. 17 |

Inhalt: Verordnung des Reichspräsidenten zum Schutz von Volk und Staat. Vom 28. Februar 1933...... S. 83

Verordnung des Reichspräsidenten zum Schutz von Volk und Staat. Vom 28. Februar 1933.

Auf Grund des Artikels 48 Abs. 2 der Reichsverfassung wird zur Abwehr kommunistischer staatsgefährdender Gewaltakte folgendes verordnet:

§ 1

Die Artikel 114, 115, 117, 118, 123, 124 und 153 der Verfassung des Deutschen Reichs werden bis auf weiteres außer Kraft gesetzt. Es sind daher Beschränkungen der persönlichen Freiheit, des Rechts der freien Meinungsäußerung, einschließlich der Pressefreiheit, des Vereins- und Versammlungsrechts, Eingriffe in das Brief-, Post-, Telegraphen- und Fernsprechgeheimnis, Anordnungen von Haussuchungen und von Beschlagnahmen sowie Beschränkungen des Eigentums auch außerhalb der sonst hierfür bestimmten gesetzlichen Grenzen zulässig.

§ 2

Werden in einem Lande die zur Wiederherstellung der öffentlichen Sicherheit und Ordnung nötigen Maßnahmen nicht getroffen, so kann die Reichsregierung insoweit die Befugnisse der obersten Landesbehörde vorübergehend wahrnehmen.

§ 3

Die Behörden der Länder und Gemeinden (Gemeindeverbände) haben den auf Grund des § 2 erlassenen Anordnungen der Reichsregierung im Rahmen ihrer Zuständigkeit Folge zu leisten.

§ 4

Wer den von den obersten Landesbehörden oder den ihnen nachgeordneten Behörden zur Durchführung dieser Verordnung erlassenen Anordnungen oder den von der Reichsregierung gemäß § 2 erlassenen Anordnungen zuwiderhandelt oder wer zu solcher Zuwiderhandlung auffordert oder anreizt, wird, soweit nicht die Tat nach anderen Vorschriften mit einer schwereren Strafe bedroht ist, mit Gefängnis nicht unter einem Monat oder mit Geldstrafe von 150 bis zu 15 000 Reichsmark bestraft.

Wer durch Zuwiderhandlung nach Abs. 1 eine gemeine Gefahr für Menschenleben herbeiführt, wird mit Zuchthaus, bei mildernden Umständen mit Gefängnis nicht unter sechs Monaten und, wenn die Zuwiderhandlung den Tod eines Menschen verursacht, mit dem Tode, bei mildernden Umständen mit Zuchthaus nicht unter zwei Jahren bestraft. Daneben kann auf Vermögenseinziehung erkannt werden.

Wer zu einer gemeingefährlichen Zuwiderhandlung (Abs. 2) auffordert oder anreizt, wird mit Zuchthaus, bei mildernden Umständen mit Gefängnis nicht unter drei Monaten bestraft.

§ 5

Mit dem Tode sind die Verbrechen zu bestrafen, die das Strafgesetzbuch in den §§ 81 (Hochverrat), 229 (Giftbeibringung), 307 (Brandstiftung), 311 (Explosion), 312 (Überschwemmung), 315 Abs. 2 (Beschädigung von Eisenbahnanlagen), 324 (gemeingefährliche Vergiftung) mit lebenslangem Zuchthaus bedroht.

Mit dem Tode oder, soweit nicht bisher eine schwerere Strafe angedroht ist, mit lebenslangem Zuchthaus oder mit Zuchthaus bis zu 15 Jahren wird bestraft:

1. Wer es unternimmt, den Reichspräsidenten oder ein Mitglied oder einen Kommissar der Reichsregierung oder einer Landesregierung zu töten oder wer zu einer solchen Tötung auffordert, sich erbietet, ein solches Erbieten annimmt oder eine solche Tötung mit einem anderen verabredet;

2. wer in den Fällen des § 115 Abs. 2 des Strafgesetzbuchs (schwerer Aufruhr) oder des § 125 Abs. 2 des Strafgesetzbuchs (schwerer Landfriedensbruch) die Tat mit Waffen oder in bewußtem und gewolltem Zusammenwirken mit einem Bewaffneten begeht;

3. wer eine Freiheitsberaubung (§ 239) des Strafgesetzbuchs in der Absicht begeht, sich des der Freiheit Beraubten als Geisel im politischen Kampfe zu bedienen.

§ 6

Diese Verordnung tritt mit dem Tage der Verkündung in Kraft.

Berlin, den 28. Februar 1933.

Der Reichspräsident
von Hindenburg

Der Reichskanzler
Adolf Hitler

Der Reichsminister des Innern
Frick

Der Reichsminister der Justiz
Dr. Gürtner

---

57 "Decree for the Protection of People and State," *Reichsgesetzblatt*, Part 1, No. 17, February 28, 1933. (See Abstract 1 in Appendix).

Kommunistische Literatenabteilung in der Berliner Künstlerkolonie
Laubenheimerplatz ausgehoben!

Mit der Feuerwehrleiter steigt man am schnellsten ein

Blutrote Fahnen und blutrünstige Transparente werden verbrannt

Jetzt Schluss damit!

DIE LITERATEN DER KOMMUNE WERDEN VERHAFTET

Deutschland hatte durch den Vertrag von Versailles beileibe nicht alle seine Kolonien eingebüßt. Unter dem starken Protektorat marxistischer Kulturpolitik wanderte die Blüte seiner Intelligenz nach Berlin-Wilmersdorf aus und gründete dort in einem großen, von moderner Sachlichkeit strotzenden Block am Südwestkorso von Wilmersdorf eine der wertvollsten aller Kolonien, die das Reich je besessen hat, die sogenannte „Berliner Künstlerkolonie".

Ungeistig und barbarisch, wie das neue Regime nun schon einmal ist, hat es am 15. März den Oberleutnant Olze mit einer Bereitschaft Schutzpolizei ausgerechnet in diese Musenkolonie geschickt, um sie abzuriegeln und zu durchsuchen. Man ist ja so argwöhnisch geworden, seit das Dasein des Herrn Grzesinsky samt Isidor ein so idyllenfeindliches Ende nahm. Und es geschah, daß die Kommißstiefel der Schutzpolizisten, die früher höchstenfalls auf dem Parkett des Deutschen Reichstages noch denkbar waren, in die

Wer sucht, der findet!

geheiligten Bezirke des Geistes stapften, jenes Geistes, der mit Thomas Mann inbrünstig das „grandiose Experiment des Bolschewismus" verehrte.

Die kulturellen Folgen, um diese vorwegzunehmen, stempeln sothane Instinktlosigkeit der Berliner Schutzpolizei zu einem Vernichtungskampf gegen „den Geist" schlechthin!

Wo soll er jetzt noch einen Hort finden, wo sollen ferner seine roten Pomeranzen und faulen Pflaumen reifen? Es ist doch ein offenes Geheimnis, daß die linksgerichtete jüdische Intelligenz die einzige Karte war, die Deutschland im internationalen Kampf der Geister überhaupt noch abzugeben hatte, daß die deutsche Literatur jetzt brach liegen wird!

Betrachten wir nur die geistig belasteten Gesichtlein der aus der „Künstlerkolonie" jählings ausgehobenen „Dichter und Denker", und wir wissen, daß sie „ohnegleichen" sind.

58   Police raid of the artists' colony on Laubenheimer Platz, Berlin, on March 15, 1933.
Those arrested in the police car are, from left to right: Walter Zadek, Theodor Balk (Dragutin Fodor), Manès Sperber, a journalist by the name of Feist, and an unknown person. (See Abstract 2 in Appendix).

59   Göring (left) and Himmler in Berlin, 1932.

60   SS-Auxiliary Policeman and Berlin Policeman on the day of the election to the *Reichstag*, March 5, 1933.

61   Loading of confiscated files from the (Communist) Karl-Liebknecht-Haus on February 2, 1933.

List of Stormtroopers' pubs [SA-Sturmlokale] and Stormtroopers' barracks in Berlin that served in 1933 as concentration camps for anti-fascists ("wild concentration camps")

Rosinenstrasse (Charlottenburg)
Friedrichstrasse (Charlottenburg)
Stormtroopers' pub Keglerheim, today Bersarin-strasse 94 (Friedrichshain)
Stormtrooper's pub Gladenbecksche Villa, Müg-gelseedamm 132 (Köpenick)
Stormtroopers' pubs Jägerheim, Demuth, Seidler (Köpenick)
Stormtroopers' barracks Hedemannstrasse, Friedrichstrasse 234 (Kreuzberg)
Prinzenstrasse 100 (Kreuzberg)
Stormtroopers' barracks Unter den Eichen (Lich-terfelde)
Stormtroopers' barracks Jüdenstrasse (Mitte)
Stormtroopers' pub Novalisstrasse (Mitte)
Dragonerstrasse (Mitte)
Kastanienallee 62 (Mitte)
Rudowerstrasse (Neukölln)
Stormtroopers' barracks Niederschöneweide (Niederschöneweide)
Stormtroopers' barracks Wasserturm Kolmarer/ Knaackstrasse (Prenzlauer Berg)
Stormtroopers' pub Sturmvogel Malmöer-/ Überkmünder Strasse (Prenzlauer Berg)
Stormtroopers' barracks General Pape (Schöne-berg)
Universum-Landesausstellungspark ("ULAP"), In-validenstrasse (Tiergarten)
Stormtroopers' pub Liebenwalder Strasse (Wedding)
Genter Strasse (Wedding)
Utrechter Strasse (Wedding)
Stormtroopers' barracks Germania (?)
(Compiled from Laurenz Demps, "Konzentrations-lager in Berlin, 1933–1945." In: Jahrbuch des Märkischen Museums 3 [1977], p. 16f.)

62   Members of the Stormtroopers (SA) are given identification cards designed to identify them as Auxiliary Police in February, 1933.

63   Berlin Policemen practice for the 9th Indoor Sports Festival held on March 17, 1934 in the Berlin Sports Palace [*Sportpalast*].

64   Stormtroopers in action, March 1933.

65   Arrested anti-fascists in a "wild concentration camp" run
by Stormtroopers, end of March 1933.

66   **Hans Otto** (1900–1933), actor.
Born on August 10, 1900 in Dresden as the son of an official.
After graduation from High School [*Realgymnasium*] he decided to become an actor. He started his artistic career in
1921 at the *Künstlertheater* in Frankfurt am Main. He had further engagements at the Hamburger Kammerspiele, the Reus-
sische Theater Gera and the Hamburger Schauspielhaus. He
went to Berlin in 1929 and was first at the Theater on Stresemannstrasse and landed in 1930 at the Schauspielhaus. Since
1923 he was a member of the German Communist Party (KPD).
In the summer of 1931 he led the left opposition within the
Trade Union of German Stage Performers [*Genossenschaft
Deutscher Bühnen-Angehörigen*] of Berlin. He became first
chairman of the League of Workers' Theater [*Arbeiter-Thea-
ter-Bund*] in Germany, District Berlin. In March 1933 he was
dismissed from office by the Superintendent of the Schauspielhaus. He participated in the anti-fascist struggle as a member
of the Communist leadership committee of the Berlin Sub-Dis-
trict Zentrum. He was arrested on Nov. 14, 1933 and died ten
days later as the result of a fall from the top floor of a Stormtroopers' barracks on Voßstrasse – a fall induced by Stormtroopers.

67   Formation [*Appell*] of the SS-Division East in the German Stadion [*Grunewaldstadion*] on August 13, 1933. Left front is Ernst Röhm, Chief of Staff of the Stormtroopers; next to him is Himmler. At this juncture the SS was still organized as a segment of the Stormtroopers.

Text 1

The Ordeal of the Actor Hans Otto

On Wednesday evening, November 13 [1933], Hans Otto was arrested in a little restaurant on Victoria-Luise-Platz in Berlin. A traitor had led the Stormtroopers to the place. We were positioned opposite each other in the Stormtroopers' pub, "Cafe Komet," in Stralau-Rummelsburg. That's how our ordeal began. While a dance band was playing inside the cafe, we were alternately beaten up, hit in the face and kicked all over until our torturers grew tired. [...]

After four days we were dragged off to Köpenick. Here, in a damp and stinking bunker, in surroundings of downright medieval appearance, we were together with other prisoners, men and women, who had apparently been there for quite some time and who had been terribly mistreated by the Stormtroopers. [...]

From Köpenick we were moved to the Stormtrooper quarter on Möllendorfstrasse and from there to the *Gestapo* on Prinz-Albrecht-Strasse. Throughout the period we were there we were interrogated and physically maltreated. On Thursday we were moved to Voßstrasse. Since the time that we had been brought to Prinz-Albrecht-Strasse we had not been given either food or drink. But all this was a mere prelude to what now occurred at Voßstrasse. During this ghastly night I saw Hans Otto once more. It must have been approximately around midnight. He no longer was able to speak but could make only indistinct sounds. His mouth and his eyes were virtually swollen shut. [...]

A few hours later I saw him for the last time. He was half naked and I could no longer recognize his face. His body was one bloody lump. He was unconscious.

Gerhard Hinze

68   Front page of *Der Angriff*, Goebbels' Berlin news organ, "reporting" on the events of the "*Röhm Putsch*" on June 30, 1934. (See Abstract 3 in Appendix).

69   Gregor Strasser (1892–1934), in 1932.
The former National Director of Party Organization [*Reichsorganisationsleiter*] of the NSDAP and representative of the Party's "left wing" was murdered on June 30th, 1934 in the "Gestapo Prison" ["*Hausgefängnis*"] of the Secret State Police Office at Prinz-Albrecht-Strasse 8.

70   Karl Ernst (1904–1934)
Ernst, Commander of the Stormtrooper Contingent [*SA-Gruppe*] Berlin-Brandenburg, was shot on June 30, 1934 by a firing squad of the *SS-Leibstandarte Adolf Hitler* in the former Main Officer's Training School [*Hauptkadettenanstalt*].

Der Politische Polizeikommandeur der Länder

Adjutant

B.-Nr. *H. 8/35 Ads.*
Bei Rückantwort stets angugeben.

Berlin SW 11, den   18. I.   193 5.
Prinz-Albrecht-Straße 8

Einschreiben !

An

Frau Erna H ä b i c h ,

Stuttgart-Botnang,
Neue Stuttgarter Str. 48, I.

Betrifft:

Vorgang:

      Auf Grund Jhrer am 19. XI. 1934 an den Führer gerichteten und nach hier abgegebenen Eingabe teile ich Jhnen im Auftrage des Politischen Polizeikommandeurs der Länder, Reichsführer SS Himmler, mit, daß Jhr Sohn Walther H ä b i c h am 1. VII. 1934 im Zuge der Röhmrevolte standrechtlich erschossen worden ist.

      Da es sich bei der Erschiessung Jhres Sohnes um einen Akt der Staatsnotwehr gehandelt hat, liegt zu weiteren Erklärungen keine Veranlassung vor.

H e i l   H i t l e r

Hauptmann der Landespolizei

71   Notification about a summary execution of July 1, 1934, by the Chief of Political Police of the Member States [*Politischer Polizeikommandeur der Länder*] on January 18, 1935 (See Abstract 4 in Appendix).

72   Victor Lutze, Röhm's successor, leaving Wilhelmstrasse
106 on July 24, 1934.

Text 2

Law of July 3, 1934 concerning measures taken in defense of the state

The Reich Government has resolved to pass the following law which is herewith proclaimed:

Only Article:
All measures that were taken to crush the treasonable aggressions [*hoch- und landesverräterische Angriffe*] of June 30, 1934, July 1 and 2, 1934 were acts of defense of the state and therefore legally justified [*rechtens*]:

Berlin, July 3, 1934.
The Reich Chancellor
Adolf Hitler
The Reich Minister of the Interior
Frick
The Reich Minister of Justice
Dr. Gürtner

3.3. The Secret State Police

The creation of a hard hitting political police force was one of the first objectives of the NS State. In Prussia it was Hermann Göring – initially acting as Minister of the Interior, then Prussian Minister President – who set up the "Secret State Police Office" on April 26, 1933. Its first director was Rudolf Diels who had been engaged since February 1933 in creating a political police force. The Secret State Police [*Geheime Staatspolizei*], which was at once detached from the general police, was soon thereafter also removed from the jurisdiction of the Ministry of the Interior and placed directly under the authority of the Minister President. Since the beginning of May, the Secret State Police Office was located at Prinz-Albrecht-Strasse 8. From there proceeded the establishment of state police branches throughout all Prussian districts.

In April 1934 Heinrich Himmler became Inspector and Deputy Head of the Secret State Police. He appointed Reinhard Heydrich Director of the Secret State Police Office. Himmler, who had been initially Chief of the Munich police and Chief of Political Police [*Politischer Polizeikommandeur*] of Bavaria, was entrusted step-by-step with the command of the political police in nearly all non-Prussian member states [*Länder*]. Since May 1934 he coordinated the tasks of the entire political police from the headquarters of the "Chief of Political Police of the Member States" [*Politischer Polizeikommandeur der Länder*] at Prinz-Albrecht-Strasse 8. In November 1934 Göring relinquished his directive functions [over the Secret State Police in Prussia], and Himmler could accelerate the centralization of the *Gestapo*. After his appointment as "*Reichsführer-SS* and Head of the German Police" on June 17, 1936, and after having been placed pro forma under the jurisdiction of the Reich Minister of the Interior Wilhelm Frick, Himmler proceeded to reorganize the entire police force. The "Main Office [*Hauptamt*] of the Security Police" (headed by Reinhard Heydrich) included the *Gestapo* and the Criminal Police. The "Main Office of General Police" [*Ordnungspolizei*] was headed by Kurt Daluege and included Municipal Police [*Schutzpolizei*], Rural Police [*Gendarmerie*] and Local Police [*Gemeindepolizei*].

The Secret State Police Office started out in 1933 with between 200 and 300 employees in the central office. Already by April 1934 their number had risen to 680. In 1942 about 1100 persons were employed in the central office of the *Gestapo*, 477 of them on the "Prinz-Albrecht-Terrain." At this particular point of time the offices at Zimmerstrasse 16–19 immediately next door had 250 employees, most of whom were busy establishing and administering the *Gestapo's* main personnel card file.

Text 3

Law of April 26, 1933, pertaining to the establishment of a Secret State Police Office

The State Ministry has resolved to pass the following law:

§ 1.
(1) The Secret State Police Office with headquarters in Berlin is being established for the purpose of executing tasks of the Political Police parallel to or in place of those of the ordinary police (Article 2 paragraph 1 of the Police Administration Law of June 1, 1931 – Collection of Statutes, p. 77). Its position is equivalent to that of a police authority of an individual member state [*Landespolizeibehörde*] and directly subordinate to the Minister of the Interior.

73   Staircase and main hall of the Secret State Police Office,
about 1935.

(2) The technical and geographic spheres of competence of the Secret State Police Office will be determined by the Minister of the Interior.

(3) The provisions of the Police Administration Law of June 1, 1931 concerning challenges of directives issued by the police authority of an individual member state will be applied in such a way that the Berlin District Committee [*Bezirksausschuß*] shall always handle all legal complaints in suits of disputed administrative procedures [*Verwaltungsstreitverfahren*] involving directives issued by the Secret State Police Office.

§ 2.

Within the sphere of its competence, the Secret State Police Office can request all police authorities to take [the requisite] police measures.

§ 3.

All directives that are necessary for the execution of this law will be issued by the Minister of the Interior and, as far as the number and specification of officials and employees who will be assigned to the Secret State Police Office are concerned, this will be done in cooperation with the Ministry of Finance.

§ 4.

This law will become effective the day after its announcement.

Berlin, April 24, 1933
(Seal)   The Prussian Ministry of State.
        Göring,   Popitz.
conjointly also for the Minister of the Interior.

The law here presented has been resolved by the Prussian Ministry of State and is herewith proclaimed.
Berlin, April 26, 1933
For the Reich Chancellor:
The Prussian Minister President
Göring.

Text 4

Law of November 30, 1933, pertaining to the Secret State Police

The Ministry of State has resolved to pass the following law:

§ 1.

(1) The Secret State Police henceforth constitutes an independent branch within the internal administration. Its Head is the Minister President. The Minister President empowers the Inspector of the Secret State Police to take charge of all ongoing activities.

74 **Rudolf Diels** (1900–1957), in 1933
Since 1930 administrative councilor [*Regierungsrat*] in the Prussian Ministry of the Interior with the special assignment of fighting Communism. Göring appointed him Director of the Secret State Police Office that was created on April 26, 1933; he was succeeded by Himmler in April 1934.

(2) Should the Minister President as Head of the Secret State Police be prevented from carrying out his duties, the State Secretary [*Staatssekretär*] within the Ministry of State will substitute for him.

(3) The Inspector of the Secret State Police is simultaneously Director of the Secret State Police Office.

§ 2.

Within the Secret State Police's sphere of responsibilities fall the duties of the Political Police, supervised by the General and the Internal Administration. Specific duties handled by the Secret State Police are determined by the Minister President in his capacity as Head of the Secret State Police.

§ 3.

(1) All business pertaining to the Political Police heretofore taken care of by the Ministry of the Interior will pass to the Secret State Police Office as soon as this law takes effect.

(2) All police authorities on the member state level, district level and local level will carry out the instructions of the Secret State Police Office in connection with all matters pertaining to the Secret State Police.

§ 4.
To allow for the proper execution of this law the Minister of Finance is authorized to revise the state budget.

§ 5.
All articles of the Law of April 26, 1933 (Collection of Statutes, p. 122) will be suspended whenever they are not in accordance with this law.

§ 6.
This law becomes effective on the day it is proclaimed.

Berlin, November 30, 1933
(seal)   The Prussian Ministry of State.
                    Göring,   Popitz
simultaneously Minister of the Interior.

Text 5

Law of February 10, 1936, concerning the Secret State Police

The Ministry of State has resolved to pass the following law:

§ 1.
(1) The Secret State Police has the task throughout the entire State of investigating and fighting all attempts to endanger the State; to gather and evaluate the results of the investigations; to inform the State Government and to keep all other authorities [Behörden] abreast of important developments and to supply them with suggestions. The Head of the Secret State Police in cooperation with the Minister of the Interior will determine which specific tasks will be carried out by the Secret State Police.
(2) The competence of the various organs of the general administration of justice will remain unaffected.

§ 2.
(1) The Minister President is the Head of the Secret State Police.
(2) All official business is conducted by the Deputy Head of the Secret State Police who has been appointed by him.

§ 3.
(1) The highest authority of the Secret State Police within the State is the Secret State Police Office. It has simultaneously the status and functions [Be-

fugnisse] of a police authority of an individual member state [Landespolizeibehörde].
(2) The Secret State Police Office has its headquarters in Berlin.

§ 4.
The duties of the Secret State Police will be carried out on the intermediate level by State Police branches for the individual State Police districts. The duties of the Secret State Police near the frontiers are the responsibility of special frontier police authorities [Grenzkommissariate]. Otherwise, the duties of the Secret State Police will be carried out by police authorities on the district and local levels as auxiliary organs of the State Police branches.

§ 5.
The State Police branches are simultaneously subordinate to the authority of the appropriate regional governors [Regierungspräsidenten], must comply with their instructions, and must keep them informed about all police matters of a political nature. The heads of the State Police branches are simultaneously the experts for the regional governors on political affairs.

§ 6.
All appointments and dismissals of officials of the Secret State Police are dealt with by the Head of the Secret State Police in agreement with the Minister of the Interior and within the framework of the general rules determined by state law about appointments and dismissals of state officials.

§ 7.
Orders and concerns of the Secret State Police are not subject to the scrutiny of the courts of administration [Verwaltungsgerichte].

§ 8.
Instructions on how to execute this law will be issued by the Head of the Secret State Police in agreement with the Minister of the Interior.

§ 9.
The Law of April 26, 1933 pertaining to the Establishment of a Secret State Police (Collection of Statutes, p. 122), the Law of November 30, 1933, concerning the Secret State Police (Collection of Statutes, p. 413), and Articles 1 through 3 of the Decree for the Execution of the Law of March 8, 1934, concerning the Secret State Police (Collection of Statutes p. 143), are herewith rescinded.

76   The Prussian Minister President, Göring, hands over the leadership of the Secret State Police Office to Himmler on April 20, 1934, at Prinz-Albrecht-Strasse 8.

Norddeutsche Ausgabe / Ausgabe A
111. Ausg. • 47. Jahrg. • Einzelpreis 20 Pf. Ausland. 25 Pf.

Ausgabe A / Norddeutsche Ausgabe
Berlin, Sonnabend, 21. April 1934

VÖLKISCHER BEOBACHTER

Kampfblatt der national-sozialistischen Bewegung Großdeutschlands

Reichsführer S.S. Himmler übernimmt die Leitung
der Geheimen Preußischen Staatspolizei

Glückwünsche und Treuebekenntnisse für Adolf Hitler zu seinem Geburtstag — Sommerurlaub für die S.A. — Die Verforgung der Kämpfer für die nationalfozialiftifche Bewegung

75   Headline of the *Völkischer Beobachter* (Racial Observer, main organ of the NSDAP) of April 21, 1934. The banner line reads: "*Reichsführer-SS* Himmler takes over the Leadership of the Prussian Secret State Police."

Der Leiter   Berlin, den 30. November 1934.

des Geheimen Staatspolizeiamts

B.Nr. 54 758 I 1 A.   61

        Nachstehender Erlass des Herrn Preussischen Minister-
        präsidenten vom 20. 11. 1934 - St.M. P. 1317 - wird allen
        Dienststellen zur Kenntnis und Beachtung zugeleitet:
    "Der Preussische Ministerpräsident   Berlin, den 20. November 1934.
    Chef der Geheimen Staatspolizei.
        St.M.P. 1317.

        Aus organisatorischen Gründen habe ich mich veran-
        lasst gesehen, den Inspekteur der Geheimen Staatspolizei,
        Herrn Reichsführer SS H i m m l e r, mit meiner Vertre-
        tung auch in den Angelegenheiten der Geheimen Staats-
        polizei zu betrauen, deren Bearbeitung bisher unter Ein-
        schaltung des Preussischen Staatsministeriums erfolgte.
        Der Inspekteur der Geheimen Staatspolizei wird die Ge-
        schäfte der gesamten Preussischen Geheimen Staatspolizei
        nunmehr unter alleiniger Verantwortung mir gegenüber
        führen. Der Schriftwechsel erfolgt in den Angelegenhei-
        ten, die ich mir vorbehalten habe, unter der Firma
        "Preussische Geheime Staatspolizei. Der stellvertretende
        Chef und Inspekteur".
        Indem ich hiervon Kenntnis gebe, bitte ich, den
        Schriftwechsel in allen Angelegenheiten der Preussischen
        Geheimen Staatspolizei nunmehr unmittelbar und aus-
        schliesslich an das Geheime Staatspolizeiamt, Berlin SW 11,
        Prinz-Albrecht-Str.8, zu richten.
                gez. G ö r i n g ."
        Dem Herrn Preussischen Ministerpräsidenten sind
        zur Unterrichtung auch weiterhin zuzuleiten:

An

   alle Dienststellen

        im Hause.
        ----

77   Decree issued by the Prussian Minister President on November 20, 1934, pertaining to the expansion of Himmler's
authority as Director of the Secret State Police Office. (See
Abstract 5 in Appendix).

§ 10.
This law becomes effective on the day following its proclamation.

Berlin, February 10, 1936.
(seal)   The Prussian Ministry of State.
            Göring,   Frick.

I proclaim for the *Führer* and Reich Chancellor in the name of the Reich the law here presented for which the Reich Government has given its consent.
Berlin, February 10, 1936.
The Prussian Minister President.
Göring.

Text 6

Decree of June 17, 1936, pertaining to the appointment of a Chief of German Police within the Reich Ministry of the Interior.

I.
In order to have the police functions in the Reich placed on a unified and centralized basis, a Chief of German Police is being appointed within the Reich Ministry of the Interior who will simultaneously be entrusted with the direction and handling of all police functions within the jurisdiction of the Ministry of the Interior of the Reich and Prussia.

II.
(1) The Deputy Head of the Prussian Secret State Police, *Reichsführer-SS* Heinrich Himmler, is herewith appointed Chief of German Police within the Reich Ministry of the Interior.
(2) He is directly and personally responsible to the Ministry of the Interior of the Reich and Prussia.
(3) He will deputize within his range of duties for the Minister of the Interior of the Reich and Prussia in the absence of the latter.
(4) His official title will be: *Reichsführer-SS* and Chief of German Police within the Reich Ministry of the Interior.

III.
The Chief of German Police in the Reich Ministry of the Interior will participate in all meetings of the Reich Cabinet whenever his sphere of responsibility is affected.

IV.
I commission the Minister of the Interior of the Reich and Prussia with the execution of this decree.
Berlin, June 17, 1936.
The Leader and Reich Chancellor
Adolf Hitler

The Reich Minister of the Interior
Frick

Text 7

Daluege's appointment as Chief of General Police [Ordnungspolizei] and Heydrich's appointment as Chief of Security Police on June 26, 1936

Berlin, July 15, 1936
Chief of Security Police
V 1 No. 6/36

Copy.
Berlin, June 26, 1936.
The *Reichsführer-SS* and
Chief of German Police
in the Ministry of the Interior
of the Reich and Prussia.
O/S. No. 1/36

To: a) General of Police Daluege
       b) SS Major General Heydrich
Subject: The appointment of a Chief of General Police and a Chief of Security Police.

On the basis of the executive order pertaining to the decree of the Führer and Reich Chancellor on the appointment of a Chief of German Police of June 17, 1936, I herewith appoint General of Police Kurt Daluege Chief of General Police and SS, Major General Heydrich Chief of Security Police. The following operational police forces [*Vollzugspolizei*] will be placed under the command of the Chief of General Police:
The Municipal Police [*Schutzpolizei*],
The Rural Police [*Gendarmerie*],
The Local Police [*Gemeindepolizei*].
Under the command of the Chief of Security Police will be placed:
The Political Police,
The Criminal Police.
All fields of activity controlled by the Chief of German Police and not listed here will become evident from a table of duty assignments, to be distributed shortly.
signed: Himmler
[...]

78   The top leadership of the SS and Police with Hermann
Göring in 1937.

3.4. The Security Service of the Reichsführer-SS

When Reinhard Heydrich assumed the directorship of the Prussian Secret State Police Office in April 1934 he had already been head of the "Security Service of the *Reichsführer-SS*"(SD) for the preceding three years. It was the task of the SD, which had grown rapidly since it was first established, to keep the opponents of the NSDAP under surveillance and to fend off possible dangers from the Party. In 1934 Heydrich's headquarters [*Dienstsitz*] became the Prinz-Albrecht-Palais at Wilhelmstrasse 102. Subordinate to the SD-Headquarters established in 1935 were the SD regional and local commands [*(Leit)-Abschnitte*] and local SD branches [*SD-Aussenstellen*] within the respective SS main regional commands [*Oberabschnitte*]. A network of informers (*V-Männer*, or confidential agents) provided the central office with information, and the central office in turn issued situation reports at regular intervals.

In 1934 the SD was declared the sole intelligence service of the Party, and in 1937 a precise division of duties between the SD and the *Gestapo* was worked out. Through the SD Himmler secured for himself a monopoly over the entire official intelligence activities of the NSDAP. Thus, the SD remained at all times a party institution, and its employees also received their salaries from the NSDAP. Heydrich, who was in charge of both the *Gestapo* and the SD, wearing two hats, so to speak [*Personalunion*], offered the guarantee

79   Reinhard Heydrich in his Munich police office in 1934,
shortly before his transfer to Berlin.

for close cooperation between the two institutions. All official intelligence activities culminated in the regularly compiled "Reports from within the Reich", i.e., grassroots reports, by which the party leadership was kept relatively frankly informed about the internal political situation, in particular about the prevailing mood of the population.

Snooping within the Party, officially forbidden by Himmler but tacitly tolerated nevertheless, aroused from time to time displeasure among Party leaders who felt that their work was being criticized. The SD also issued informative reports about the extent of corruption within the various German administrative agencies, notably in the occupied territories.

An additional major aspect concerning the work of the SD were its official clandestine activities which in part also took place abroad. A familiar example is the fake attack on the Gleiwitz radio station whereby the SD, in close cooperation with the *Gestapo*, was able to furnish Hitler with the desired pretext for an invasion of Poland. From the ranks of the SD emerged a number of SS leaders who subsequently played a role in the "Final Solution of the Jewish Question," notably by way of the Special Units [*Einsatzgruppen*] of the Security Police and the SD. Adolf Eichmann, chief organizer of the mass deportation of Jews from all over Europe into the extermination camps also belonged to the service since 1935. He and others working in the Office of Jewish Affairs II/112 [*Judenreferat* II/112] of the SD Main Office would subsequently occupy leading positions in the machinery of the "Final Solution" within the European countries occupied by Germany.

Text 8

Decree of July 1, 1937 by the Chief of the Security Main Office and Chief of Security Police concerning the division of duties between the Gestapo and the Security Service (SD)

Copy.

Reichsführer-SS   Berlin, July 1, 1937
The Chief of Security Main Office
and Chief of Security Police.
C.d.S. D. No. 4957/37   Secret

Joint Directive for the Security Service of the *Reichsführer-SS* and the Secret State Police

Subject: Cooperation between the Security Service of the *Reichsführer-SS* and the Secret State Police.

1. The Security Service of the *Reichsführer-SS* and the Secret State Police will constitute a unified whole both in regard to the results of their work and their effect on the public. Their internal relationship will be neither competition nor superior standing and subordination, but mutual complementarity and avoidance of all duplication.

2. The following division of duties between the Security Service of the *Reichsführer-SS* and the Secret State Police will become effective immediately:

a) The Security Service of the *Reichsführer-SS* will be exclusively responsible for the following subject areas: Advanced Knowledge [*Wissenschaft*]: (Teaching, University Life, Research, Political Views),

Germanism and Germandom [*Volkstum and Volkskunde*]: (Racial Science, Public Health, Germandom, Work pertaining to Germanism [*Volkstumsarbeit*],

Art (Music, Theatre, Film, Radio),

Education (Youth Education in the school, Youth Education outside the schools, Education of University Students, Physical Education),

Party and State,

Constitution and Administration,

Foreign Countries,

Freemasonry,

Activities of associations [*Vereinswesen*].

b) The Secret State Police will be responsible exclusively for the following subject areas:

Marxism,

Treason,

Emigrants.

Der Inspekteur   Berlin, den 25. Juni 1934.

der Geheimen Staatspolizei.

B. Nr. 25 176 III H.

24

Betrifft: Nachrichtendienst der Partei.

Der Stellvertreter des Führers hat durch Befehl vom
9. Juni 1934 angeordnet,

daß nach dem 15. Juli 1934 neben dem Sicherheitsdienst des Reichsführers SS, kein Nachrichten-
oder Abwehrdienst der Partei mehr bestehen darf,
auch nicht in der Form einer Inlands- Nachrichten-
organisation für außenpolitische Zwecke.

Von dieser Anordnung ist sämtlichen Beamten und Ange-
stellten der Geheimen Staatspolizei Kenntnis zu geben.
Die Herren Staatspolizeistellenleiter mache ich persönlich
dafür verantwortlich, daß nach dem 15. Juli 1934 in ihren
Bezirken außer dem Sicherheitsdienst des Reichsführers SS,
kein Nachrichtendienst der Partei - gleichgültig ob getarnt oder nicht getarnt - mehr besteht. Über jede Zuwiderhandlung gegen die Anordnung des Stellvertreters des
Führers vom 9. Juni 1934, sei sie auch noch so geringfügi-
ger Natur, ist mir sofort zu obiger Geschäftsnummer zu be-
richten.

In Vertretung:

gez. H e y d r i c h.

Beglaubigt:

Pol.Ow.

An
die Herren Leiter
der Preußischen
Staatspolizeistellen.

80   By order of the "Leader's Deputy," Rudolf Hess, dated
June 9, 1934, the Security Service (SD) is designated as the
sole intelligence service of the Party. Other Party branches are
no longer permitted to conduct intelligence operations.
(See Abstract 6 in the Appendix).

c) All matters pertaining to the subject areas listed below that are general and fundamental (whereby active intervention by the State Police is ruled out) will be handled by the Security Service of the *Reichsführer-SS*, and all individual cases (whereby active intervention is called for) will be handled by the Secret State Police:

Churches, Sects, other religious or ideological groups,

Pacifism,

Jewry,

Rightist Movement [*Rechtsbewegung*],

other groups hostile to the State (such as the Black Front, the *bündische* Youth Movement, et al.).

Economy, Press.

[...]

10. The foregoing directions apply respectively to all proceedings taken care of under the rubric "Chief of Security Police."

Signed: Heydrich.

Confirmed:

Dr. Best.

Text 9

"Reports from within the Reich." Security Service (SD) Reports about the Reactions of the German Population to Stalingrad, January 25 to August 9, 1943

No. 353, January 25, 1943

[...] The numerous apprehensions that were voiced repeatedly because of the uncertainty during the past weeks have supposedly been confirmed by the Army Report of January 22 and thus are said to have become certainty after the Soviets have allegedly thrust into the Stalingrad area from the West. [...]

Beyond this Army Report a series of other articles have likewise eliminated all hope that the troops trapped in Stalingrad still have a chance to be relieved. Glorification of the defense of Stalingrad through terms such as "heroic onslaught," "unflinching perseverance," "heroic battle" and "heroic defense" would allow no other interpretation than that Stalingrad has been lost to us. [...]

The apprehensions of our fellow Germans [*Volksgenossen*] seem not only directed at the loss of Stalingrad but are said to reveal deep anxieties about the entire course of the war in the East. The view that "probably the whole eastern front seems to be close to collapse" is said to be heard not infrequently. The population is allegedly suspicious, wondering whether the media, despite their frankness, were in fact depicting the adversity of the situation in its entierety. [...]

No. 354, January 28, 1943

[...] Fearing that an unfavorable end of the war may now be within the realm of possibility, our fellow Germans occupy themselves seriously with the consequences of defeat. While here and there the opinion is voiced that it "would perhaps not be half as bad," the overwhelming majority is thoroughly convinced that loss of the war would be tantamount to total ruin. [...]

Nr. 355, February 1, 1943

[...] The comparison between the struggle for Stalingrad and the fight of the Nibelungs in Etzel's hall, or with the fight at Thermopylae, is to have met with acceptance, notably in the speech of the Reich Marshal [Göring]. The mass of our fellow Germans, however, is said to want the press to employ such emotional sentiments and attributes sparsely and sparingly lest such terms as "heroism," "valor," "sacrifice and martyrdom" be emptied of meaning through daily repetitions; in some newspapers they are said to have sunk to the use of terminology that was perceived as platitudinous. [...]

No. 356, February 4, 1943

Reports about the termination of the Battle of Stalingrad have shaken the entire people once again to its depth. The speeches of January 30 and the proclamation of the Führer have taken a backseat in view of this event, and play a lesser role in serious conversations on the part of our fellow Germans, than do a number of questions connected with the events at Stalingrad. First of all it is the number of casualties [*Blutopfer*] which the population wants to know. Conjectures fluctuate between 60.000 and 300.000 men. It is being assumend that the great majority of those who fought at Stalingrad have perished. Regarding those troops who have become prisoners of the Russians there are two popular conceptions. On the one hand there are those who say that imprisonment is worse than death because the Bolsheviks are bound to treat those soldiers who have fallen into their hands alive in an inhumane manner. Others believe in turn how fortunate it is that not all of them have perished; this way there remains the hope that some of them might eventually return to the homeland. Especially the relatives of those who fought at Stalingrad suffer much under this ambiguous situation and the uncertainty that results from it.

Furthermore, large segments of the population are debating whether the developments at Stalingrad were inevitable and whether the immense sacrifices were necessary. Our fellow Germans are specifically concerned with the question whether the threat to Stalingrad was at the time promptly recognized. Air reconnaissance should have spotted the concentration of Russian armies that were then moving against Stalingrad.

Furthermore, the question is being discussed why the city was not evacuated when there was still time to do so. [...]

The third issue around which the conversations of our fellow Germans revolve right now is the importance of the Battle of Stalingrad seen in the context of the war as a whole. [...]

No. 357, February 8, 1943

[...] The thoughts and discussions of the population are still fixed on Stalingrad. The initial shock, however, is over; the discussions about the causes of the defeat have also subsided somewhat. The report that 47,000 wounded could be rescued has caused general rejoicing and a certain relief, despite the fact that the actual losses are presumed to be much higher than this figure. [...] At the moment a good deal of talk deals with the estimated length of the war. The question today, it is said, is no longer how far away victory is, but how long we can continue the war with prospects for a favorable ending. [...]

No. 358, February 11, 1943

[...] Current incoming information confirms once again that Stalingrad has aroused a deep national awareness within the entire people. [...] The National Socialist fellow Germans, so the reports say, are also seriously concerned about the future, are not above criticism concerning the internal situation, and in the process go even beyond the hitherto unconditionally respected limits. [...]

No. 368, March 18, 1943

[...] The following report which relates the experience of a woman [*Volksgenossin*] during a railway journey and which was selected at random from among similar reports reflects symptomatically the lack of discipline on the part of many fellow Germans, but also the difficult situation responsible people confront when encountering similar manifestations:

"A Berliner who allegedly works in a governmental office said to a fellow traveller after a lengthy and very frank discussion of the war situation: 'I can give you a hundred percent assurance that we won't have to lose this war anymore in the future; we have lost it already! When a woman [*Volksgenossin*] retorted 'if I were a man I would box your ears!' the Berliner became rude. Politics wasn't a subject for women because they don't understand anything about it; he who was sitting in a [government] department higher up knew better. It would

be unthinkable 'that we could wiggle out of the kind of mess we have managed to get ourselves into.' The other traveller also told the woman not to get so upset as he, too, moved in authoritative circles where similar views prevailed. (The name of the traveller could be ascertained and requisite measures have been initiated)." [...]

August 9, 1943

After Stalingrad it was still possible, through increased efforts, to infuse the agitated masses with determination to ward off disaster on the horizon. Their hearts were suddenly receptive again to new propagandistic influences. But as aerial warfare is threatening the urban population with utter ruin, as all middle class citizens and workers face their own worries that are seemingly without solution — about their livelihood, their earthly possessions, about simply surviving — there arises in all of them a hitherto unknown need to think for themselves: [There is] the vexing question of "why?" and, above all, real hunger for political answers which are not just rousing phrases and slogans, but which can restore once again the imperiled or even destroyed livelihood and calm the spreading fear for one's life. Not only their disappointed sentiments must be addressed, but also their traumatized minds, upset as they are by horrible events.

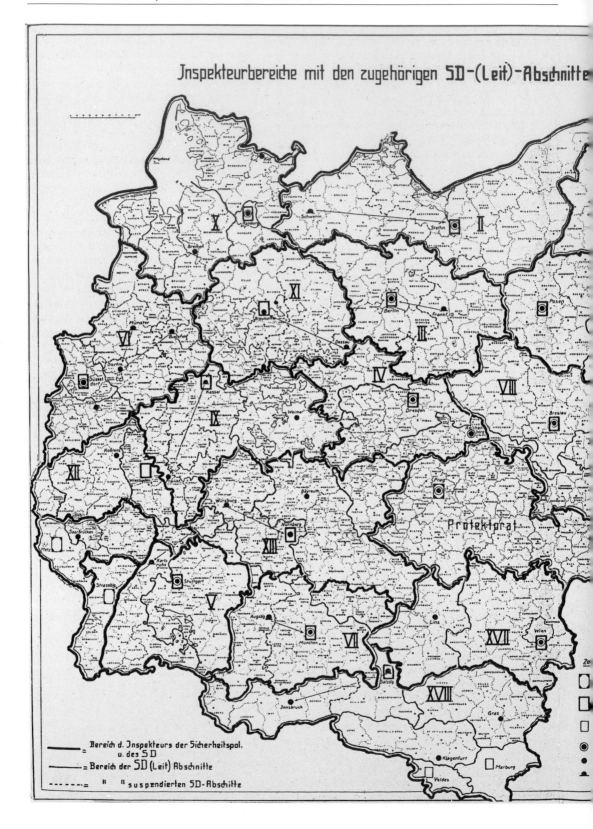

81   Map of the Regional and Local Commands [*SD-(Leit)-Abschnitte*] of the Security Service as of 1940/41.
Pertaining to the legend on the map, lower left:
Zone of the Chief [*Inspekteur*] of Security Police.
Zone of the Regional and Local Commands [*SD-(Leit)-Abschnitte*] of the Security Service.
Zone of suspended Security Commands.

3.5. The Reich Security Main Office

With the establishment of the Reich Security Main Office (RSMO) — [*Reichssicherheits-hauptamt (RSHA)*] on September 27, 1939, Himmler concentrated all forces organized within the State's Main Security Police Office (Secret State Police and Criminal Police) and those active within the Party's Security Service Main Office [*SD-Hauptamt*] into one institution. He appointed Reinhard Heydrich Head of the Reich Security Main Office and Chief of Security Police and the Security Service.

This organizational fusion, however, did not mean that the existing departments were dissolved. Whenever business was conducted with other departments, Department IV, for instance, the former name was maintained, in this case "Secret State Police Office." The term "Reich Security Main Office" was only used for internal correspondence. For this reason, too, the RSMO had no central building. Its departmental branch offices were scattered throughout the city. The building at Prinz-Albrecht-Strasse 8 in Berlin South West 11 remained headquarters, however; it was also the RSMO's postal address. It also remained the official address of the *Reichsführer-SS* and his personal staff.

Subordinate to the RSMO was a wide network of branch offices. In 1943 alone, there were 70 State Police and 66 Criminal Police branch offices. In the occupied territories, mobile and stationary branch offices held sway: there were either the Special Units [*Einsatzgruppen*] and Special Commandos [*Einsatzkommandos*], or else, chiefs and commanders of Security Police and Security Service with the units under their command. Even in the concentration camps, Secret State Police officials selected specially for the job by the RSMO worked in the "Political Offices."

Himmler and Heydrich had established with the RSMO the most important agency of National Socialist Rule devoted to oppression and terror. Through a perverse combination of bureaucratic procedure and unrestrained arbitrariness, the RSMO issued its instructions and orders for the "Third Reich's" politics of persecution and extermination. This office selected the personnel for the "Special Units" that carried out mass executions by which hundreds of thousands of victims were killed. Staff members of this office developed gassing vans which were used for a while to murder the Jewish population. The Office of Protective Custody [*Schutzhaftreferat*] decided which people were to be sent to concentration camps. The Institute for Criminal-Technical Matters [*Kriminaltechnisches Institut*] of Department V experimented on prisoners with poisoned ammunition. These are just a few examples.

Besides the guards at concentration camps and extermination camps, the most important and most dreaded instruments of National Socialist politics of persecution, oppression and extermination were the Security Police, i.e., Secret State Police [*Gestapo*] and Criminal Police [*Kripo*]. In addition, there were units of the Security Service [*Sicherheitsdienst (SD)*], and police battalions of the Main Office of the General Police [*Hauptamt Ordnungspolizei*].

Of the approximately 3400 employees in the central administrative offices of the Reich Security Main Office, approximately 1500 were located in 1942 on the "Prinz-Albrecht-

Terrain." And while an additional 500 worked in offices in the immediate vicinity, roughly another 100 employees of the *Reichsführer-SS'* Personal Staff were also operative on the terrain proper.

Text 10

Decree of September 27, 1939 by the Reichsführer-SS and Chief of German Police pertaining to the establishment of the Reich Security Main Office

Berlin, Sept. 27, 1939
The *Reichsführer-SS* and
Chief of German Police
S-V 1 No. 719/39 – 151 –
/1

Distribution *per procura*

Subject: Fusion of the central departments of Security Police and Security Service.

1. The following departments:
Main Office Security Police
Main Office Security Service
of the *Reichsführer-SS*
Secret State Police Office
Reich Criminal Police Office
will be fused to form the Reich Security Main Office in accordance with the following stipulations. The position of these departments within the Party and governmental administration will not be affected by this fusion.

2. The following structure and designations with respect to all internal office transactions will be in effect as of October 1, 1939:

a) Department "Administration and Law" of the Main Office of Security Police, Department I (I,1 I,2 and I,4) of the Main Security Office, Section [*Abteilung*] I of the Secret State Police Office will form Department I of the Reich Security Main Office (unless the table of duty assignments [*Geschäftsverteilungsplan*] specifies the jurisdiction of another department). Its director will be SS Brigadier General and Assistant Administrative Secretary [*Ministerialdirigent*] Dr. Best.

b) Central Section II 1 of the previous Department II and I 3 of the Security Main Office of the *Reichsführer-SS* will form Department II of the Reich Security Main Office in accordance with the directives of the revised table of duty assignments. Its director will be SS Colonel Professor Dr. Six.

c) Central Section II 2 of the previous Department II of the Security Main Office of the *Reichsführer-SS* will henceforth form Department III of the Reich Security Main Office in accordance with the directives of the revised table of duty assignments. Its director will be SS Colonel Ohlendorf.

d) Department Political Police of the Main Office of Security Police and Sections II and III of the Secret State Police Office will form Department IV of the Reich Security Main Office. Its director will be *SS-Oberführer* [no equivalent rank in U.K. or U.S.A.; ranks between colonel and brigadier general] and Reich Detective Superintendent [*Reichskriminaldirektor*] Müller.

e) Department Criminal Police of the Main Office of Security Police and the Reich Criminal Police Office will form Department V of the Reich Security Main Office. Its director will be *SS-Oberführer* and Reich Detective Superintendent Nebe.

f) Department III of the Security Main Office of the *Reichsführer-SS* will become Department VI of the Reich Security Main Office in accordance with the directives of the revised table of duty assignments. Its director will be SS Brigadier General Jost.
[...]

Signed: H. Himmler

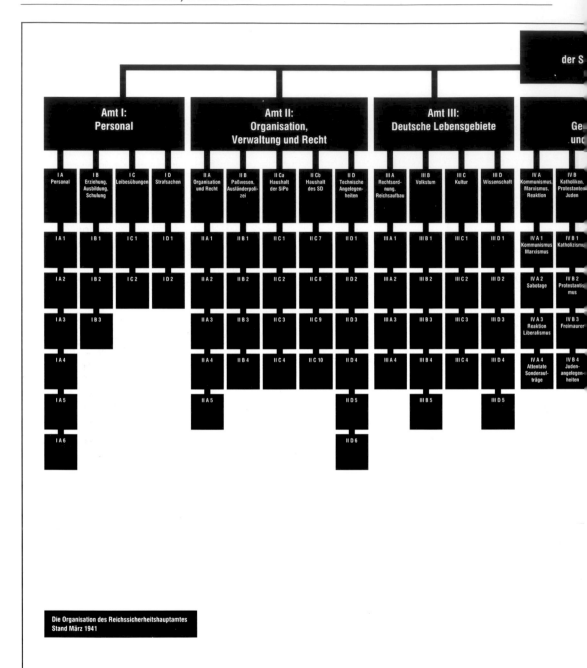

Die Organisation des Reichssicherheitshauptamtes Stand März 1941

82   Organization of the Reich Security Main Office as of March 1, 1941.

Chief of Security Police and Security Service
(Below, from left to right):

Department I: Personnel.
I A Personnel. I B Education, Training, Indoctrination. I C Physical Education. I D Criminal Matters.

Department II: Organization, Administration and Law.
II A Organization and Law. II B Passport Matters, Alien Police.

II C a Budget of Security Police. II C b Budget of the Security Service (SD). II D Technical Matters.

Department III: German Controlled Territories [Lebensgebiete]
III A Matters pertaining to the Legal System and Building Up the Reich. III B Germanism [*Volkstum*]. III C Cultural Matters. III D Economy.

Department IV: Investigation of and Fighting Opponents.
IV A Communism, Marxism, Reactionaries. IV B Catholics, Protestants, Jews. IV C Protective Custody. IV D Protectorate [Bohemia, Moravia], southeastern Poland [*Generalgouverne-*

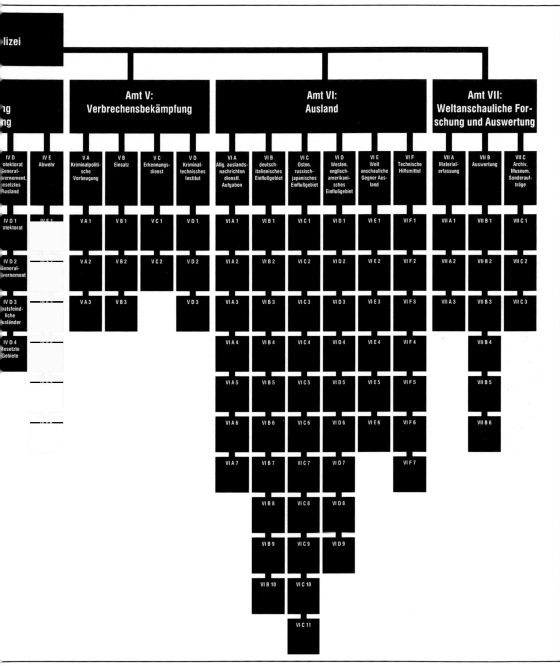

...lizei													

Amt V: Verbrechensbekämpfung — **Amt VI: Ausland** — **Amt VII: Weltanschauliche Forschung und Auswertung**

IV D Protektorat Generalgouvernement, besetztes Ausland	IV E Abwehr	V A Kriminalpolitische Vorbeugung	V B Einsatz	V C Erkennungsdienst	V D Kriminaltechnisches Institut	VI A Allg. auslandsnachrichtendienstl. Aufgaben	VI B deutschitalienisches Einflußgebiet	VI C Osten, russischjapanisches Einflußgebiet	VI D Westen, englischamerikanisches Einflußgebiet	VI E Welt anschauliche Gegner Ausland	VI F Technische Hilfsmittel	VII A Materialerfassung	VII B Auswertung	VII C Archiv, Museum, Sonderaufträge
IV D 1 Protektorat	IV E 1	V A 1	V B 1	V C 1	V D 1	VI A 1	VI B 1	VI C 1	VI D 1	VI E 1	VI F 1	VII A 1	VII B 1	VII C 1
IV D 2 Generalgouvernement		V A 2	V B 2	V C 2	V D 2	VI A 2	VI B 2	VI C 2	VI D 2	VI E 2	VI F 2	VII A 2	VII B 2	VII C 2
IV D 3 Staatsfeindliche Ausländer		V A 3	V B 3		V D 3	VI A 3	VI B 3	VI C 3	VI D 3	VI E 3	VI F 3	VII A 3	VII B 3	VII C 3
IV D 4 Besetzte Gebiete						VI A 4	VI B 4	VI C 4	VI D 4	VI E 4	VI F 4		VII B 4	
						VI A 5	VI B 5	VI C 5	VI D 5	VI E 5	VI F 5		VII B 5	
						VI A 6	VI B 6	VI C 6	VI D 6	VI E 6	VI F 6		VII B 6	
						VI A 7	VI B 7	VI C 7	VI D 7		VI F 7			
							VI B 8	VI C 8	VI D 8					
							VI B 9	VI C 9	VI D 9					
							VI B 10	VI C 10						
								VI C 11						

ment], Occupied Territories. IV E Counterintelligence [*Abwehr*]. IV A 1 Communism, Marxism. IV B 1 Catholicism. IV C 1 Central card index [*Hauptkartei*]. IV D 1 Protectorate. IV A 2 Sabotage. IV B 2 Protestantism. IV C 2 Protective Custody. IV D 2 *Generalgouvernement* IV A 3 Reactionaries, Liberalism. IV B 3 Freemasons. IV C 3 Press. IV D 3 Enemy Aliens. IV A 4 Assassinations, Special Assignments. IV B 4 Jewish Affairs. IV C 4 Structural Components of the Party. IV D 4 Occupied Territories.

Department V: Crime Fighting.
V A Protection against Political Crimes. V B Deployment for Action [*Einsatz*]. V C Criminal Identification Service. V D Institute for Criminal – Technical Matters.

Department VI: Foreign Countries. VI A Intelligence Work Abroad, General tasks. VI B German-Italian Sphere of Influence. VI C The East: Russo-Japanese Sphere of Influence. VI D The West: Anglo-American Sphere of Influence. VI E Ideological Opponents Abroad. VI F Technical Aids.

Department VII: Ideologies – Research and Evaluation. VII A Collection of Material. VII B Evaluation. VII C Archive, Museum, Special Assignments.

83   Reinhard Heydrich (1904–1942)
Born in Halle on the Saale. Attended a Catholic highschool emphasizing science and languages. Joined the Navy in 1922. After having been cited before a court of honor, he was discharged as a First Lieutenant (Navy) in 1928. Joined the NSDAP and SS in 1931. In August 1931 he was put in charge of building up an intelligence service in the *SS-Oberstab* [no equivalent in English; approx. SS higher headquarters] in Munich. In March 1933 he became acting Head of the Political Division within Munich's police headquarters and Chief of Bavaria's Political Police. In November 1933 he became Head of the Security Service of the *Reichsführer-SS*. On April 22, 1934 he became Head of the Prussian Secret State Police Office, and then, in 1936, was appointed Chief of Security Police (Secret State Police and Criminal Police). When the Reich Security Main Office was established on September 27, 1939, Heydrich became its Head. In September 1941, when the Reich Protector of Bohemia and Moravia fell ill, he was appointed his substitute. Heydrich died in June 1942 in Prague as the result of an assassination attempt.

84   Ernst Kaltenbrunner (1903–1946)
Born in Ried (Inn District). Doctor of Law in 1926. Joined the NSDAP in 1930, the SS in 1931. Was appointed State Secretary for Public Safety in March 1938 in the Austrian Cabinet of Seyss-Inquart. After the "*Anschluß*" [annexation of Austria] he became Head of *SS-Oberabschnitt* [approx. Main Regional Command] Danube, and simultaneously Higher SS and Police Leader for the same region. On January 30, 1943, he was appointed Heydrich's successor as Chief of Security Police and Security Service, and also as Head of the Reich Security Main Office. Towards the end of the war he moved his headquarters to Alt-Aussee in Styria. Sentenced to death by the International Military Tribunal at Nuremberg he was executed in 1946.

85   Werner Best (1903–1989)
Born in Darmstadt. Doctor of Law, since 1929 Precinct Judge [*Amtsrichter*] in Hesse. Joined the NSDAP in 1930. Discharged from state service in Hesse in December 1931. 1931 until 1933 NSDAP District Leader and also its delegate to the [Hesse] Diet. In March 1933 State Police Commissioner for Hesse. Joined the SS in June 1933. In July 1933 appointed Chief of Police in Hesse. Since January 1935 he headed a department within the Secret State Police Office. In 1936 Head of Department I (Administration and Law) in the Security Police Main Office and Deputy to the Chief of Security Police. After the Reich Security Main Office was established in September 1939 he remained Head of Department I. In 1940 he became chief administrator at the staff of the commanding general in Paris. From November 1942 until the end of the war he was in charge of the German Embassy in Copenhagen. In 1948 he was sentenced to death in Denmark for war crimes committed, but was pardoned in August 1951. All legal proceedings pending against him in the German Federal Republic were suspended in 1972 because of his unfitness to stand trial; in 1982 they were dismissed.

Administrative departments of the Reich Security Main Office in Berlin
Status as of December 7, 1943

1. Prinz-Albrecht- Strasse 8
Head of Department IV (Investigating and fighting enemies) and Headquarters of Department IV.
Departmental Sections:
IV N   (Liaison)
IV A   (Opposition, sabotage, protective service [Schutzdienst])
IV A 1   (Communism, marxism and aligned organizations, crimes in wartime, illegal and enemy propaganda)
IV A 4   (Protective service, assassination reports, surveillance)
IV D   (Greater German spheres of interest – parts of them)

2. Wilhelmstrasse 102
Chief of Security Police and Security Service (SD)
Attaché Group
Head of Department I   (Personnel, training and organization of the Security Police and Security Service)
Headquarters of Department I.
Departmental Sections:
I Org   (Organizational matters, project files, editorial office of the command roster, decree file)
I A 4   (Personal data, Security Service)
I A 5   (Personal data, Party members and SS)
Head of Department III (German controlled territories [Lebensgebiete])
Headquarters of Department III, including Section III A 1 (General aspects concerning tasks in the controlled territories)

3. Wilhelmstrasse 103
Section II A (Budget, payroll and general accounting for Security Service)

4. Wilhelmstrasse 106
Departmental Sections:
III A   (Matters pertaining to the legal system and to building up the Reich [Reichsaufbau])
III A 2   (Legal matters [Rechtsleben])
III A 4   (The People's overall way of life)
III A 5   (General legal questions pertaining to the police, constitutional questions pertaining to the police, special laws pertaining to the police)
III A 6
III D   (Economy)
III D 1   (Food production and distribution)
III D 3   (Economy of finance, currency, banks and stock exchanges, insurance business)
III D 4   (Industrial and energy economics)
III D 5   (Matters pertaining to labor and social welfare)
III D West   (Occupied territories, West)
III D East   (Occupied territories, East)

5. Wilhelmstrasse 20
Departmental Sections:
I A 2   (Personnel files, Gestapo)
I A 3   (Personnel files, Criminal Police)
III D 2   (Commerce, skilled trades, and transportation)

6. Wilhelmstrasse 34
Section:
IV D 4   (Greater Germany's spheres of influence: France, Belgium, Holland, Norway, Denmark)

7. Zimmerstrasse 16–18
Departmental Sections:
IV C   (card index of individuals [Personenkartei], administration of files on individuals, protective custody, press and Party.
IV C 1   (Evaluation of central card index, administration of files on individuals, information center on alien surveillance liaison center)
IV C 2   (Matters pertaining to protective custody), liaison center
IV D 5   (Occupied eastern territories)

8. Kochstrasse 64
Head of Department II (Budget and economy)
Headquarters of Department II
Departmental Sections:
II A   (Budget, payroll and billing)
II A 1   (Budget of Security Police, foreign currency)
II A 2   (Payroll, supply, travel expenses of Security Police)
II B 1   (Billeting, raw materials, confiscated property)
II B 2   (Clothing supplies, business needs)
II B 3   (Prisoners overall aspects [Gefangenenwesen])
II B 4   (Justiciary affairs)

9. Hedemannstrasse 14
Section:
II A 3   (Accounting office, building management)

10. Hedemannstrasse 22
Departmental Sections:
III B   (Germanism [Volkstum])
III B 1   (Tasks relating to Germanism)
III B 2   (Minorities)
III B 3   (Racial and national health)
III B 4   (Nationality and naturalization)
III B 5   (Occupied territories)
III C   (Cultural matters)
III C S
III C R

11. Hermann-Göring-Strasse 5
Administrative Department of the Deputy to the Director of Medical Matters (The administrative department of the director was in Dresden).
Departmental Sections:
I A 1   (General personnel matters), liaison center.
I A 6   (Welfare)

12. Hermann-Göring- Strasse 8
Departmental Sections:
IV F   (Alien Police)
IV F 2   (Passports)
IV F 3   (Matters pertaining to proof of identity and identification cards)
IV F 4   (Alien Police)

13. Burgstrasse 26
Departmental Sections:
II   (Technical matters)
II C 2   (Telegraph and telephone services)
II C 3   (Automotive matters)
II C 5   (Moving up supplies [Nachschub])
III A 3   (Constitution and administration)

14. Werderscher Markt 5–6
Head of Department V (Crime Fighting)
Headquarters of Department V
Departmental Sections:
V A   (Protection against political crimes)
V A 1   (Legal questions, international cooperation and research into criminality)

V A 3   (Female Criminal Police)
V A 4   (Registration with the police)
V B 3   (Sex crimes)
V D 2   (Chemical and biological science research)
V D W   (Work and repair shops)

15. Berliner Strasse 120 (Pankow)
Section:
IV F 5   (Central visa office)

16. Wörthstrasse 20
Departmental Sections:
V B   (Joint deployment with national headquarters of
                the Reich Criminal Police Office)
V B 1   (Capital crimes)
V B 2   (Fraud)

17. Lindenstrasse 51–53
Cashier's and accounting office of the RSMO

18. Jägerstrasse 1–2
Clothing supply office of Section II B 2 (Kochstrasse 64)

19. Hauptstrasse 144
Departmental Sections:
V C   (Search operations, matters pertaining to police
                dogs, information)
V C 1   (Headquarters of search operations)

20. Eisenacher Strasse 12
Head of Department VII (Ideologies – research and evalu-
ation)
Headquarters of Department VII
Section:
VII A 2   (Reporting, examination and use of press reports)

21. Kurfürstenstrasse 115–116
Section:
IV B 4   (Jewish affairs, evacuation procedures, confis-
                cated property of enemies of the people and
                state, abrogation of German citizenship)

22. Meinekestrasse 10
Departmental Sections:
IV B   (Political churches, sects and jews)
IV B 1   (Political catholicism)
IV B 2   (Political Protestantism, sects)
IV B 3   (Other churches, freemasonry)
IV C 3   (Matters pertaining to the press and literature)
IV C 4   (Matters pertaining to the Party [Nazi] and its or-
                ganizational structure)

23. Kurfürstendamm 140
Departmental Sections:
IV A 2   (Defense and countermeasures against sabot-
                age; political forgery activities)
IV E   (Counterintelligence)
IV E 1   (General counterintelligence aspects; expert tes-
                timonies concerning high and national treason
                [Hoch- und Landesverrat])
IV E 3   (Counterintelligence West)
IV E 4   (Counterintelligence North)
IV E 5   (Counterintelligence East)
IV E 6   (Counterintelligence South)
IV F 1   (Frontier Police)

24. Emser Strasse 12 (Wilmersdorf)
Departmental Sections:
VII A   (Collection of [relevant] material)
VII A 1   (Library)
VII C   (Archive, museum, and special assignments per-
                taining to advanced knowledge [wissenschaftli-
                che Sonderaufträge])

VII C 1
VII C 2

25. Berkaer Strasse 32
Head of Department VI (Security Service abroad)
Headquarters of Department VI
Departmental Sections:
VI A   (Organization of the intelligence service abroad)
VI B   (Intelligence service in western europe)
VI C   (Intelligence service in the Russo-Japanese
                sphere of influence)
VI D   (Intelligence service in North and South America,
                England and Scandinavia)
VI G   (Methodical scientific research service)
VI Wi   (Incorporation of the economy into the intellig-
                ence service abroad)

26. Schloßstrasse 1 (Charlottenburg)
Departmental Sections:
I B   (The next generation, education and training)
I B 1   (Political-ideological and SS-oriented edu-
                cation)
I B 2   (The next generation)
I B 3   (Training, advanced training, and special schoo-
                ling)
I B 4   (Physical education and military defense train-
                ing)
I B 5   (Career guidelines, examination office, admi-
                nistration of funds)

27. Am Grossen Wannsee 71
Departmental Sections:
IV C 1   (These are three of 13 sections of the area
IV C 2   "inteligence service in the russo-japanese
IV C 3   sphere of influence").

28. Delbrückstrasse 6a (Grunewald)
Section:
VI F   (Technical aids for the intelligence service ab-
                road)

29. Fürstenwalder Damm (Rahnsdorf)
Section:
V C 3 a   (Police dog training school)
V D 4 W   (Workshops: Photocopying)

30. Münchener Strasse 32
Storage Depot of Department VII

31. Potsdamer Chaussee/Corner Theodor-Fritsch-Allee (Police Barracks)
Main Office of Department II

32. Wrangelstrasse 6–7 (Steglitz)
Departmental Sections:
IV D   (Greater German spheres of influence), liaison
                center
IV D 1   (Protectorate Bohemia-Moravia, Czechs inside
                Germany, Slovakia, Croatia and remaining
                Yugoslavia, Greece)
IV D 2   (Generalgouvernement, Poles inside Germany)
IV D 3   (Collection centers for informer's reports
                [Vertrauensstellen], enemy aliens, emigrants)

33. Wielandstrasse 42
Section:
II C 1   (Aspects pertaining to broadcasting, photogra-
                phy and film)

86 **Bruno Streckenbach** (1902–1977)
Attended highschool through the 11th grade. Joined a Free
Corps in 1919. Business training with a Hamburg import firm.
Joined the NSDAP and the Stormtroopers in 1930, the SS in
1931. Chief of Hamburg's Political Police in September 1933.
Member of the Security Service as of December 1933. In February 1938 Inspector of Security Police and the Security Service in Defense District X (Hamburg). 1939 Commander of
Special Unit [*Einsatzgruppe*] I. Commander of Security Police
and the Security Service in the *Generalgouvernement*. In January 1941 Head of Department I (Personnel) in the Reich Security Main Office. Transferred to the Combat SS [*Waffen-SS*] in
December 1942, on his own request. Tried by a court-martial
in Moscow in 1952 he was sentenced to 25 years of hard labor for war crimes committed. Was discharged in 1955 into
the custody of the German Federal Republic. Proceedings instituted against him for crimes committed under National Socialism were halted in 1976 because of his permanent inability
to stand trial.

87 **Alfred Franz Six** (1909–1975)
Born in Mannheim. Joined the Stormtroopers and the NSDAP
in May 1930. From 1933 on he led various Stormtroop units.
PH.D. degree in 1934. Assistant at a Heidelberg Institute. In
the Fall of 1934 he became the national official in charge of
the German Student League in Berlin. Habilitation in 1936. In
1935: full-time member of the Security Service and transfer
into the SS. In 1937 he became a Department Head in the Security Service Main Office.
When the Reich Security Main Office was established in September 1939 he became Head of Department II. Dean of Fa-
culty for Studies of Foreign Countries at the University of Berlin
at the end of 1939. As of January 1, 1941, Head of Department VII (Research of Ideologies) in the Reich Security Main
Office. In June and July 1941, Commander of the "Advance
Party Moscow" of Special Unit B. As of September 1, 1942, Director of the Cultural-Political Division of the German Foreign
Office. In 1948 sentenced by a U.S. Military Court to 20 years
imprisonment. Released in 1952.

88 **Otto Ohlendorf** (1907–1951)
Born in Hoheneggelsen nr. Hildesheim. Studied Law and Economics. Joined the NSDAP in 1925, the SS in 1926. In October
1933 he became an Assistant at the Institute for Global Economy at Kiel, and in January 1935 Department Chairman at the
Institute for Applied Economics in Berlin. Specialist for Economics with the Security Service in 1936. From 1939 until 1945
Head of Department III (German Controlled Territories [*Deutsche Lebensgebiete*] in the Reich Security Main Office. In this
capacity he was responsible for issuing the "Reports from
within the Reich [*Meldungen aus dem Reich*]." From June 1941
until July 1942 he led Special Unit D in the Soviet Union. In addition to his duties as Department Head in the Reich Security
Main Office, he became also the manager of a committee for
foreign trade in the Reich Ministry of Economics in 1943. In the
"Special Units Trial" he was sentenced to death by the U.S. Military Court II in 1948 and executed in 1951.

Administrative departments of the Reich Security Main Office outside of Berlin:

Potsdam, Priesterstrasse 11–12:
Investigating officer for the Chief of Security Police and Security Service

Dresden, Devrientstrasse 2:
A 1
Director of Medical Matters

Bernau, Dammühle (?):
Section:
I A 1   (General personnel matters)

Rauscha, Sagan District:
II C 4   (General weaponry)

Bernau, Security Service Academy:
Departmental Sections:
III A S
III C 1   (Advanced knowledge)
III C 2   (Education and religious life)
III C 3   (National culture of the people and art)

Fürstenberg, Security Police Academy:
Departmental Sections:
V A 2   (Preventive measures against crime)
V C 2   (Operational means for search operations)
V C 3 b
V C 3 c   (Aspects pertaining to police dogs)
V C 3 d
V D 1 b

Schloss Grambow/Mecklenburg:
Departmental Sections:
V D   (Institute for Criminal-Technical Matters)
V D 1 a
V D 3   (Verification of original documents)

Hernskretschen:
Central Institute of Criminal Biological Matters

Vienna:
Central Institute for Criminal-Medical Matters (in the starting phase)

Vienna 50, Theresianusgasse 18:
Section:
VI E   (Intelligence service in Central Europe)

Friedenthal nr. Oranienburg:
Section:
VI S   (Special assignments: acts of sabotage, fighting behind enemy frontlines)

Schloss Plankenwarth nr. Graz:
Wannsee Institute

Schlesiersee, Glogau District:
VII A 3   (Confidential information office)
VII C 3

Reich Security Main Office: Table of Duty Assignments
Status as of March 1, 1941

Chief of Security Police and Security Service: SS Major General Reinhard Heydrich

DEPARTMENT I: PERSONNEL

Head:	SS Brigadier General and Brigadier General of Police Streckenbach (simultaneously Inspector of the Security Police and Security Service Academies)
Division I A:	Personnel
Director:	SS Colonel and Senior Administrative Councilor Brunner
Section I A 1:	General personnel matters (SS Major and Administrative Councilor Mohr)
Section I A 2:	Personal data, *Gestapo* (SS Major and Administrative Councilor Tent)
Section I A 3:	Personal data, Criminal Police (SS Major, Administrative Councilor and Criminal Police Councilor Schraepel)
Section I A 4:	Personal data, Security Service (SS Major Braune)
Section I A 5:	Personal data, Party and SS (vacant)
Section I A 6:	Welfare (SS Lieutenant Colonel and Senior Administrative Councilor Trinkl)
Division I B:	Education, training and indoctrination
Director:	SS Colonel Schulz
Deputy:	SS Major Dr. Sandberger
Section I B 1:	Ideological training (SS Major Dr. Engel, Substitute: SS Major Zapp)
Section I B 2:	The next generation (SS Major Hotzel, Substitute: SS Major Thomas)
Section I B 3:	Structuring lesson plans for the academies (Administrative Councilor Sandberger; Substitute: Criminal Police Director Zirpins)
Section I B 4:	Additional lesson plans (Administrative Councilor and Criminal Police Councilor Rennau)
Division I C:	Gymnastics
Director:	SS Colonel and Senior Administrative Councilor von Daniels
Section I C 1:	General aspects pertaining to gymnastics (vacant)
Section I C 2:	Physical and military training (vacant)
Division I D:	Penal matters
Director:	Streckenbach (acting)
Deputy:	SS Major Haensch
Section I D 1:	Punishable offense while in service (SS Major and Administrative Councilor Schulz)
Section I D 2:	Disciplinary matters, SS (Haensch)

DEPARTMENT II: ORGANIZATION, ADMINISTRATION AND LAW

Head:	SS Colonel and Colonel of Police Dr. Nockemann
Division II A:	Organization and law
Director:	Presently vacant
Deputy:	SS Major and Senior Administrative Councilor Dr. Bilfinger

Section II A 1: Organization of Security Police and Security Service (SS Captain and Administrative Assessor [no engl. equivalent] Dr. Schweder)

Section II A 2: Legislation (SS Major and Administrative Councilor Neifeind)

Section II A 3: Justiciary matters, indemnity claims (SS Major and Administrative Councilor Suhr)

Section II A 4: National defense matters (SS Major and Administrative Councilor Renken)

Section II A 5: Miscellaneous (Determining hostility toward people and state; confiscation of financial assets; abrogation of citizenship — all of them will subsequently become IV B 4) (SS Major and Administrative Councilor Richter)

Division II B: Basic questions pertaining to passport matters and Alien Police

Director: Administrative Councilor Krause

Section II B 1: Passport matters I (Administrative Councilor Dr. Hoffmann, Administrative Councilor Dr. Baumann)

Section II B 2: Passport matters II (Administrative Councilor Weintz)

Section II B 3: Matters pertaining to proof of identity, identification cards (Administrative Councilor Kelbing)

Section II B 4: Basic questions pertaining to Alien Police and securing the frontiers (Senior Administrative Councilor Kröning)

Division II C a: Budget and economy of the Security Police

Director: SS Colonel and Administrative Councilor Dr. Siegert

Section II C 1: Budget and payroll (SS Colonel and Administrative Councilor Dr. Siegert)

Section II C 2: Supplies and material costs (SS Major and Administrative Councilor Kreklow)

Section II C 3: Housing; prisoners-overall aspects (SS Major and Administrative Councilor Dr. Bergmann)

Section II C 4: Economy office (SS Major and Office Councilor Meier)

Division II C b: Budget and economy of the Security Service

Director: Presently vacant

Deputy: SS Lieutenant Colonel Brocke

Section II C 7: Budget and payroll of the Security Service (SS Captain Radtke)

Section II C 8: Procurement, insurance, contracts, real estate Matters, automotive matters (SS Major Schmidt)

Section II C 9: Checking and auditing (Brocke)

Section II C 10: Cash Accounting and rendering accounts (SS Lieutenant Colonel Wittich)

Division II D: Technical matters

Director: SS Lieutenant Colonel Rauff

Section II D 1: Aspects pertaining to broadcasting, photography, film (SS Major and Police Councilor Gottstein)

Section II D 2: Telegraph and telephone services (SS Major and Police Councilor Walter)

Section II D 3 a: Automotive organization of the Security Police (SS Captain and Captain of Municipal Police Pradel)

Section II D 3 b: Automotive organization of the Security Service (SS Captain Gast, SS Lieutenant Heinrich)

Section II D 4: General weaponry (SS Major and Police Councilor Lutter)

Section II D 5: Aviation (SS Major and Major of Municipal Police Leopold)

Section II D 6: Managing the technical funds of the Security Police and Security Service (Police Councilor Kempf)

DEPARTMENT III: GERMAN OCCUPIED TERRITORIES

Head: SS Colonel Ohlendorf

Division III A: Questions pertaining to the legal system and building up the Reich Director: SS Major Dr. Gengenbach

Deputy: SS Captain Dr. J. Beyer

Section III A 1: General questions pertaining to work in the German controlled territories (SS Captain Dr. Beyer)

Section III A 2: Legal situation (SS Captain and Administrative Councilor Dr. Malz)

Section III A 3: Constitution and administration (presently run by the Head of Division)

Section III A 4: The people's overall way of life (presently vacant)

Division III B: Germanism

Director: SS Lieutenant Colonel Dr. Ehlich

Deputy: SS Major and Administrative Councilor Dr. Müller

Section III B 1: Tasks related to Germanism (SS Captain Hummitzsch)

Section III B 2: Minorities (presently vacant)

Section III B 3: Race and national health (SS Captain Schneider)

Section III B 4: Immigration and resettlement (SS Major and Administrative Councilor Dr. Müller)

Section III B 5: Occupied territories (SS Major von Loew zu Steinfurth)

Division III C: Cultural matters

Head: SS Major Dr. Spengler

Deputy: SS Captain von Kielpinski

Section III C 1: Advanced knowledge (SS Captain Dr. Turowski)

Section III C 2: Education and religious life (SS Captain Dr. Seibert)

Section III C 3: National culture and art (SS Captain Dr. Roessner)

Section III C 4: Press, literature, broadcasting (SS Captain von Kielpinski)

Division III D: Economy

Head: vacant

Deputy: SS Major Seibert

Section III D 1: Food production and distribution (presently vacant)

Section III D 2: Commerce, skilled trade, Transportation (SS Major Seibert)

Section III D 3: Finance economy, currency, banks and stock exchanges, insurance companies (SS Captain Kröger)

Section III D 4: Industrial and energy economics (presently vacant)

Section III D 5: Labor and social welfare (SS Major Dr. Leetsch)

DEPARTMENT IV: INVESTIGATION AND FIGHTING OF ENEMIES

Head: SS Brigadier General and Brigadier General of Police Müller

Division IV A:
Director: SS Lieutenant Colonel and Senior Administrative Councilor Panzinger
Section IV A 1: Communism, marxism and aligned organizations, crimes in wartime, illegal and enemy propaganda (SS Major and Criminal Police Director Vogt)
Section IV A 2: Defense and countermeasures against sabotage, authorized political police representatives for counterintelligence, political forgery (SS Captain and Commissioner of Criminal Police Kopkow)
Section IV A 3: Reactionaries, opposition, legitimists, liberalism, emigrants, political perfidy aspects (unless covered by IV A 1) (SS Major and Criminal Police Director Litzenberg)
Section IV A 4: Protection service, assassination reports, surveillance, special assignments, search operation troops (SS Major and Criminal Police Director Schulz)

Division IV B:
Director: SS Major Hartl
Deputy: SS Major and Administrative Councilor Roth
Section IV B 1: Political catholicism (SS Major and Administrative Councilor Roth)
Section IV B 2: Political protestantism, sects (Roth)
Section IV B 3: Other churches, freemasonry (presently vacant)
Section IV B 4: Jewish affairs, evacuations (SS Major Eichmann)

Division IV C:
Director: SS Lieutenant Colonel and Senior Administrative Councilor Dr. Rang
Deputy: SS Major, Administrative Councilor and Criminal Police Councilor Dr. Berndorff
Section IV C 1: Evaluations, central card index, administration of files on individuals, information, A-File index (file of suspects), Alien surveillance, central visa office (Police Councilor Matzke)
Section IV C 2: Protective custody (SS Major, Administrative Councilor and Criminal Police Councilor Dr. Berndorff)
Section IV C 3: Aspects of the press and literature (SS Major and Administrative Councilor Dr. Jahr)
Section IV C 4: Aspects pertaining to the Party [NSDAP] and its organizational structure (SS Major and Criminal Police Councilor Stage)

Division IV D:
Director: SS Lieutenant Colonel Dr. Weinmann
Deputy: SS Major and Administrative Councilor Dr. Jonak
Section IV D 1: Aspects pertaining to the Protectorate; Czechs in the Reich (Jonak)
Section IV D 2: Matters pertaining to the *Generalgouvernement*; Poles in the Reich (Administrative Assessor [no English equivalent] Thiemann)
Section IV D 3: Collection center for informers'reports; enemy aliens (SS Captain and Criminal Police Councilor Schroeder)
Section IV D 4: Occupied territories: France, Luxembourg, Alsace and Lorraine, Belgium, Holland, Norway, Denmark (SS Major and Administrative Councilor Baatz)

Division IV E:
Director: SS Major and Administrative Councilor Schellenberg

Section IV E 1: General counterintelligence aspects; expert testimonies concerning high and national treason... protecting work places [*Werkschutz*]; professional guards [*Bewachungsgewerbe*](SS Captain and Captain of Police Lindow)
Section IV E 2: General economic matters; defense against economic espionage (Administrative Assessor Sebastian)
Section IV E 3: Counterintelligence West (SS Captain and Criminal Police Councilor Dr. Fischer)
Section IV E 4: Counterintelligence North (Criminal Police Director Dr. Schambacher)
Section IV E 5: Counterintelligence East (SS Major and Criminal Police Director Kubitzky)
Section IV E 6: Counterintelligence South (SS Captain and Criminal Police Councilor Dr. Schmitz)

DEPARTMENT V: FIGHT AGAINST CRIME

Head: SS Brigadier General and Brigadier General of Police Nebe.

Division V A: Prevention of political crimes
Director: SS Major, Senior Administrative Councilor and Criminal Police Councilor Werner
Deputy: Administrative Councilor and Criminal Police Councilor Dr. Wächter
Section V A 1:   Legal questions, international cooperation and research into criminality (Administrative Councilor and Criminal Police Councilor Dr. Wächter)
Section V A 2:   Protection against political crimes (SS Major and Administrative Councilor Dr. Riese)
Section V A 3:   Female Criminal Police (Criminal Police Director Wieking)

Division V B: Deployment for Action
Director: Administrative Councilor and Criminal Police Councilor Galzow)
Deputy: Administrative Councilor and Criminal Police Councilor Lobbes)
Section V B 1:   Capital crimes (Administrative Councilor Lobbes)
Section V B 2:   Fraud (Criminal Police Director Rassow)
Section V B 3:   Sex crimes (Criminal Police Director Nauck)

Division V C: Criminal identification and searches
Director: Senior Administrative Councilor and Senior Criminal Police Councilor Berger
Deputy: Criminal Police Director Dr. Baum
Section V C 1:   National center for criminal identification (SS Major and Criminal Police Director Müller)
Section V C 2:   Search operations (Criminal Police Director Dr. Baum)

Division V D: Security Police: Institute for Criminal-Technical Matters
Director: SS Major, Senior Administrative Councilor and Criminal Police Councilor Dr. of Engineering, habilitated, Heeß
Deputy: SS Captain and Criminal Police Councilor Dr. of Engineering Schade
Section V D 1:   Identification of clues (SS Captain and Criminal Police Councilor Dr. of Engineering Schade)
Section V D 2:   Chemistry and biology (SS Lieutenant Dr. of Engineering Widmann)
Section V D 3:   Verification of original documents (Criminal Police Councilor and MA in Chemistry Wittlich)

89 **Heinrich Müller** (1900–?)

Born in Munich. Trained as an airplane mechanic. Entered police service after the First World War. 1933 Senior Police Secretary. Joined the SS in April 1934 and was transferred to the Secret State Police Office in Berlin. Because of his former employment with the Bavarian Political Police the NSDAP in Munich had grave misgivings about letting him join the Party; as a result, he did not become a member of the NSDAP until 1939. From 1939 until 1945 he was Head of Department IV (Investigation and Fighting of Enemies; identical to the Secret State Police Office) of the Reich Security Main Office.

90 **Arthur Nebe** (1894–1945)

Born in Berlin. After taking his *Notabitur* (final examinations in highschool taken prematurely on account of the war) he volunteered for service during the First World War. Entered police service in 1920. Joined the NSDAP and the Stormtroopers in 1931 and became a contributing member of the SS. Was appointed Criminal Police Councilor in the Prussian State Police Office in April 1933. In December 1936 he transferred from the Stormtroopers into the SS. Was appointed Reich Criminal Police Director in July 1937, and from 1939 until 1944 he was Head of Department V (Crime Fighting; identical to the Reich Criminal Police Office) of the Reich Security Main Office. Served from June until November 1941 as commander of Special Unit B in the Soviet Union. Went underground in July 1944 because of connections with the Resistance fighters of the 20th of July. Arrested in January 1945, he was executed in March of the same year.

91 **Heinz Jost** (1904–1964)

Born in Holzhausen. Joined the NSDAP in 1927 and worked as a local Party functionary [*Ortsgruppenleiter*], District Propaganda Director and Organizational Leader. Joined the Stormtroopers in 1929. Practiced law in Lorsch, 1931. Provisional Chief of Police in Worms, in March 1933, and from October 1933 in Giessen. In July 1934 full-time employee of the Security Service and simultaneously transfer from the Stormtroopers to the SS. Became Division Chief in the Security Service Main Office in January 1936. After the Reich Security Main Office was established in September 1939 he became Head of Department VI. Served in 1942 as commander of Special Unit A and also commanded the Security Police and Security Service in the "*Reichskommissariat Ostland*" (Occupied Territory so renamed by the Nazis; it comprised Estonia, Lithuania, Latvia and parts of Belo-Russia). Became Plenipotentiary of the Reich Minister for the Occupied Territories in the East with the High Command of Army Group A at Nikolajew. In April 1944 he was drafted into the Combat SS. In 1948, the U.S. Military Court II sentenced him to life imprisonment. He was prematurely released in 1951.

92 **Walter Schellenberg** (1910–1952)

Born in Saarbrücken. In March/April 1933 he joined the SS and the NSDAP. In 1934 he entered the Security Service. After his second law examination in 1936 he became an *Assessor* [no Engl. equiv.] in the Secret State Police Office. When the Reich Security Main Office was established in September 1939, he became Director of Division IV E (Defense against Espionage inside Germany). In July 1942 he became Director of Department VI of the RSMO (Security Service Abroad). The U.S. Military Tribunal IV sentenced him to six years in prison. He was prematurely released in December 1950.

DEPARTMENT VI: FOREIGN COUNTRIES

Head: SS Brigadier General and Brigadier General of Police Jost

Division VI A: General responsibilities involving intelligence work abroad, comprising seven sections

Director: SS Lieutenant Colonel Dr. Filbert

Deputy: SS Major and Administrative Councilor Finke
The staff members responsible for the seven sections and their respective assignments are as follows:
- the Authorized Official of Department VI is responsible for checking out all intelligence contacts, including the securement of contacts and courier routes, and for all intelligence measures taken by Department VI at home and abroad (responsible: Division Director VI A)
- the Authorized Officials of Department VI are responsible for checking and securing all assignments given to the regional commands of the Security Service abroad (vacant)
- the Authorized Official I (West) is responsible for the regional commands of the Security Service in Münster, Aachen, Bielefeld, Dortmund, Cologne, Düsseldorf, Koblenz, Kassel, Frankfurt/Main, Darmstadt, Neustadt, Karlsruhe, Stuttgart (SS Lieutenant Colonel Bernhard)
- the Authorized Official II (North) is responsible for the regional commands of the Security Service in Bremen, Brunswick, Lüneburg, Hamburg, Kiel, Schwerin, Stettin, Neustettin (SS Lieutenant Colonel Dr. Lehmann)
- the Authorized Official III (East) is responsible for the regional commands of the Security Service in Danzig, Königsberg, Allenstein, Tilsit, Thorn, Poznan, Hohensalza, Litzmannstadt [Lodz], Breslau, Liegnitz, Oppeln, Kattowitz, Troppau, the *Generalgouvernement* (SS Major von Salisch)
- the Authorized Official IV (South) is responsible for the regional commands of the Security Service in Vienna, Graz, Innsbruck, Klagenfurt, Linz, Salzburg, Munich, Augsburg, Bayreuth, Nuremberg, Würzburg, Prague (SS Major Lapper)
- the Authorized Official V (Center) is responsible for the regional commands of the Security Service in Berlin, Potsdam, Frankfurt/Oder, Dresden, Halle, Leipzig, Chemnitz, Dessau, Weimar, Magdeburg, Reichenberg, Karlsbad (SS Lieutenant Colonel Thiemann)

Division VI B: German-Italian sphere of influence in Europe, Africa, and the Near East with 10 sections (not listed) Director: presently vacant

Division VI C: The East: Russo-Japanese sphere of influence with 11 sections (not listed)

Director: presently vacant

Division VI D: The West: Anglo-American sphere of influence with 9 sections (not listed)

Director: presently vacant

Division VI E: (Department Head IV is empowered to provide subject related guidance): Searches for ideological opponents abroad (with six sections, not listed)

Director: SS Lieutenant Colonel Knochen

Deputy: SS Captain Loose

Division VI F: Technical aids for intelligence service abroad with seven sections (not listed)

Director: SS Lieutenant Colonel Rauff

Deputy: SS Lieutenant Colonel Fuhrmann

DEPARTMENT VII: IDEOLOGIES — RESEARCH AND EVALUATION

Head: SS Colonel Professor Dr. Six

Division VII A: Collection of Material

Director: SS Lieutenant Colonel and Senior Administrative Councilor Mylius

Section VII A 1:   Library (SS Captain Dr. Beyer)

Section VII A 2:   Reporting, translation service, selection and use of press material (SS Captain Mehringer)

Section VII A 3:   Confidential investigation office and liaison center (SS Captain Burmester)

Division VII B: Evaluation

Director: presently vacant

Section VII B 1:   Freemasonry and jewry (presently vacant)

Section VII B 2:   Political churches (SS Captain Murawski)

Section VII B 3:   Marxism (SS Lieutenant Mahnke)

Section VII B 4:   Other opposition groups (SS First Lieutenant Mühler)

Section VII B 5:   Individual scientific research on German domestic problems (SS Captain Dr. Schick)

Section VII B 6:   Individual scientific research on problems abroad (presently vacant)

Division VII C: Archive, museum, special research assignments

Director: presently vacant

Section VII C 1:   Archive (SS Captain Dittel)

Section VII C 2:   Museum (vacant)

Section VII C 3:   Special research assignments (SS Lieutenant Colonel Dr. Levin)

94   Gun carriage with Heydrich's casket in front of the Prinz-Albrecht-Palais, his headquarters as Head of the Reich Security Main Office, on June 9, 1942.
Heydrich died in June 1942 in Prague as the result of an assassination attempt.

93   A meeting following the assassination attempt (on Hit-
ler's life) held at the *Bürgerbräu* Beerhall on November 8,
1939. From the left: Franz-Josef Huber (Vienna *Gestapo*
Chief); Arthur Nebe (Chief of the Criminal Police); Himmler,
Heydrich (Head of the Reich Security Main Office); Heinrich
Müller (Chief of the *Gestapo*).

3.6. Gestapo Prison ["Hausgefängnis"] and Political Prisoners (1933–39)

In the late summer of 1933 a prison was installed in the building of the Secret State Police Office at Prinz-Albrecht-Strasse 8. Its purpose was to hold prisoners slated for interrogation in the building by the *Gestapo*. Despite repeated additions, the total number of cells remained limited. At most fifty persons could be accomodated in the 38 solitary cells and one communal cell. Many political prisoners were held in the police prison on Alexanderplatz or (until 1936) in Concentration Camp Columbiahaus from where they were then transported for the day to Prinz-Albrecht-Strasse 8 for interrogation.

Interrogation of inmates in the "*Gestapo* Prison" could extend over several hours or days, but also over many weeks and months. Long-range stays in the prison, however, were the exception rather than the rule. Still, Kurt Schumacher was held here for four months in the summer of 1939, Rudolf Breitscheid and Kurt Lehmann in 1941/1942 for eleven months, Berthold Jacob in 1942–1944 for two years. For most prisoners, though, the *Gestapo* Prison was a way station on their journey through the prisons and concentration camps of the SS-State.

95   View of the cell block the *Gestapo* built in 1933. It was situated in the lower basement section, adjacent to Prinz-Albrecht-Park, 1948.

Prinz-Albrecht-Strasse 8 became infamous above all because of the brutal tortures the *Gestapo* applied while trying to extract the desired information. Several prisoners were only able to escape this terror by committing suicide. "Intensified interrogations" as the tortures were called in German bureaucratic jargon did not take place in the basement prison cells but in the offices on the floors above. During the initial years the victims were for the most part Communists, Social Democrats and members of labor unions, but also members of the Socialist youth movement, of smaller socialist parties and resistance organizations that ranged from the Socialist Workers Party to the Group "New Beginnings." In addition, there were others equally unwilling to submit to the National Socialist State's claim to power, for instance Jehovah's Witnesses or individual representatives of the Churches. Furthermore, the SS also used the *Gestapo* Prison to hold oppositional National Socialists or SS men who had committed punishable offenses. Yet it was for the most part a place where those opponents of the NS-System stayed and suffered whose interrogations were of special interest to the machinery of persecution.

Text 11

Directive of May 14, 1935 by the Deputy Director and Inspector of the Prussian State Police, pertaining to the transport of prisoners to the Secret State Police Office for interrogation

Berlin, May 14, 1935
Prussian Secret State Police
Deputy Director and Inspector
B.No. 705/35 – I A –

Subject: Regulating prisoner transports
Secret State Police Office – Concentration Camp Columbia – Police Headquarters, Berlin.

In order to relieve the Secret State Police's motor pool of congestion, I herewith issue the following directive, effective immediately:
Transports of prisoners will henceforth rely exclusively on police vans [*Schubwagen*]. Use of passenger cars for prisoner transports will be restricted exclusively to exceptional cases [...]
The department sections of the Secret State Police Office will put in requests for prisoners from Concentration Camp Columbia wanted for interrogation by means of a claim form, made out in duplicate, and directed to the prison of the Secret State Police Office. The top sheet of the claim form must bear the official seal of the appropriate section, with signature. Claim forms for prisoners who are to be picked up with the initial transport on the day in question must be submitted to the Secret State Police Office the previous day, during weekdays by 4:30 p.m. at the latest, and on Sundays or holidays latest by 11 a.m. Furthermore, all claim forms must be handed in to the Secret State Police Office at least half an hour prior to the departure of the police van.

All prisoners to be delivered from the Secret State Police Office to either Concentration Camp Columbia or to Berlin Police Headquarters are to be brought to the prison of the Secret State Police Office at all times half an hour prior to departure of the police van with their transfer papers or, as the case may be, with written requests by the agencies responsible for the return transport of the interrogated individuals.

Command Headquarters of Concentration Camp Columbia must see to it that all prisoners to be sent to the Prison of the Secret State Police Office as well as the food rations of the prison inmates will be available and ready on time so as not to delay the next transport. Noon rations for prisoners from Concentration Camp Columbia who will stay at the Secret State Police Office during noontime must be sent by Concentration Camp Columbia to the prison of the Secret State Police Office via the police van operating at 1 p.m.

Requests for the required rations will be handled in the following manner:
The prison of the Secret State Police Office sends each day a preliminary notice with the police van operating at 1 p.m. to Concentration Camp Columbia, stating how many rations will most likely be required during the following day for meals of

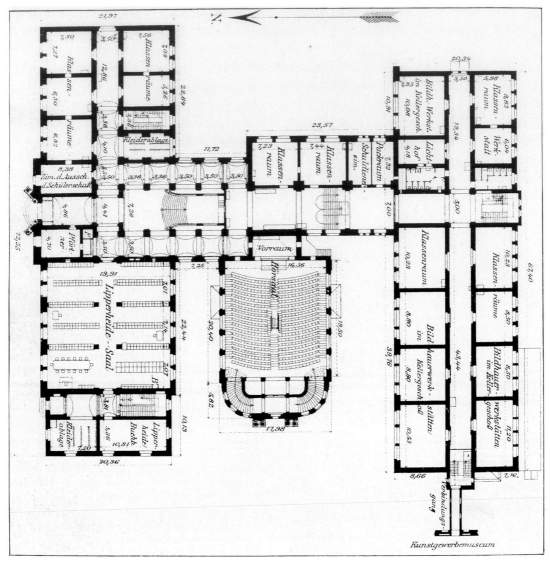

96 · Floor plan of the ground floor of the School of Industrial Arts and Crafts, 1905.

After the *Gestapo* moved into the building in the spring of 1933, the former classrooms in the northern wing were used as offices for around the clock duty and field service. The former sculptors' studios in the southern wing were transformed into prison cells in 1933 and 1936 respectively. Furthermore, the rooms of the Lipperheide Collection (a part of the Art Library) were taken over by the *Gestapo* in 1934.

prisoners held at the prison of the Secret State Police Office. The final notice regarding the required rations for meals in the morning, at noon, and in the evening will be sent to Concentration Camp Columbia by whatever transport carriage is leaving to pick up rations. On the requisition form of the Secret State Police Office for the noon rations, the number of prisoners from Concentration Camp Columbia who will stay during noontime at the Secret State Police Office will be simultaneously noted down.

Signed: H. Himmler

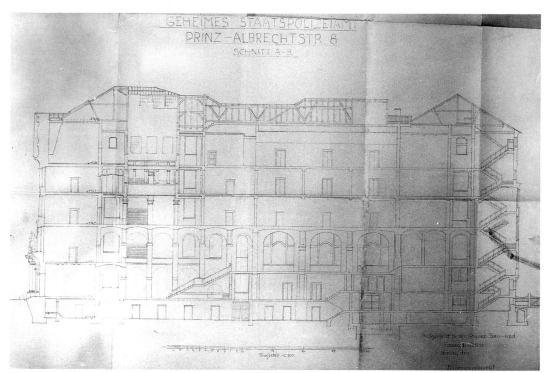

97   Sectional view of the building Prinz-Albrecht-Strasse 8, displayed about 1934 by the Prussian Construction and Finance Directory.
The view follows the central axis of the building from the main entrance portal at Prinz-Albrecht-Strasse (left) to the stairway of the southern wing. By the spring of 1933, the former School of Industrial Arts and Crafts was almost completely at the disposal of the Secret State Police Office and, after the Art Library was evicted from its rooms in the western part of the building in July 1934, completely so.

98   The central hall of *Gestapo* Headquarters with busts of Goering (left) and Hitler, around 1935.

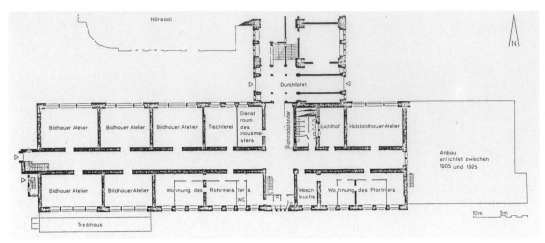

99   Basement (floor plan) of the School of Industrial Arts and Crafts, 1905–1925.

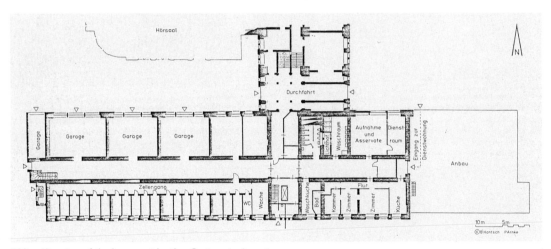

100   Alteration of the basement by the *Gestapo* in August 1933.

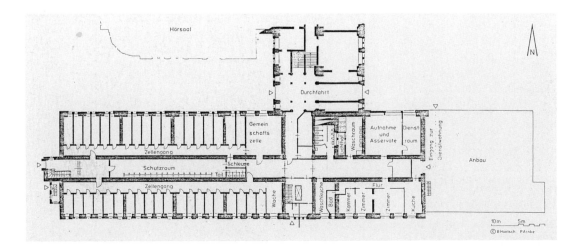

Dauerdienst I A					Eingelieferte Perfonen					Berlin, den	193	
Lfd. Nr.	Name Zu- Vor-		Stand	Geburtsdatum und Ort	Wohnung	Wo festgenommen	Grund	Eingeliefert Tg. Std.	Partei-zugehörig-keit	Verbleib Jfoliert-gewahrsam / Entlassen		Bemerkungen (Berlegungen, ab-genommene Sachen)
29	Schäfer, Friedrich			30.6.84 Berlin	Hohenneuendorf			29.1.37			14	
30.	Woyte, Karl			18.1.98 Brln	Berlin Lichtenberg 23			2.1.37	SPD			
31.				16.9.10				21.1.37	SPD			
32	Marx geb. Gessinger, Gabriel			26.04 Brln	Berlin Güntzelstr. 126		Schutzhaft	5.3.37 7.30	SPD	233/37		
33	Jonas, Julius			26.7.12 Brln		Saarbrücken		19.5.37 15°°		464/37		
34	Marcus, Harry			26.3.11 Berlin	Charlottenburg	Berlin		27.5.37		410/37		
35	Karger, Wilhelm			25.9.02 Brln		Meiningen		7.6.37 9°°	SAP	488/37		
36.	Wittich, Otto			24.12.09 Lagerd.	Kopenhagen	Lübeck		16.6.37	SPD	527/37		
37.	Snell, Twinton			13.6.93 Brln		Benthiem		4.7.37 18°°		555/37		
38.	Petersdorf, Hugo			8.7.77	Berlin	Berlin		7.7.37 6°°	SPD	563/37		
39.	Göring, Gerhard			21.11.97 Berlin		Berlin		7.7.37 7°°	SPD	564/37		
40.	Gottfried, Hans			7.2.96 Berlin		Berlin		7.7.37 7°°	SPD	566/37		
41	Werner, Hermann	Ing.		31.10.91 Oppeln		Neukölln		7.7.37 7°°	SPD	567/37		
42.	Jorgmann, Mauritz			30.4.98				25.7.37				
43.	Goldbeck, Amandus			26.11.07				26.8.37 12 Uhr		685/37		
44	Selmer, Margarete			6.3.80 Berlin				14.9.37 9°°	SPD	736/37		
45.	Hermann, Wilhelm			14.12.04				27.9.37		763/37		
46.	Schroeder, Ludwig			5.8.94				22.10.37				
47.	Loewenz, Werner			31.12.				11.37				
48.	Weller, Paul			17.5.96				26.11.37		937/37		
49	Hambelmann, Rolle			8.1.04				26.10.37		937/37		
50.	Rakow, Hans			16.7.98				27.11.37		935/37		
51	Mierendorff, Karl	Schriftst.		24.3.97				16.12.37		97/37		

102 Excerpt from the arrest pad for the period January 29 to December 16, 1937. Among other entries there is that of Karl (Carlo) Mierendorff, No. 52.

103 Outside view of the cells in the northern section of the *Gestapo* Prison seen from the interior courtyard of the former School of Industrial Arts and Crafts; after 1945.
At the left edge of the picture one can see the entrance to the lecture hall which the *Gestapo* used on and off for showing movies.

101 Expansion of the *Gestapo* Prison in the summer of 1936.
By the end of 1935, plans were drawn up for an expansion of the *Gestapo* Prison by way of a second cell block. The drawing conveys the extent of the main prison as it looked from the fall of 1936 when the expansion had been completed until the end of the war. There were 20 solitary cells and a guard room in the original cell block (below), built in 1933, and 18 additional cells as well as one communal cell in the block created by the expansion. In front of all cells were walkways, in between a controlled passage, and an air raid shelter which served simultaneously as a guard room.

104   **Edith Walz** (born 1911), in 1929.
Member of the Socialist Workers' Youth [*Sozialistische Arbeiterjugend* (SAJ)] and the SPD, later of the Socialist Youth Association [*Sozialistischer Jugendverband* (SJVD)], the youth organization of the Socialist Workers' Party [*Sozialistische Arbeiterpartei* (SAP)]. In 1933, members of the latter organization distributed leaflets and wrote slogans against the Nazi Regime on the walls of houses. Edith Walz was arrested on December 6, 1933, and taken to Prinz-Albrecht-Strasse 8. There she was interrogated and eventually released. No criminal proceedings were instituted against her.
Edith Walz lives today in West Berlin.

105   **Willi Gleitze** (born 1904) in 1928.
Social Democrat since 1921, and from 1930–1933 Youth Secretary of the Socialist Worker's Youth in Leipzig. He participated prominently in illegal activities carried out by SPD and SAJ.
On December 27, 1933, the *Gestapo* arrested him and took him to the "*Gestapo* Prison" at Prinz Albrecht-Strasse 8. After the interrogations were over — in the course of which he was systematically beaten — he was transferred on the same day to Concentration Camp Columbiahaus. He was tried in August 1934 at the Berlin Superior Court of Justice [*Kammergericht*] and acquitted.
Gleitze lives today in West Berlin.

Text 12

After I was taken to the *Gestapo* Building on Prinz-Albrecht- Strasse I was interrogated by a *Gestapo* official named Müller. He told me to talk about all my activities since the dissolution of the SAJ in Leipzig, and subsequently here in Berlin ... Our talk proceeded along these lines for quite some time. Suddenly six youngish men showed up in the room (which was pretty large). They positioned themselves in a circle and at their respective places picked up equipment for beating people that had been put there beforehand. There were rubber truncheons, cowhide whips, riding whips, and clubs. Very soon Müller rose from his seat whereupon everybody pounced upon me and started to beat me indiscriminately.

I tried to protect myself as far as possible. I slid into the open space beneath the office desk but was pulled out. Then I sought refuge on top of a pile of books, succeeded in shielding myself there fairly well for some time, but then was dragged down and continued to be beaten until Müller ordered them to stop.

The interrogation proceeded but remained inconclusive as far as Müller was concerned. I stuck to my earlier statements. After a considerable period of time another gang of thugs showed up and took again their places by the equipment for beating people. Shortly thereafter Müller got up again, and the same abuse as before was resumed. I had to endure all this for two hours. Müller always stopped the beatings whenever he thought that he would reach his objective through further interrogation. During these two hours, five different gangs of thugs took turns beating me.

At one point, one of the thugs placed a chair into the middle of the room. He ordered me to raise my right arm and give the Hitler salute. I refused. Thereupon everybody who stood around beat me again. I remained stubborn and the beatings continued. Finally I realized that I would have to give in. After I had rendered the Hitler salute, the same thug [who had given the original order] said: "This fellow has the cheek to salute us with 'Heil Hitler.'" I was beaten again until Müller put a stop to it.

Willi Gleitze

106   Georgi Dimitroff (1882–1949), around 1933.
Co-founder of the Bulgarian Communist Party in 1919. Since 1929 Dimitroff lived in Berlin as an exile and ran the West European office of the Communist International (Comintern).
After his acquittal in the Reichstag Fire Trial on December 23, 1933, he was taken to the "*Gestapo* Prison." As late as February 27, 1934, he was finally granted permission to depart for the Soviet Union.
From 1935 until 1934 Dimitroff was General Secretary of the Comintern, and from 1946 until 1949 Minister President of the Bulgarian People's Republic.

108   Franz Neumann (1904–1974), in November 1945.
From 1920 on he was a member of the Social Democratic Party [SPD]. Youth Welfare worker with the Berlin Municipal Council. Delegate for Reinickendorf District and President of the Metal Worker Youth [organization] until 1933. Since Spring 1933 active in the Social Democratic resistance movement.
He was arrested on January 4, 1934, and taken to Prinz-Albrecht-Strasse 8. After the interrogations were over he was moved to Concentration Camp Columbiahaus. He was sentenced to a year and a half in prison.
1946 Deputy Mayor of Reinickendorf District. Co-chairman of the Berlin Welfare Office for Workers, 1946–1960, a member of Berlin's municipal council and the municipal chamber of deputies. 1951–1958 chairman of its delegation. 1946–1958 chairman of the SPD in Berlin. 1949–1969 member of the lower house of the German Federal Parliament. 1971 honorary citizen of the City of Berlin.

107   Walter Hoeppner (1900–1984), around 1960.
Social Democrat. In his Tegel housing development "Free Plot of Land" [*Freie Scholle*] he was active in the Resistance Movement, alongside Franz Neumann and other Social Democrats. Like many other members of the resistance group around Neumann he was arrested on January 3, 1934, and taken to Prinz-Albrecht-Strasse 8 where he was severely beaten during interrogation. Further stations of his ordeal were Concentration Camp Columbiahaus, the Police Headquarters prison at Alexanderplatz, and the pretrial detention prison in Moabit. After sentencing in June 1934 he remained in Tegel Penitentiary until July 25, 1935.

109   Ernst Thälmann (1886–1944), in the Court of Justice prison, Hanover, in 1943.

1903 member of the SPD, in 1917 of the USPD [Independent Social Democratic Party], since 1920 of the German Communist Party [KPD].

Thälmann was arrested on March 3, 1933. From January 9–23, 1934, he was imprisoned at Prinz-Albrecht-Strasse 8 where he was interrogated and badly manhandled. Thereafter he was taken to the pretrial detention prison in Moabit. No trial was ever held. Until he was murdered in Concentration Camp Buchenwald on August 18, 1944, he remained uninterruptedly imprisoned.

Text 13

It is nearly impossible to relate what happened for four and a half hours, from 5 p.m. to 9:30 p.m. in that interrogation room. Every conceivable cruel method of blackmail was used against me to obtain by force and at all costs confessions and statements both about comrades who had been arrested, and about political activities. It began initially with that friendly "good guy" approach as I had known some of these fellows when they were still members of Severing's Political Police [during the Weimar Republic]. Thus, they reasoned with me, etc., in order to learn, during that playfully conducted talk, something about this or that comrade and other matters that interested them. But the approach proved unsuccessful. I was then brutally assaulted and in the process had four teeth knocked out of my jaw. This proved unsuccessful too. By way of a "third act" they tried hypnosis which was likewise totally ineffective ... But the actual highpoint of this drama was the final act. They ordered me to take off my pants and then two men grabbed me by the back of the neck and placed me across a footstool. A uniformed *Gestapo* officer with a whip of hippotamus hide in his hand then beat my buttocks with measured strokes. Driven wild with pain I repeatedly screamed at the top of my voice.

Then they held my mouth shut for a while and hit me in the face, and with a whip across chest and back. I then collapsed, rolled on the floor, always keeping face down and no longer replied to any of their questions. I received a few kicks yet here and there, covered my face, but was already so exhausted and my heart so strained, it nearly took my breath away. And then there was that terrible thirst.

Ernst Thälmann

110   **Franz Bobzien** (1906–1941), around 1930.
From 1925 on member of the SPD and the Socialist Workers' Youth (SAJ). Since 1931 member of the Socialist Workers' Party (SAP). Chairman of Germany's Socialist Youth Association (SJVD) in Hamburg and member of its national leadership. In February 1934 he was forced across the border by Dutch officials and thus fell into the hands of the *Gestapo*. On March 1, 1934, he was taken to Prinz-Albrecht-Strasse 8. Sentenced to three years in a penitentiary in the summer of 1934, he was transferred after serving his term to Concentration Camp Sachsenhausen. On March 28, 1941, he died while working with a bomb disposal squad.

111   **Theodor Haubach** (1896–1944).

Social Democrat since 1922. 1924–1928 Editor-in-Chief of the Social Democratic newspaper *Hamburger Echo*. 1927–1928 member of Hamburg's municipal chamber of deputies. 1928–1932 Press Secretary in the Reich Ministry of the Interior. 1930–1932 Press and Public Relations Officer at Berlin Police Headquarters. Held leading positions in the *Reichsbanner Schwarz-Rot-Gold* [a left-of-center political defense organization].

After his first arrest in 1933 he was held at Prinz-Albrecht-Strasse 8 from November 24 until December 21, 1934 and then was moved directly to Concentration Camp Esterwegen. After his release in the summer of 1936 he was employed in the private sector of the economy but was again briefly imprisoned in August 1939. As a member of the "Kreisau Circle" ["Kreisauer Kreis," the resistance group around Count von Moltke] – Haubach was earmarked as Minister for the Press and People's Enlightenment in the event the Nazi Regime was successfully overthrown – he was arrested on August 9, 1944 and was taken from the Lehrter Strasse Prison to Prinz-Albrecht-Strasse 8, presumably for interrogation. On January 15, 1945, he was sentenced to death and was executed at Plötzensee Prison on January 23.

113   **Ferdinand Friedensburg** (1886–1972), in 1932.
Reichstag delegate for the German Democratic Party [DDP]. From 1925 to 1927 Berlin's Deputy Chief of Police. From 1927–1933 Chief District Administrator [*Regierungspräsident*] in Kassel.

Arrested on February 6, 1935, he was taken to Prinz-Albrecht-Strasse 8. Six weeks after preliminary proceedings initiated against him on charges of "national treason" had been dismissed, he was released from detention.

After the war, Friedensburg became co-founder of the Catholic Democratic Union [CDU] and Mayor of the City of Berlin from 1946 to 1951. He served from 1948 to 1950 on its municipal council. From 1950 to 1952 he was a member of the Berlin House of Deputies, and from 1952 until 1965 a member of the lower house of Germany's Federal Parliament. From 1954 to 1965 he was also a member of the European Parliament. In 1971 he became an Honorary Citizen of the City of Berlin.

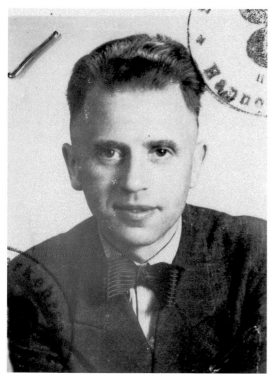

112   **Alfred Nau** (1906–1983), around 1947.
Member of the SPD and the Socialist Workers' Youth (SAJ). 1928–1933 Secretary of the SPD Party Executive. From 1933 on, he was involved in illegal activities for the Party.
On December 2, 1934, he was taken to Prinz-Albrecht-Strasse 8 and was kept there imprisoned for several months. In 1946, Nau became a member of the SPD Executive and Party Treasurer, and in 1958 a member of its Presidium. From 1975 until his death he was chairman of the Friedrich-Ebert-Foundation.

114   **Berthold Jacob** (1898–1944), on September 18, 1935.

Pacifist. From 1920 on active in journalism, for the *Berliner Volkszeitung* and *Weltbühne*. 1924 co-founder of the German Republican Party. Joined the SPD in 1928, and in 1931 became a member of the Socialist Workers' Party (SAP). 1928–1929 eight months of fortress imprisonment because of his campaign against the clandestine rearmament of the German Army [*Reichswehr*]. Emigrated to Strasbourg in 1932, and in 1933 was deprived of his German citizenship.

Jacob's carefully researched reports on German rearmament prompted the *Gestapo* to lure him with the help of an informer to Basel on March 9, 1935. From there, they kidnapped him to Germany. From March 11 on he was held in detention at Prinz-Albrecht-Strasse 8 but was released on September 17, 1935, as a result of international pressure. In September 1939, while in exile in Paris, he was interned by the French authorities. In 1941 he managed to flee to Spain and subsequently to Portugal.

On September 25, 1941, he was once again kidnapped by *Gestapo* agents and taken back to Berlin where he was held for two years at Prinz-Albrecht-Strasse 8 before being transferred to the Police Prison on Alexanderplatz. In February 1944 he was moved to the Berlin Jewish Hospital where he died on February 26, 1944.

116   **Werner Pünder** (1885–1973), around 1970.
Berlin lawyer and distant relative of Erich Klausener, President of "Catholic Action" in the Diocese Berlin, who was murdered by the *Gestapo* in 1934.
Werner Pünder was legal advisor to the Klausener family which did not accept the official version of suicide circulated by the *Gestapo*.
Because of his courageous engagement in this connection he was held in prison at Prinz-Albrecht-Strasse 8 from April 16 until May 16, 1935. After the war he resumed his law practice.

115   **Hermann Brill** (1895–1959), after 1945.
Member of the SPD from 1921 on (USPD member 1918–1922). From 1919–1933 first a delegate to the Diet of Gotha, then of Thuringia. Reichstag delegate in 1932.
Brill was taken to Prinz-Albrecht-Strasse 8 on March 21, 1935, because of "suspected illegal activities." It is not known when exactly he was released. He was again imprisoned from September 21, 1938 until December 1938 in the "*Gestapo* Prison." Sentenced to twelve years in a penitentiary, he spent from 1939 until 1945 in Brandenburg Penitentiary and Concentration Camp Buchenwald. In 1945, Brill became Minister President of Thuringia and from 1946 to 1949 served as Director of the State Chancellory of Hesse. Was a member of the German Federal Parliament from 1949 to 1953.

117   **Werner Finck** (1902–1978), around 1930.

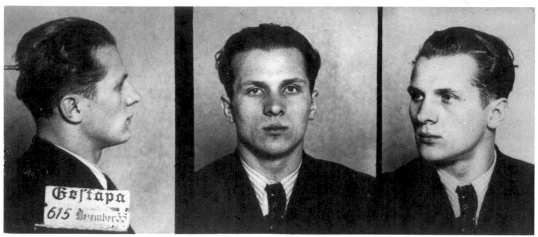

Staff member of *Berliner Tageblatt*. Cabaret artist and actor. In 1929 he joined the cast of the cabaret "*Katakombe*" in Berlin, and in 1931 became its director. Since February 1935 the "*Katakombe*" was under surveillance by the *Gestapo* and was closed by the police in May 1935.

The same day, Finck was arrested and taken to Prinz-Albrecht-Strasse 8 for interrogation. After the interrogation had ended he was transferred to Concentration Camp Columbiahaus and from there to Concentration Camp Esterwegen where he remained imprisoned until July 1, 1935. He was charged with having violated the "Perfidy Law" [*Heimtückegesetz*] but was acquitted on October 26, 1935. Four years later he was expelled from the "Reich Culture Chamber" [*Reichskulturkammer*] and in 1942 was once again imprisoned for nine months.

After 1945, Finck was a successful book author, cabaret artist, and theater and film actor.

118   **Georg Banasch** (1888–1960), around 1931.

Doctor of Political Science, Clerical Councilor [*Ordinariatsrat*] and Canon since 1939, Prelate in the Bishopric Berlin. Director of the "Information Office of Germany's Episcopal Authorities" which collected and distributed critical information about those legal proceedings which the Nazi judiciary had initiated in 1935/1936 againts representatives of the Catholic Church.

In conjunction with this, Banasch was arrested on November 22, 1935, and taken to the "*Gestapo* Prison" at Prinz-Albrecht-Strasse 8. Although the proceedings pending against him were stayed in the beginning of January 1936, he remained in prison until March 6, 1936.

Banasch resumed his work as Clerical Councilor and Canon in Berlin after 1945.

119   **Erich Honecker** (born 1912), in *Gestapo* detention, December 1935.

In 1926 he became a member of the German Communist Youth League (KJVD), and in 1930 he joined the German Communist Party (KPD). From 1931 on Secretary of the KJVD in the Saar region. After 1933 a member of the illegal central committee of the KJVD; he also took charge of KJVD resistance activities in southern Germany.

Honecker was arrested on December 4, 1935, and taken first to Prinz-Albrecht-Strasse 8. In 1937, after a year and a half in pretrial detention, he was sentenced to a ten year penitentiary term. He remained imprisoned in Brandenburg Penitentiary until the end of the war.

1946–1955 First Chairman of the Free German Youth [*Freie Deutsche Jugend* (FDJ)]. Since 1950 a delegate to the Parliament [*Volkskammer*] of the German Democratic Republic (GDR). Since 1971 First Secretary of the Central Committee of the Socialist Unity Party of Germany and a member of the Council of State of the GDR. Since 1976 General Secretary of the Central Committee and Chairman of the Council of State of the GDR.

Text 14

In the forenoon of the following day, however, I was arrested just as I was leaving my apartment on Brüsseler Strasse in the Berlin Wedding district. What followed during the days after the 4th of December, 1935, in *Gestapo* Headquarters on Prinz-Albrecht- Strasse and in the barracks of the *Leibstandarte "Adolf Hitler"* [lit. Bodyguard Regiment A.H.] in Berlin-Tempelhof did not reoccur in quite the same way during my subsequent ten years of imprisonment. They were really days one never forgets. And yet, for a person whose entire life lay still ahead of him — I was then 23 years old — they were days that tested my character. Nothing could make me renounce my Communist ideology, neither physical nor psychological tortures by *Gestapo* officials nor the numerous interrogations conducted by Fascist investigating judges during my year and a half of pretrial detention.

Erich Honecker

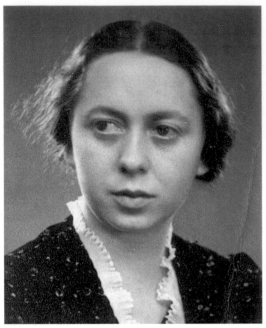

120 **Hildegard Schröder**, née Hirche (1911–1970), in 1938.
Member of the Socialist Workers' Youth (SAJ) since 1925, since 1928 of the SPD. Illegal activities since 1933.
She was arrested, together with her husband, on April 7, 1936, interrogated at Prinz-Albrecht-Strasse 8, and thereafter was taken to the prison on Alexanderplatz. She was sentenced to a year and a half in prison for "aiding and abetting High Treason."

121 **Heinz Schröder** (born 1910), around 1935.

Member of the SPD since 1928. Was active in the *Reichsbanner Schwarz-Rot-Gold* and in the Socialist Workers' Youth (SAJ). Illegal activities since 1933.
He was arrested, together with his wife, on April 7, 1936, and taken to Prinz-Albrecht-Strasse 8 where both of them were interrogated. On the same day he was sent to Concentration Camp Columbiahaus. Heinz Schröder was sentenced to two years and three months in a penitentiary. In 1942 he was assigned to the Penal Battalion "999," a so-called "probationary unit" [*Bewährungseinheit*] of the Regular Army [*Wehrmacht*]. In 1946 he became a member of the German Socialist Unity Party [*Sozialistische Einheitspartei Deutschlands (SED)* and is today Chairman of the "Association of Persons Persecuted by the Nazi Regime (VVN)" in Berlin (West).

Text 15

[..] soon we arrived at the Gestapo building on Prinz-Albrecht- Strasse. Then, abrupt and harsh, "get out!" Then, "go in there, move to the wall, then go upstairs." Both of us walked upstairs, hugging the wall. The cops walked along the banisters, where the light well was. Only later did we find out why this was so. Some prisoners unable to endure further tortures had hurled themselves down the light well [...] A dead Communist or Social Democrat was useless to the Nazis as they could no longer beat any information out of him. After we arrived on the sixth floor we had to sit down on a bench, and a hulking SS man of the "Bodyguard Regiment Adolf Hitler" placed himself between us. We were no longer allowed to talk to each other, were not even allowed to move our heads and look at each other once more. My Hilde was called in first [...]; then it was my turn. I had to sit down with my back to the desk. Next to me a typist Gestapo broad took her place and typed everything I said immediately into the machine [...] And then the questions came hard and fast, question after question, with four men crossexamining, and in the process they pinched me, hit me with their fists, though all of it still relatively harmless [...] And yet, they got no results. At the end of the interrogation Schüttauf said: "Whenever I have a Communist here, I slug him in the mug; but you Social Democrats are no worthy oponents, you are neither fish nor fowl." Then I was taken down to the basement. Here were the cells, 36 of them in all, among them also a rather spacious community cell. All doors had blankets hanging on the outside, but I still could hear the moans and whimpers.

Heinz Schröder

Text 16

My first trip was to the basement prison of the Secret State Police Office on Prinz-Albrecht-Strasse. When the doors had closed behind me

122 **Werner Peuke** (1905–1949), during wartime.
Member of the KPD. Since 1933, member of the Socialist resistance group "New Beginning."
Peuke was arrested at Easter, 1936, and taken to Prinz-Albrecht-Strasse 8 on April 14, 1936. There he remained for four days in the "*Gestapo* Prison" before he was transferred to Concentration Camp Columbiahaus. From there he was taken nearly every day to Prinz-Albrecht-Strasse 8 for interrogation. From Fall 1936 until 1939 he was imprisoned in Concentration Camp Sachsenhausen.
After the war Peuke participated in the establishment of municipal administration in the Soviet Sector of Berlin. In 1948, after conflicts with the SED, he moved to the western sector of the city.

123 **Eberhard Hesse** (1911–1986), around 1935.
He was active in the Socialist Workers' Youth (SAJ) and became a member of the SPD in 1930. From 1933 on he was engaged in resistance work and was also associated with the group "New Beginning."
On April 23, 1936, he was taken to Prinz-Albrecht-Strasse 8 and was subsequently sentenced to a year and half in prison. From 1947 to 1974 he was director of the August-Bebel-Institute. From 1951 to 1961 he headed the SPD's Berlin Press Office, and from 1961–1971 he was Regional Managing Director of the SPD in Berlin. He also sat in Berlin's House of Deputies from 1956 until 1975.

and I was led into the brightly lit reception room, that familiar oppressive feeling returned. This time, though, it did not last hours but only minutes. Strangely enough, I did not even have to give my name. The man seemed to know everything. "Hand over your valuables, take out your shoe laces, take off your tie." Everything was stuffed into my hat. Suddenly he handed me a briefcase. When I opened it I found some toilet articles and my fiancée's handbag. Then it became clear to me that she, too, must have been arrested. The cell into which I was pushed had only one small window — a few centimeters square, more like a ventilator — a table, a chair, a wooden bunk without blankets. On the wall I detected some graffiti: "This is a murder basement," "Down with Hitler." The light in the cell burned all night.

Werner Peuke

124 **Karl (Carlo) Mierendorff** (1897–1943), around 1930.

Doctor of Philosophy, member of the SPD since 1920. 1926–1928 Secretary of the Social Democratic Reichstag delegation. 1928–1930 Press and Public Relations Officer to the Hessian Minister of the Interior, Wilhelm Leuschner (SPD). From 1933 until January 1938 he was imprisoned in Darmstadt and the Concentration Camps Osthofen, Papenburg, Börgermoor, Torgau, Lichtenburg and Buchenwald. On December 16, 1937, he was taken to the "Gestapo Prison" at Prinz-Albrecht-Strasse 8. He was probably released on February 2nd, 1938. Between 1938 and 1940 he established contact with friends who were in the Social Democratic resistance movement, among them Haubach, Leuschner, Maaß and Leber. From 1941 to 1943 he worked with the "Kreisau Circle" ["Kreisauer Kreis," the resistance group around Count von Moltke]. On December 4, 1943, Mierendorff perished during a bombing raid on Leipzig.

Doctor of Philosophy, since 1918 a member of the SPD. 1942–1931 a delegate to the Württemberg Diet and 1930–1933 to the Reichstag. He sat on the executive committee of the SPD's Reichstag delegation from 1932 until 1933. For a period of ten years, from July 1933 on, he was uninterruptedly held in various concentration camps. In the summer of 1939 he was taken from Concentration Camp Dachau to Prinz-Albrecht-Strasse 8 for interrogation and remained for four months in the communal cell of the "Gestapo Prison" where Fritz Erler was also held for a while. After July 20, 1944, he was arrested again and imprisoned in Concentration Camp Neuengamme.
From 1946 until his death on August 20, 1952, Schumacher was chairman of the SPD and in 1949 became also a delegate to the German Federal Parliament where he chaired the SPD delegation.

125   **Franz Künstler** (1888–1942), while an inmate in Concentration Camp Oranienburg, November 3, 1933.
Member of the SPD since 1906, from 1917 to 1922 of the USPD. From 1924 to 1933 Chairman of the SPD in Berlin. From 1920 to 1933 a delegate to the Reichstag.
From July 1933 until September 1934 he was held in various prisons and concentration camps. As he was suspected of "preparation to commit high treason," he was held from August 1 to November 28, 1938, in the "Gestapo Prison" at Prinz-Albrecht-Strasse 8. He died on September 10, 1942, as a result of health damages incurred while he was held in prison.

126   **Kurt Schumacher** (1895–1952), around 1930.

127   **Fritz Erler** (1913–1967), around 1947.
Member of the Socialist Workers' Youth (SAJ) in 1928, and in 1931 of the SPD. Until 1933 he was also district leader in charge of canvassing for the SAJ Prenzlauer Berg, Berlin, and chairman of the Socialist Union of Greater Berlin's students [highschool]. In 1933 he joined the resistance group "New Beginning" and became a member of its political steering committee in 1936.
He was arrested on November 3, 1938. In August of the following year he was held prisoner in the communal cell of the "Gestapo Prison" at Prinz-Albrecht-Strasse 8. After ten months of pretrial detention he was sentenced on September 15, 1939, to ten years in a penitentiary for illegal political party activities. He managed to escape in April 1945 while he and other prisoners were being transferred.
After the war, Erler was District Administrator [Landrat] in Biberach/Riß. Since 1946 he was a member of the Advisory State Assembly [Beratende Landesversammlung] and a delegate to the Diet of Württemberg-Hohenzollern. From 1949 to 1967 he was a member of the German Federal Parliament. From 1957–1964 he was deputy chairman of the SPD delegation in the German Federal Parliament, and from 1964 to 1967 its chairman. During the latter period he was also deputy chairman of the SPD.

3.7. "Protective Custody"

One of the most severe measures which the National Socialist State applied against any-body who had been declared an "Enemy of State and People" was protective custody. As a rule, the individual State Police branches applied for this category of arrest. Then the Protective Custody Section within the Secret State Police Office processed the case and eventually issued the requisite order after the respective approval of either the Chief of the *Gestapo*, Heinrich Müller, or of Heydrich, and in very special cases of Himmler himself had been obtained. Protective custody was implemented in the concentration camps.

Already in October 1939 it became a rule that ordinarily nobody was to be released from protective custody during the duration of the war. From May 1943 on, the local *Gestapo* branches could, on their own authority, place Polish prisoners into protective cus-tody and then send them to a concentration camp. The Reich Security Main Office merely had to be informed of the matter.

The precise number of arrest orders resulting in protective custody can no longer be as-certained. When Heydrich assumed his duties as Head of the Secret State Police Office in 1934, all such orders were marked by the initial letter of the arrested person's last name and was followed by a consecutive number. One of the last orders still extant by which protective custody was imposed bears the number "M 34 591." This means that at least 34 591 persons whose last name began with an "M" were held in protective custody until 1945.

With the abrogation of fundamental rights by the Decree of February 28, 1933, following the fire of the Reichstag building and with the elimination of formal reviews of *Gestapo* procedures by courts of law, *Gestapo* imposition of protective custody and its implemen-tation in concentration camps cleared the way for whatever "special treatment" [*Sonder-behandlung*] the National Socialist leadership wanted to employ, in other words, the physical liquidation of any individual prisoner.

The official who had been in charge of the Reich Security Main Office's Protective Cus-tody Section stated after the war: "As an official accustomed to obey orders I could not possibly imagine that the Reich leadership which had been formally recognized by all foreign powers would issue unlawful orders. And with regard to the more severe orders that were issued, those I considered justified measures taken in wartime."

Text 17

Directive of April 26, 1935 by the Secret State Police Office, pertaining to the check on sentences imposed by the courts against "Enemies of the State"

Frankfurt/Main, November 16, 1935.

State Police branch
for the administrative district Wiesbaden
in Frankfurt am Main
II L 3623/35.

I am handing the following copy [of a directive] from the Secret State Police Office in Berlin to all officials and employees of II L for your information and files.
By authorization
signed: Wüst
witnessed: Schäfer,
Office Employee

Copy.

Berlin, April 26, 1935

Secret State Police Office
B. No. 64479/35 222 II/I

I receive constant complaints that some courts do not treat or punish enemies of the State with the severity one might think would be justified in view of what they have done. Criminal proceedings are said to have been suspended with insufficient reason. In other instances, punishment according to public sentiment seems much too light. Acquitals are said to have occured although the public generally expects and hopes that punishment will surely be forthcoming. Moreover, police authorities frequently complain that persons arrested and awaiting a decision were released, although the grounds for issuing an arrest warrant most certainly existed. Thus, arrest warrants have been repeatedly denied in cases where Communists had been proven guilty and had confessed to illegal activities in behalf of the KPD. (See the most recent case at State Police Branch II L involving the affair of high treason by Apel and accomplices; here a councilor of a lower court [Amtsgerichtsrat] did not want to issue an arrest warrant although evidence that illegal activities had been engaged in existed).
The Political Police is understandably greatly interested in seeing political criminals justly punished by German law courts in view of what they have done. It [i.e., the Political Police] has no authority of its own to punish and therefore is nearly completely dependent on the court decisions. But as it has been given the task to fight enemies of the State and as this responsibility has been placed on its shoulders, it must make it its business to see to it that the courts do take suitable measures to subdue enemies of the State.
Every State Police branch must therefore report each inadequate performance by the courts. Such a report must include a brief summmary of the case in question, with emphasis on those aspects that reveal an unsatisfactory performance by the court.

Text 18

Directive of May 3, 1935 by the Secret State Police Office, pertaining to surveillance of released prisoners

Copy!

Berlin, May 3, 1935

Secret State Police Office
B. No. 64594/ 35–228-II 1

To all Prussian State Police branches:
It appears essential to place released protective custody prisoners or other enemies of the State considered to be especially dangerous under continuous surveillance. In order not to have their surveillance interrupted when they change domicile, the local police authorities must report an intended change of domicile by a released prisoner promptly to their appropriate State Police branch. That State Police branch will thereupon notify the local police authority of the released prisoner's new domicile. Now should that person move his new domicile to the district of a different State Police branch, then that branch must be notified accordingly by the State Police branch of the district where the person had resided previously. The local police authority of the person's new domicile must be instructed in each case to continue surveillance and to forward relevant information to the State Police branch.
Should any of these persons not arrive at the new place of residence for which he registered [with the local police] when he handed in his change of address card [Abmeldung], then the State Police branch of the designated new domicile must check back with the local police authorities or the State Police branch of his previous place of residence in order to determine whether the person has left his erstwhile domicile or has subsequently decided not to make the intended move after all. In the former instance, the State Police branch of his previous place of residence must list the person in the Deutsche Kriminalblatt [approx.: German Journal of Criminality] in order to initiate a search for his whereabouts. It may prove useful for the proper execution of this directive to mark the residence-

registration cards [*Meldekarten*] of the persons concerned with the following endorsement: "In case of a change of domicile the State Police branch must be notified." The local police authorities are to be informed accordingly. It is their responsibility to see to it that these endorsements do not come to the attention of the persons in question.

By authorization
signed. Signature

Text 19

Instruction [Weisung] of March 23, 1936 by the Chief of Police of all German Member States [Länder] to the Inspector of Concentration Camps pertaining to a more severe detention for prisoners who are committed to a concentration camp for the second time

Copy!
The Political Commander of Police of all German Member States
Berlin SW 11, March 23, 1936
Prinz-Albrecht- Strasse 8
B. No. [...]. 55/36 Ads.
Restricted! [*Verschlossen*]

To the
Inspector of Concentration Camps
SS Major General Eicke

In all concentration camps special detachments are to be formed for prisoners who are in a concentration camp for a second time. The protective custody files of all those who are in a concentration camp for a second time are not to be submitted again, on principle, for three years. The usual quarterly detention reviews are not applicable to these prisoners.

As to correspondence, I allow four times a year for writing and receiving a letter.
Working time: ten hours a day.
No smoking will be permitted.
Money received from home cannot exceed 10 *Reichsmarks* quarterly.
Packages may not be received at all.
These prisoners shall be singled out by special markings on their clothing.

Signed : H. Himmler.

Text 20

Directive of January 25, 1938 by the Reich Minister of the Interior to the Secret State Police Office pertaining to "Protective Custody"

Copy

Berlin, January 25, 1938
Reich Minister of the Interior

1.S-V 1 No. 70/37–179-g
To
the Secret State Police Office.
Subject: Protective Custody
The following regulations pertaining to protective custody will become effective as of February 1, 1938. [...]
[...]

§ 1.
Applicability.
Protective Custody may be authorized by the Secret State Police as a coercive measure in combating all hostile activities toward people and state on the part of individuals whose atitude puts the existence and security of people and state at risk. Protective custody may not be imposed for penal purposes or as a substitute for penal imprisonment. Actions subject to punishment must be tried in courts of law.

§ 2.
Jurisdiction.
(1) Protective custody may be imposed exclusively by the Secret State Police Office.
(2) Requests for the imposition of protective custody are to be directed by the Regional Commands of the Secret State Police or the Secret State Police branches, respectively, to the Secret State Police Office. Each request must be thoroughly substantiated whereby the arguments of the person arrested must be taken into consideration. A copy of the interrogation report of the temporarily arrested individual is to be forwarded immediately.
(3) Protective custody may only be imposed after the accused has had a chance to be heard beforehand on the charges against him.

§ 3.
Temporary Arrest.
(1) The Secret State Police Office, the Regional Commands of the Secret State Police and the State Police branches are authorized, according to the preconditions laid down in § 1, to order the temporary arrest of an individual
a) if there is concern that he will abuse his state of freedom to engage in activities hostile to the state,

b) if he threatens to eliminate evidence,
c) if he is suspected of planning to escape.
(2) The accused must be informed by deposition within 24 hours after his arrest at the latest that he is under temporary arrest.
(3) An individual held under temporary arrest must be released not later than ten days after the day he was arrested, unless the Secret State Police has in the meantime imposed protective custody (5).
[...]

§ 6.
Implementation.
Protective custody is to be implemented on principle in state-run concentration camps.
[...]

§ 9.
Implementing Regulations.
The requisite implementing regulations will be issued by the Chief of Security Police.

Signed: Frick

Text 21

Directive of October 26, 1939, by the Reich Security Main Office, Department IV (Gestapo), pertaining to "implementation of Protective Custody"

Berlin, October 26, 1939
Top Secret!
Reich Security Main Office
Department IV
B. No. 409 39 g. Rs. [Top Secret]

a) To all Regional and Local Commands of the Secret State Police
b) To the Secret State Police Office (according to short distribution list C),
for information purposes
a) To all Inspectors of Security Police and Security Service,
b) To the General Inspector of the reinforced SS Death's Head Regiments (with 8 copies for the camps).
Subject: Implementation of Protective Custody.

By order of the *Reichsführer-SS* and Chief of German Police all protective custody prisoners committed to a concentration camp during wartime are to be assigned to a separate punitive detachment. Only protective custody prisoners who have been sent to a camp by the police as a preventive measure (especially A-File), or who have been explicitly exempted as stated in their letter of transfer, will be exempt from this order.
These exceptions, however, require the approval

of the Secret State Police Office and, if applicable, must be applied for at Section II D.
In order to achieve a more far-reaching deterring effect the following must be observed in each individual case:

1) If a protective custody prisoner who was sent to a concentration camp had worked in a factory [*Betrieb*], and if his hostile attitude to the State and his alienation from the community had been conducive to influence the discipline or, respectively, the will to work etc. on the part of his fellow workers, then care must be taken to make his commitment to a concentration camp public by means of a public notice.
2) In more severe cases it might be added to such an announcement that the person committed to a camp has been assigned to a punitive detachment because of his conduct.
3) Under no circumstances must the duration of detention be mentioned even if, for instance, the *Reichsführer-SS* and Chief of German Police, or the Chief of Security Police and Security Service respectively should have already determined the duration of detention.
To the outside, the duration of detention in a concentration camp must always be indicated as "indefinitely."
Conversely, there are no objections to a cleverly launched whispering campaign which in more severe cases may heigthen the deterring effect, conceivable along the line of it having been said that the individual committed, given the severity of his case, would not be released for another two or three years.
4) In individual cases the *Reichsführer-SS* and Chief of German Police will impose corporal punishment in addition to commitment to a concentration camp. In the future, such orders will also be communicated to the requisite Regional and Local Command of the State Police. In cases like these there are also no objections if, as in No. 3, paragraph 3, word of the heightened severity [of the punishment] be spread around as long as this will be conducive to increase the deterring effect.
5) It is understood that only particularly suitable and reliable persons will be chosen for the dissemination of such information.
6) The Regional and Local Commands of the State Police will submit to me a brief report on their respective experiences by February 2, 1940.

Acting as deputy:
signed: Müller
Witnessed:
Office employee [female].

Text 22

Directive of January 31, 1940 by the Reichsführer-SS and Chief of German Police pertaining to contacts between German women and prisoners of war

Berlin, January 31, 1940

Reichsführer-SS
and Chief of German Police
in the Reich Ministry of the Interior
S I V 1 No. 861 VI/39 – 176 -7 – Sdb. StGB [Criminal Code].

To:
a) The Regional and Local Commands of the State Police,
b) Commanders of Security Police and Security Service,
   for your information
[...]

Subject: Contacts with Prisoners of War.

I. German women and girls whose contacts with prisoners of war are of a nature which grossly offends the sound instincts of the people are to be taken into protective custody until further notice, and are to be committed to a concentration camp for at least one year. A gross offense of the sound instincts of the people would be any social intercourse (e.g. parties, dances), and especially all sexual intercourse.
II. Should women and girls of a locality want to pillory the woman in question publicly, or want to shave off her hair prior to her transportation to a concentration camp, the police is not to intervene.

Signed: Himmler
Witnessed:
Administrative Secretary.

Text 23

Directive of August 27, 1941 by the Chief of Security Police and Security Service pertaining to the arrest of "elements hostile to the State" after onset of war with the Soviet Union.

Berlin, August 27, 1941.
Chief of Security Police
and Security Service
IV C 2 Allg. No. 41 334.
Confidential!

To:
a) Regional and Local Commands of the State Police,

b) Commanders of Security Police and Security Service,
c) All sections of Department IV of the RSMO,
d) Department V.
For your information
To:
e) The Inspectors of Security Police and Security Service
f) The Commanders of Security Police and Security Service
g) IV GSt. for the file of directives (2 copies)
h) Division I B (12 copies)

Subject: Fundamental Directive of the *Reichsführer-SS* and Chief of German Police pertaining to the arrest of elements hostile to the state after the onset of the campaign against the Soviet Union.

In response to reports of important events relating to the domain of the State Police the *Reichsführer-SS* and Chief of German Police has ordered in individual cases extended protective custody and transport to a concentration camp. The agencies concerned have been kept informed of all relevant decisions in order to take further appropriate initiatives.

In view of mounting activities and comments hostile to the state since the campaign against the Soviet Union has begun, the *Reichsführer-SS* and Chief of German Police has now come to the fundamental determination that "all slanderous priests [*Pfaffen*], Czechs and Poles hostile to Germany as well as Communists and similar scum will be sent to a concentration camp for an extended period of time as a matter of principle."

In order to make sure that this directive does not remain restricted to applications for protective custody submitted in the usual manner, but can be considered prior to the submission of applications, I notify [you] of this directive.

As far as the initiation of criminal proceedings is concerned, an application should be made for renewed arrest [*Rücksistierung*]. I thereby ask all public prosecutors to cooperate with the State Police in matters of general pardons, cases of parole, etc.

This directive is to be treated as confidential. Neither the prisoners nor any other person must know about it.

This directive is not meant for local or district police authorities.

Acting as deputy:
signed: Müller
Witnessed:
Office employee (female).

"Protective Custody" and "Preventive Custody" [Vorbeugungshaft] for Homosexuals

Homosexuals in the Third Reich were persecuted with particular vehemence and way beyond the existing provisions of the criminal law code. They were not only subject to "protective custody" but to "preventive custody" as well. Both led to imprisonment in a concentration camp. Male homosexuality was seen as a threat to the "people's community" (*Volksgemeinschaft*) and was incompatible with the principles of racial population policies. The widespread prejudices against homosexuality were also used by the National Socialist leadership for propaganda purposes: in 1934, when Röhm was murdered; in 1936/1937, during the staged "moral trials" of Catholic priests and members of religious orders; and in 1938, when General von Fritsch was deprived of his high command of the Army.

In 1936, a "Central Reich Agency to fight Homosexuality and Abortion" was established in the Prussian State Office of the Criminal Police; and as early as 1934, a "Special Department Homosexuality" had been created within the Secret State Police Office. From 1939 on, both institutions belonged to the Reich Security Main Office. In 1935, Article 175 of the criminal code was expanded, with more severe provisions added to it. Thousands of homosexuals — there are no precise figures — were imprisoned in concentration camps. These "men with the pink triangle" were subject to special harassment on the part of the guards; their death rate was markedly higher than that of other categories of prisoners.

128   On June 29, 1935 the State Police Office in Düsseldorf placed into protective custody a young man suspected of homosexuality. (See Abstract 7 in Appendix).

129   Arrest report of April 8, 1936 by the supervisory political branch of the Secret State Police in Essen, pertaining to the arrest of a person suspected of homosexuality. (See Abstract 7 in Appendix).

Text 24:

A report of March 11, 1935 by SS First Lieutenant Carl Marks, pertaining to a raid made by *Gestapo* and SS on homosexuals in Berlin

Carl Marks
SS First Lieutenant
Leibstandarte SS Adolf Hitler
11th Company [*Sturm*]

Berlin-Lichterfelde, March 11, 1935

Report!

On March 9, 1935, the company under my command provided 20 men for a commando to support officers of the *Gestapo* during a raid on homosexuals.

The Commando departed from the barracks in two trucks at 9:15 p.m. and reported as ordered to Chief Inspector Kanthak at 10 p.m. In addition to our commando, 10 to 12 police officers had been assigned to participate in the raid. Some of them were appointed to make sure beforehand that the execution [of the raid] would proceed as planned. A few of them returned before our deployment began. Meanwhile Chief Inspector K. briefed me on the operation.

At 10:45 p.m. we departed from *Gestapo* headquarters and rode in several trucks to the restaurant "Weinmeister Klause" on Weinmeisterstrasse where many persons with homosexual tendencies were believed to hang out. According to prior arrangements, two of our men sealed off the exits of the restaurant; they had been given orders not to allow anybody to leave but to admit everybody who wanted to come in. Eight men, previously designated, blocked off the space in front of the bar from the other part of the restaurant. Two men searched the toilets. Chief Inspector K. and his officers removed all suspicious looking persons from the tables and ordered them to join those who had been previously told to line up in front of the bar. Then they were loaded onto the trucks and, guarded by our men, were taken to *Gestapo* headquarters. Among those arrested was also a woman who was said to be in posession of inflammatory Soviet-Russian pamphlets. From the courtyard of *Gestapo* headquarters those arrested were taken, again under guard, to the hallway on the fourth floor and to the sections that handled such cases. Here they had to line up in alphabetical order and, guarded by our men, with their faces to the wall, wait for their interrogation. The interrogation began at once, conducted by most of the previously mentioned police officers. After these men had been interrogated they were moved to another part of the hallway where they had to wait for the decisions regarding their guilt or innocence. Here too they were guarded by our men.

Once the interrogations of those first arrested had started, Chief Inspector K. and some of his men not immediately needed for interrogations resumed the raid, accompanied by the rest of our men.

[...]

130   **Josef Meisinger** (1899–1947), around 1940.
Josef Meisinger, a Bavarian Criminal Police official, worked from 1934 on in the Secret State Police Office in Berlin. His special assignment was to monitor activities within the National Socialist Party and its various affiliated organizations (for example, corruption). In addition, he was also in charge of Section II S, which handled homosexual matters, and from 1936 on headed the "Central Reich Agency to fight Homosexuality and Abortion." In 1939 he became Deputy Commander of Special Unit IV, and in April 1940 was appointed Commander of Security Police and Security Service in Warsaw. In October 1940 he was assigned to Tokyo as a police attaché. There he was arrested by the Americans in 1945, was extradited to Poland in 1946 and executed in Warsaw in 1947 because of crimes committed while commanding the Security Police there.

3.8. Concentration Camps

Next to the standardization of the Political Police it was Himmler's second objective to centralize the concentration camps. During the period 1933–1934 the "wild," i.e. inofficial camps run by Stormtroopers were closed down or placed under the administration of the state. On July 7, 1934, the *Reichsführer-SS* appointed Theodor Eicke, who had run Camp Dachau since the summer of 1933, as Inspector of Concentration Camps. In addition to the reorganization of the camps, Eicke systematized the terrorist treatment of prisoners in conjunction with the guard units under his command, subsequently known officially as "Death's Head Units." In 1939, six camps existed with roughly 21.000 prisoners: Dachau, Sachsenhausen, Buchenwald, Flossenbürg, Mauthausen and Ravensbrück.

Although the camps were initially under the direction of the SS Main Office, Eicke always preserved his independent position. In 1942, Himmler placed the camps, now in the charge of Eicke's successor, Richard Glücks, under the control of the Main Office for Economic Administration [*Wirtschaftsverwaltungshauptamt*] of the SS as Departmental Division D 5. The enormous increase of the number of inmates once war had broken out increased the already existing tendency of exploiting camp inmates systematically for labor. From this point on it was merely a small step toward that murderous treatment of prisoners referred to as "extermination through labor," which hit the Jewish prisoners worst of all.

The composition of prisoners changed during the war, and in 1945 roughly 90% of them were non-Germans. In 1944, 20 concentration camps with 165 satellite forced labor camps existed. Two figures will reveal the disastrous conditions in the camps, where inmates were defenseless and totally at the mercy of their guards: during the second half of 1942, 57.503 inmates out of 95,000 died, and in the first eight months of 1943, over 60,000. In January 1945 over 700,000 human beings were imprisoned in the camps, 200,000 of them women. 40,000 guards secured this portion of the SS State at the end of the war.

132 Rudolf Diels, Head of the Secret State Police Office, addresses inmates of Concentration Camp Oranienburg prior to their release in December 1933.

131   Entrance gate to Concentration Camp Oranienburg, in 1933.

133   Inspection on May 8, 1936, of a pictorial sign pointing to Concentration Camp Dachau. From the left: Karl Wolff (Chief of the *Reichsführer-SS*' personal staff), Himmler and Rudolf Hess. .

135   Map of the concentration camps.
Top left reads: The most important concentration camps in the Third Reich. Lower right, legend:
Concentration camps
cities
frontiers of 1937
Greater German Reich, 1942.

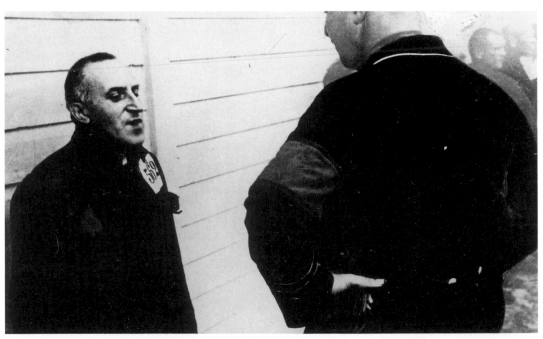

134   Carl von Ossietzky (former editor of *Die Weltbühne*) in Concentration Camp Papenburg-Esterwegen.

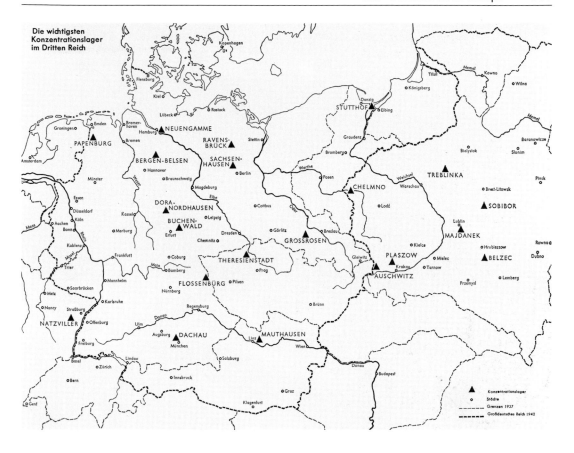

Die wichtigsten Konzentrationslager im Dritten Reich

136   Forced labor by inmates in Concentration Camp
Neuengamme, around 1941/1942.

137   Standing formation in Concentration Camp Sachsenhausen, around 1940/41.

138   Prisoner in the electric fence of a concentration camp.

4. Persecution, Extermination, Resistance

4.1. The German Jews 1933–38

Beyond the fight against and the elimination of political opponents, the terror of the NS State was directed above all against the Jewish population, the "racial-political main enemy." Ever since Hitler's rule began, it had been a primary objective of National Socialist Germany to slander, isolate and expel the German Jews. Within the range of prevailing political opportunities between 1933 and 1939, Jews were deprived of their occupational possibilities, became targets of anti-Semitic hatred and slander campaigns in every sphere of public life, and were forced with all available means into emigration.

Increasingly isolated from the rest of the population by the promulgation of the "Nuremberg Laws," deprived of any long-range hopes for making a living because of the beginning "Aryanization," and by their systematic exclusion from one occupation after the other, Jews were deprived step by step of all opportunities to live in their homeland. The November pogrom of 1938 had the objective of excluding German Jews once and for all from economic life, pushing them toward emigration by the increasing pressure of mass arrests. Whereas until 1938 the most important initiators of anti-Jewish campaigns had been primarily agencies of state and party, the year 1938 marked the transfer of this initiative to the Secret State Police. From January 1939 on it was Reinhard Heydrich who was in charge of the "Solution of the Jewish Question."

Chronology – until December 1938 – of all measures taken to persecute the Jews and to deprive them of their rights

April 1, 1933
"Boycott" of all Jewish places of business by Stormtroopers and SS throughout the entire Reich.

April 7, 1933
Law to "Restore Professional Bureaucracy" results in the discharge of "non-Aryan" officials.

July 14, 1933
"Law of Annulment of Previous Naturalization and of Revocation of German Citizenship"; this was directed primarily against Jews from the former German territories in the east who had obtained citizenship after 1918.

September 22, 1933
Law of the Reich Cultural Chamber: Exclusion of Jewish artists and all Jews active in the cultural sector.

October 4, 1933
Law of Editors: Exclusion of Jewish editors.

May 21, 1935
Military Service Act: "Aryan descent" becomes prerequisite for military service.

Summer 1935
"Jews not wanted here!" – Signs at village entrances, places of business and in restaurants are on the increase.

September 15, 1935
At a special session held in conjunction with the NSDAP's "Reich Party Rally," the Reichstag passes the anti-Semitic "Nuremberg Laws," i.e. the "Reich Citizenship Law," and the "Law for the Protection of German Blood and German Honor" ["*Blutschutzgesetz*"].

November 14, 1935
The 1st Ordinance supplementing the "Reich Citizenship Law" defines the meaning of "Jew" and leads to the abrogation of the right to vote and to hold public office. It also leads to the discharge of all Jewish officials, including former frontline fighters [in the First World War] and defines "persons of mixed blood" ["*Mischlings*"-*status*].

November 14, 1935
The 1st Ordinance supplementing the "*Blutschutz-gesetz*" leads to the prohibition of marriages between Jews and "persons of mixed blood in the second degree."

June 12, 1937
Secret directive by Heydrich ordering "protective custody" for all "defilers of race" once the regular legal proceedings are concluded.

March 28, 1938
The law on the legal situation of Jewish religious communal associations deprives Jewish congregations of the status of corporations under public law.

April 22, 1938
Ordinance concerning the "camouflage of Jewish business establishments."

April 26, 1938
The ordinance about registration of all Jewish capital above 5000,— Reichsmarks is a preparatory step toward the future exclusion [of Jews] from the economy.

June 1938
Finance offices and police stations draw up lists of wealthy Jews.

June 9, 1938
Destruction of the Munich synagogue.

June 14, 1938
The 3rd Ordinance supplementing the "Reich Citizenship Law" leads to the registration and marking of all Jewish business establishments.

June 15, 1938
During the so-called "June Action," 1,500 Jewish citizens with a police record, including, for instance, anyone convicted of traffic violations, are arrested and sent to concentration camps.

July 23, 1938
Adoption of a special identification card for Jews as of January 1, 1939.

July 25, 1938
The 4th Ordinance supplementing the "Reich Citizenship Law" strikes all Jewish physicians off the Medical Register as of September 30, 1938, and henceforth permits them medical practice only in exceptional cases and as "caretaker of the sick" [*Krankenbehandler*], exclusively for Jews.

August 10, 1938
Destruction of the Nuremberg synagogue.

August 17, 1938
The 2nd Ordinance pertaining to the execution of the "Law about Changes of Family Names and First Names" forces Jewish citizens to adopt the mandatory first names of "Israel" and "Sara" respectively as of January 1, 1939.

September 27, 1938
The 5th Ordinance supplementing the "Reich Citizenship Law" deprives all Jewish lawyers of their right to practice law as of November 30, 1938, and permits further activity only for Jews, as so-called "Jewish Advisers" [*Konsulenten*].

October 5, 1938
All passports of Jews are stamped with a "J".

October 28, 1938
Expulsion of between 15,000 and 17,000 so-called "stateless" and originally Polish Jews to Poland, many of whom had lived in Germany for decades.

November 7, 1938
Fatal assassination attempt on the German Embassy Councillor vom Rath in Paris by Herschel Grynszpan, whose parents were affected by the expulsion.

November 9/10, 1938
A state-run pogrom against the Jewish population throughout all of Germany, the so-called "Reich Crystal Night." The destruction included synagogues, business establishments, apartment buildings. Over 26,000 male Jews were arrested, many severely maltreated.

November 12, 1938
Ordinance about a "Punitive Payment" [*Sühne-leistung*] of the Jews to the amount of one billion Reichsmarks.

November 12, 1938
The ordinance to exclude all Jews from the German economy results in the closing of all Jewish business establishments and further measures along similar lines.

November 12, 1938
The ordinance pertaining to the "Restoration of Clean Streets" ["*Wiederherstellung des Strassenbildes*"] by Jewish commercial enterprises forces the Jews themselves to pay for all damages suffered on November 9 and 10.

November 12, 1938
The Jewish population is henceforth excluded from all cultural functions such as theater, movies, concerts, variety shows, exhibitions and circuses.

November 15, 1938
Jewish children are barred from attending school as of this date.

November 28, 1938
A police ordinance about Jews appearing in public restricts Jewish citizens from moving about freely and finding places to live.

December 3, 1938
All Jewish citizens must hand in their driver's licenses. In Berlin, establishment of a zone Jews are forbidden to enter [*Judenbann*].

December 13, 1938
An ordinance pertaining to the forced sale of Jewish commercial enterprises, business establishments, etc., so-called "Aryanization." Jews must sell their property at ridiculously low prices and then deposit the proceeds in blocked accounts. During wartime these assets were then confiscated by the German Reich.

139   An advertising pillar in Berlin with an appeal for joining the anti-Jewish "boycott" on April 1, 1933.

140   Stormtrooper sentries in front of a Jewish-owned store
in Berlin on April 1, 1933.

141   A shop window in Berlin with anti-Semitic graffiti and
"boycott" slogans on April 1, 1933.

Text 25:

"Law for the Protection of German Blood and German Honor" of September 15, 1935

Imbued with the realization that the purity of German blood is a prerequisite for the continued existence of the German people, and inspired by the inflexible will to protect the German Nation for all times to come, the Reichstag has unanimously passed the following law which is herewith promulgated:

§ 1
(1) Marriages between Jews and subjects of German or related [*artverwandt*] blood are forbidden. Marriages concluded in spite of it are null and void, even if concluded abroad to circumvent this law.
(2) Only the State Attorney may initiate an annulment claim.

§ 2
Extramarital sexual intercourse between Jews and subjects of German or related blood is forbidden.

142   Virulent anti-Semitic propaganda in a special issue of the weekly *Der Stürmer*, published by Julius Streicher, in May 1934. (See Abstract 8 in Appendix).

143   Entrance to a German village in 1935. The sign in the picture reads: "Jews enter this village at their own risk."

§ 3
Jews may not employ in their households female subjects of German or related blood under 45 years of age.

§ 4
(1) Jews are forbidden to fly the national flag of the Reich or display the national colors.
(2) They may, however, show the Jewish colors. The right to do so is protected by the State.

§ 5
(1) Anybody violating the injunction listed in § 1 will be punished by detention in a penitentiary.
(2) Any male violating the injunction listed in § 2 will be punished by either a prison term or a penitentiary term.
(3) Anybody violating any of the provisions listed in either § 3 or § 4 will be punished by imprisonment up to one year and a fine, or by either of these penalties.

§ 6
The Reich Minister of the Interior, in agreement with the Führer's Deputy and the Reich Minister of Justice, will issue the legal and administrative stipulations reqired to implement and supplement this law.

§ 7
The law becomes effective the day after it is promulgated, Article 3, however, only as of January 1, 1936.

Nuremberg, September 15, 1935,
at the Reich Party Rally of Liberty [Reichsparteitag der Freiheit]

The Führer and Reich Chancellor
Adolf Hitler

Reich Minister of the Interior
Frick

Reich Minister of Justice
Dr. Gürtner

The Führer's Deputy
R. Hess
Reich Minister without portfolio

Text 26

Telex Message of November 9, 1938 from the Secret State Police Office, Department II, to all Regional and Local Commands of the State Police, pertaining to the preparation of the pogrom against Jews

Berlin, No. 234 404 November 9, 1938
To all Regional and Local Commands of the State Police -Attention: Chiefs or Deputies
This telex must be delivered at once in the fastest possible manner.

1. Operations against Jews, in particular against their synagogues, will commence very soon throughout Germany. There must be no interfer-

Jüdisches Geschäft!   Wer hier kauft wird photographiert

144 "April Boycott," 1933. The sign reads: "Jewish business! Whoever buys here will be photographed."

ence. However, arrangements should be made, in consultation with the General Police, to prevent looting and other excesses.

2. Any vital archival material that might be in the synagogues must be secured by the fastest possible means.

3. Preparations must be made for the arrest of from 20.000 to 30.000 Jews within the Reich. In particular, affluent Jews are to be selected. Further directives will be forthcoming during the course of the night.

4. Should Jews be found in the possession of weapons during the impending operations, the most severe measures must be taken.
SS Verfügungstruppen [forerunner of the Combat (*Waffen*)-*SS*] and General SS may be called in for the overall operations. The State Police must under all circumstances maintain control of the operations by taking appropriate measures.

Addendum for the Cologne State Police:
The Cologne synagogue contains particulary important material. This must be secured at once in the fastest possible manner and in consultation with the Security Service.

Gestapo II Müller
This telex is classified "Secret."

Text 27

Decree of November 12, 1938 pertaining to a Punitive Payment [Sühneleistung] by all "Jews who are German Subjects"

The hostile attitude of Jewry toward the German People and Reich, an attitude which does not even shrink from committing cowardly murder, demands decisive resistance and severe retaliation. Pursuant to the Decree for the Execution of the Four-Year-Plan of October 18, 1936 (*Reichsgesetzblatt* I, p. 887), I therefore issue the following decree:

§ 1
A payment of 1,000,000,000 Reichsmarks is herewith imposed upon all Jews collectively who are German subjects.

§ 2
Stipulations for implementation will be issued by the Reich Minister of Finance in agreement with the other Reich ministers concerned.

Berlin, November 12, 1938.
Plenipotentiary for the Four-Year-Plan
Göring
Field Marshal

145 Destroyed stores in Berlin on November 10, 1938, the morning after the pogrom.

4.2. The German Jews 1939−45

When the deportations of German Jews began in October 1941, only 163,969 of the roughly 500,000 Jews who had lived in Germany in 1933 still resided in the so-called "*Altreich*" [Germany with its 1937 borders]. Under the direction of the Jewish Section (IV B 4) in the Reich Security Main Office and with the participation of all police agencies as well as other state agencies as far as they had jurisdiction to do so, the Jews were deprived of their remaining property and deported to the east. Destinations of the deportation trains were at first the ghettos of Lodz (Litzmannstadt), Kovno, Riga, Warsaw, Minsk, and several localities in the Lublin district. There they became victims of the execution commandos of SS and police units or were taken to the extermination camps in Poland. Since mid-1942 the destination of the death trains was increasingly Auschwitz-Birkenau. The Security Police deported persons over the age of 65 to the so-called "Senior Citizens Ghetto" [*Altersghetto*] Theresienstadt, where large numbers of them fell victim to the devastating conditions there, or they were moved on to the extermination sites and camps further east.

The Secret State Police and participating state agencies within the territory of the Reich saw to it, through an unprecedented process of expropriation, that the Jewish population died a "civic death" before being physically annihilated.

Chronology of how the Jews between 1939 and 1945 were deprived of their civil rights, persecuted and exterminated

January 17, 1939
8th Ordinance supplementing the Reich Citizenship Law (Jewish dentists, veterinarians, and apothecaries lose the right to practice their respective professions).

January 24, 1939
Founding of the "Reich Central Agency for Jewish Emigration."

April 30, 1939
Law on the housing of Jews. Preparations are made to consolidate Jewish families in "Jewish houses" [*Judenhäuser*].

July 4, 1939
10th Ordinance supplementing the Reich Citizenship Law (establishment of the "National Association of Jews in Germany" [*Reichsvereinigung der Juden in Deutschland*].

September 1, 1939
Restrictions on movements. In summertime, curfew at 9 p.m., in wintertime at 8 p.m.

September 23, 1939
Confiscation of all radio receivers.

October 12, 1939
First deportations from the "*Ostmark*" [Austria] and the "Protectorate of Bohemia and Moravia" to Poland.

November 23, 1939
All Jews in the *Generalgouvernement* are obligated to be clearly marked as Jews.

February 12/13, 1940
Deportation of the Stettin Jews to Poland (Lublin District).

April 20, 1940
Secret directive of the Supreme Command of the Army (Persons of mixed blood [*Mischlinge*] and husbands of Jewish wives must be discharged.

October 22, 1940
Deportation of Jews from Alsace-Lorraine, the Saar region and Baden to southern France.

September 1, 1941
Police directive about obligatory distinguishing marks for Jews (introduction of the "Jewish star" in Germany as of September 19, 1941).

October 17, 1941
Deportations of the German Jews (from the "*Altreich*") begin, first to Lodz, Kovno, Minsk, Riga and the Lublin District, subsequently to Auschwitz.

October 23, 1941
Ban on Jewish emigration.

November 25, 1941
11th Ordinance supplementing the Reich Citizenship Law (confiscation of Jewish capital at the time of deportation).

January 20, 1942
Wannsee Discussion ("Wannsee Conference") about the deportation and extermination of European Jewry ("Final Solution").

March 26, 1942
Announcement of marking Jewish apartments in Germany.

April 24, 1942
Ban on the use of public transportation.

June 2, 1942
Deportations to Theresienstadt begin.

June 30, 1942
All Jewish schools within Germany must permanently close.

February 27, 1943
Deportation of those German Jews working in Berlin in the armament industry ("Factory Action").

July 1, 1943
13th Ordinance Supplementing the Reich Citizenship Law (all Jews in Germany are placed under police law [*Polizeirecht*].

Text 28

Decree of October 23, 1941 by the Reich Security Main Office, pertaining to the ban on Jewish emigration.

Berlin, October 23, 1941
Reich Security Main Office
IV B 4b(RZ) 2920/41g (984)
To the Authorized Representative of the Chief of Security Police and Security Service for Belgium and France
Att. SS Brigadier General Thomas, Brussels

Subject: Emigration of Jews   Secret!
Reference: none

The *Reichsführer-SS* and Chief of German Police has directed that the emigration of Jews is to be halted at once. (The evacuation operations remain unaffected by this decree). I ask you to notify the appropriate German authorities within their administrative regions of this decree.

Only in individual cases of a very particular nature, for instance, if national interests might be positively affected, may the emigration of some individual Jews be granted as long as a ruling to this effect has been obtained beforehand from the Reich Security Main Office.

Acting as deputy signed: Müller

Text 29

Express letter of October 24, 1941 by the Chief of General Police, pertaining to the deportation of Jews from the "Altreich" and the "Protectorate of Bohemia and Moravia."

Berlin, October 24, 1941
NW 7, Unter den Linden 74
Chief of General Police
Kdo.g2 (01) No. 514 II/41 (g)
Secret!

Express Letter
Subject: Evacuation of Jews from the *Altreich* and the Protectorate.

1.) During the period November 1 to December 4, 1941, the Security Police of the *Altreich*, the *Ostmark* [Austria] and the Protectorate of Bohemia and Moravia will ship 50,000 Jews to the east into the vicinities of Riga and Minsk. Resettlement will take place by means of railway transports [*Reichsbahn*], with each train carrying 1,000 persons. The transport trains will be assembled in Berlin, Hamburg, Hanover, Dortmund, Muenster, Duesseldorf, Cologne, Frankfurt/Main, Kassel, Stuttgart, Nuremberg, Munich, Vienna, Breslau, Prague, and Brünn.

2.) Based on agreements with the Chief of Security Police and Security Service, the transport trains will be guarded by General Police, which will furnish escort units, each 1 [person in command] to 12 [policemen] in strength. Details must be worked out with the appropriate local administrative branches of the Security Service.
The task of the escort units will be completed as soon as they have delivered the transports properly to the appropriate Security Police branches at the places of destination. They will then return without delay to their home stations.

3.) The costs arising from furnishing escort units will be born by the Chief of Security Police. An account of the costs incurred by the police administrations is to be handed in to the Chief of Security Police at the termination of each transport.

signed: Daluege.

Text 30

Report of November 13, 1941 by the Sector Command North, Litzmannstadt (Lodz), pertaining to the arrival of transports of deported Jews.

Litzmannstadt, November 13,1941
Sector Command North
— 1 a (J) —

Report of Developments

Subject: Shipment of 20,000 Jews and 5,000 Gypsies to the Ghetto Litzmannstadt.
Reference: Special Orders — S 1a (J) — of October 14, 1941 and November 5, 1941.

I. Jews:
During the period of October 16, 1941 until November 4, 1941 inclusively, 19,827 Jews were received from the *Altreich* at Radegast Station and sent to the ghetto. The Jews (primarily older women and men) arrived here daily during the period previously stated with 20 transports in special trains of the *Reichsbahn* (passenger carriages), carrying on the average 1,000 persons.

Arrivals were as follows:
5 transports from Vienna . . . . . . with 5,000 Jews
5 transports from Prague . . . . . . with 5,000 Jews
4 transports from Berlin . . . . with 4,187 Jews
2 transports from Cologne . . . . with 2,007 Jews
1 transport from Luxembourg . with   512 Jews
1 transport from Frankfurt . . . . with 1,113 Jews
1 transport from Hamburg . . . . with 1,034 Jews
1 transport from Düsseldorf . . with   984 Jews

20 transports . . . . totalling 19,837 Jews
[...]
[Signature illegible]
Captain of Municipal Police
and Deputy Sector Commander

Text 31

Eleventh Ordinance supplementing the Reich Citizenship Law, dated November 25, 1941.

[...]
§ 2
A Jew loses German citizenship
a) as soon as this ordinance becomes effective, if, once this ordinance becomes effective, his regular domicile is abroad,
b) if and when he subsequently moves his regular domicile abroad.

§ 3
(1) The property of a Jew will accrue to the German Reich once he loses his German citizenship pursuant to this ordinance. [...]

§ 4
(1) Persons whose property has accrued to the Reich in accordance with § 3 will be unable to inherit anything from a German citizen who has died.
(2) Gifts by German citizens to persons whose property has accrued to the Reich in accordance with § 3 are prohibited. [...]

§ 7
(1) All persons in possession of a portion of property that has been forfeited, or who still owe a debt to the accumulated property must report the possession of this portion of the property or, respectively, the debt they owe to it to the Senior Finance Director in Berlin within six months after the property has been forfeited (§ 3) [...].

§ 10
(1) All subsequent claims [*Verfolgungsansprüche*] by Jews who, pursuant to § 2 have lost their German citizenship will be null and void at the end of the month in which loss of citizenship becomes effective. [...]

Berlin, November 25, 1941.

Reich Minister of the Interior
Frick

Head of the Party Chancellory
M. Bormann

Reich Minister of Finance
Acting as deputy
Reinhardt

Reich Minister of Justice
The authorized representative
in charge of affairs
Dr. Schlegelberger

Text 32

Report of March 9, 1942 about a conference on March 6, 1942, in the Reich Security Main Office, pertaining to the "technical implementation" of the deportation of Jews

Düsseldorf, March 9, 1942

Report
about the conference which took place on March 3, 1942 in the Reich Security Main Office, Department IV B 4.

SS Lieutenant Colonel Eichmann spoke initially by way of introduction about the subsequent evacuation of 55,000 Jews from the *Altreich*, the *Ostmark*, and the Protectorate.

Among others, Prague, with 20,000 and Vienna with 18,000 Jews to be evacuated will be most strongly affected by this. The size of the other transports will depend proportionally on the number of Jews still present in each of the respective regional commands of the State Police. Thus, Düsseldorf has been again assigned a transport of 1,000 Jews.

[...]

The report went on to discuss the technical implementation of the transports. — Here it is important [to know], first of all, that the exact timing of transports is not possible. Only empty trains for the transport of Russians resp. workers into the *Altreich* are available. They were to move back empty to the *Generalgouvernement* but are now used, in agreement with the Supreme Command of the Army, by the Reich Security Main Office. The day of departure will be communicated to the State Police branches, six days ahead of time, under the code word DA, by telephone because of faster transmission and better preservation of secrecy. The telephone conversation must be confirmed immediately by telex to Section IV B 4.

The hours of departure, which must be observed to the minute, can be ascertained from the timetable.

Although the trains have a capacity for only 700 persons, 1,000 Jews must be put into them. For this reason it is advisable to order sufficient freight cars for the baggage from the *Reichsbahn* ahead of time. There should also be a passenger carriage for the escort unit. If necessary, the latter will have to be content with riding in a carriage of the Russian train.

The commander of the escort unit must be instructed to see to it that baggage cars from the *Altreich* be sent back immediately after their arrival at the place of destination.

Then followed an exchange of information between such State Police branches already familiar with the handling of evacuations and others that are now facing them as a new task.

The conference ended at approximately 4.30 p.m.

[signature illegible]
Police inspector.

Text 33

Notification of June 30, 1942 by the National Association of Jews in Germany [Reichsvereinigung], pertaining to transactions of "contracts for buying into a home" ["Heimeinkaufsverträge"]

National Association of Jews in Germany

Berlin-Charlottenburg 2, June 30, 1942
                    Kantstrasse 158   Tel. 919141

To the
Jewish religious associations [*Kultusvereinigungen*] [and]
district branches of the National Association of Jews in Germany.

Subject: Transactions of home contracts for communal accomodations
V Dr. E./My   42/198/334

The supervisory authority has directed us to make the following announcement:

1. Those persons earmarked for communal accomodations must transact contracts for buying into a home through the appropriate district branches or, respectively, Jewish religious associations of the *Reichsvereinigung* [...]

2. Those eligible for communal accomodations are:
a) residents with whom contracts for buying into a home [*Heimeinkaufverträge*] or contracts for admission into a home [*Heimaufnahmeverträge*] — but no home contracts were concluded,
b) persons who have had private living quarters until they were housed on a communal basis.

3. a) Contracts for admission into a home must be immediately switched to contracts for buying into a home as a matter of principle.
b) Persons with whom so far no home contracts have been concluded, contracts for buying into a home must be transacted at once. Hereby the following guidelines (see 4) must be taken into account:

4. a) Contracts for buying into a home — with the prevailing regulations having been broadened — are to be transacted whenever readily available property assets of at least 1000 Reichsmarks are present. Readily available property assets also include stocks and bonds which can be deposited with the *Reichsvereinigung* after proper permission has been obtained. Applications for selling stocks and bonds in order to remit the corresponding cash value are not admissable, as a matter of principle. Furthermore, claims laid to life insurance companies are considered readily available property assets if one can borrow against them.
b) Property assets which are to be transferred to the *Reichsvereinigung* in connection with the contracts for buying into a home must be restricted to liquid funds (including stocks and bonds) and to readily convertible claims. The inclusion of prop-

erty assets whose conversion into cash value — after departure [*Abwanderung*] has taken place — would require an application in accordance with Article 7, Paragraph 2 of the Eleventh Ordinance supplementing the Reich Citizenship Law of November 26, 1941 [*Reichsgesetzblatt* (National Register of Published Laws) 1, p. 722] or, respectively, in accordance with Article 39 of the Law of December 12, 1939 pertaining to compensation when property has been confiscated or transferred (*Reichsgesetzblatt* 1, p. 1333) is inadmissible, as a matter of principle.

[...]

5. a) Transfers of property assets to the *Reichsvereinigung* while processing contracts for buying into a home must be completed with the greatest possible speed.

b) For the time being, all surplus amounts are to be entered into the accounts as usual, but as soon as communal accomodations become effective, they must be deposited into special account "H" of the *Reichsvereinigung* at the banking house of Heinz, Tecklenburg & Company, Berlin W 8, Wilhelmplatz 7.

National Association of Jews in Germany
Welfare Section
Dr. Paul Israel Epstein   Johanna Sara Karminski

Text 34

Guidelines of February 20, 1943 by the Reich Security Main Office, pertaining to the "technical implementation" of the deportation of Jews to Auschwitz

Berlin, February 20, 1943
Reich Security Main Office
IV B 4 a 2093/42 g (391)

Guidelines
for the technical implementation
of the evacuation of Jews to the east.
(Concentration Camp Auschwitz)

The following guidelines for the evacuation of Jews from the territory of the Reich and from Bohemia and Moravia to the east have been established and must be strictly observed in all respects. They supersede all previously issued directives.

1. Appropriate Administrative Agencies.
Implementation is the duty of the Regional and Local Commands of the State Police (in Viennna, as up to now, it will be the operational section of the Central Office for Jewish Emigration, Vienna, in coordination with the Regional Command of the

State Police in Vienna; in the Protectorate, the Commander of Security Police and Security Service at the Central Office for Regulating the Jewish Question in Bohemia and Moravia, Prague). Additional tasks of these administrative agencies, besides concentration and roundup of the persons to be evacuated, will be the deportation of Jews in special trains of the German Railway in accordance with a timetable established by the Reich Security Main Office in agreement with the Reich Transportation Ministry, and the settlement of all legal matters pertaining to property.

[...]

III. Transport.
It is advisable to concentrate Jews to be evacuated prior to their transportation. Transports will always be assembled, at a strength of 1,000 each, in accordance with the timetable issued by the Reich Security Main Office, and in agreement with the Reich Transportation Ministry; it will be made available to the administrative agencies concerned.

Each person must take the following items:
Travel rations for approximately five days,
1 suitcase or knapsack each with items of equipment, namely:
1 pair of sturdy work boots,
2 pairs of socks,
2 shirts,
2 pairs of underpants,
1 pair of overalls,
2 woolen blankets,
2 sets of bed linen (top and bottom sheets)
1 dinner pail
1 drinking cup
1 spoon and
1 pullover.

The following items may not be taken:
stocks and bonds, foreign currency, savings deposit books, etc.,
valuables of any sort (gold, silver, platinum, except for a wedding ring),
pets [*lebendes Inventar*],
ration cards (to be taken away prior to departure and handed over to the local economy agencies).
Before the transports leave, searches must be made for arms, ammunition, explosives, poison, foreign currency, jewelry, etc.
Jewish aides are to be appointed to maintain peace and order during the journey; they must also clean the trains before leaving them.
When Jews file change-of-address cards prior to leaving, the forms in the registration offices must not list the final destination but merely "moved — address unknown".

IV. Transport Escorts.

For the security of the transports, each transport train will be assigned an appropriately equipped escort unit (as a rule, General Police at a strength of one person in charge and 15 men). They must be thoroughly briefed – with special reference to the constantly attempted escapes – about their duties and about the measures to be taken with regard to attempted escapes. The person in charge of the escort unit must be handed a roster, in duplicate, with the names of all persons on the train; the roster is intended for the administrative agency that receives the transport.

In addition to personal data, the transport roster must also list occupations. [...]

By order:

signed: Günthers.

Witnessed:

Office employee (female).

Text 35

Communication of March 8, 1943 to the Main Office for the Economy and Administration [Wirtschafts-Verwaltungshauptamt] pertaining to the fate of Jewish deportees from Berlin and Breslau ("Operation Factory") in Auschwitz

Telephone Message March 8, 1943
Main Office for the Economy and Administration
Department D II
Oranienburg

Subject: Transport of Jewish workers.

The following prisoner transports arrived on March 5 and 7:

Transport from Berlin, arrival March 5, 1943, total strength 1,128 Jews. 389 men were assigned for work (Buna), and 96 women. 151 men and 492 women and children received special treatment. Transport from Breslau, arrival March 5, 1943, total strength 1,405 Jews. 406 were assigned for work (Buna), and 190 women. 125 men and 684 women and children received special treatment. Transport from Berlin, arrival March 7, 1943, total strength 690 including 25 prisoners in protective custody. 153 men and 25 prisoners in protective custody were assigned for work (Buna), and 65 women. 30 men and 417 women and children received special treatment.

signed: Schwarz
SS First Lieutenant

146   Deportation of Jews, Hanau railway station, on May 18, 1942.

4.3. The Gypsies

In addition to the Jews, the Gypsies (Sinti and Roma) were likewise subject to racial persecution in the "Third Reich." During the Second World War, genocide was committed against the Gypsies in all countries under National Socialist domination, with hundreds of thousands of victims.

The agency in charge of persecuting Gypsies was the Reich Criminal Police Office (since September 1939: Department V of the Reich Security Main Office) after the central "Police Section for Gypsies" [*Zigeunerpolizeistelle*] in Munich was incorporated into it in October 1938 to form the "Central Reich Administration for Combating Gypsy Malefaction" ["*Reichszentrale zur Bekämpfung des Zigeunerunwesens*"]. As early as 1936 the Gypsies were subjected to centralized "racial-hygenic" and "criminal-biological" investigations. In the so-called "Basic Gypsy Directive" ["*Zigeuner-Grunderlaß*"] of December 1938, Himmler gave instructions to "tackle the settlement of the Gypsie Question with the nature of this race in mind." Deportation of the Gypsies from the territory of the Reich began in May 1940; in the spring of 1942 began the systematic deportation from the occupied European countries. Deported and local Gypsies were murdered by the Special Units, above all in Poland and the Soviet Union, and in extermination camps. On August 2, 1944 alone, 2897 Gypsies died in Auschwitz-Birkenau in the gas chambers.

Chronology of the Persecution and Extermination of Gypsies under National Socialist Rule

1936
Commentary to the Nuremberg Laws of September 1935 by Stuckart and Globke: "In Europe, only Jews and Gypsies are infallibly of alien blood."

November 1936
Dr. Dr. Robert Ritter begins investigations of "Gypsies and Gypsy *Mischlinge*" [Gypsies of mixed blood] at the "Research Department for Racial Hygiene and the Biology of Populations" at the Reich Health Office; this became of fundamental importance for subsequent racial persecution.

October 1, 1938
The Police Section for Gypsies at the Munich Police headquarters is incorporated into the Reich Criminal Police Office (since September 27, 1939 it was Department V of the Reich Security Main Office) to form the "Central Reich Administration for Combating Gypsy Malefaction."

December 8, 1938
Himmler issues a circular directive on "Combating the Gypsy Plague" (the so-called "Basic Gypsy Directive").

September 21, 1939
During a conference of the department heads of Security Police and Commanders of Special Units, with Heydrich presiding, the deportation of the "remaining 30,000 Gypsies" from the German territory to Poland becomes policy.

October 17, 1939
The so-called "Freezing-of-Movement Directive" ["*Festsetzungserlaß*"] by the Reich Security Main Office: Gypsies and "Gypsies of mixed blood" may no longer leave their towns of residence or, as the case may be, their present whereabouts.

April 27, 1940
Himmler orders the deportation of 2500 Gypsies from different parts of German territory to the *Generalgouvernement*. The deportations are carried out in May 1940.

August 7, 1941
Himmler issues a circular directive on the "evaluation of racial-biological testimonies by experts concerning persons of Gypsy origin." Distinctions are drawn between "tribally pure Gypsies" and different groups of "Gypsies of mixed blood."

January 1942
Approximately 5000 Gypsies who were brought from the Lodz ghetto to Chelmno are murdered in the extermination camp Chelmno in gassing vans.

March 13, 1942
Directive by the Reich Labor Ministry about the employment of Gypsies: the special regulations drafted for Jews in the area of social law shall also apply to Gypsies.

August 29, 1942
Memorandum by the head of the administrative staff ot the German military administration in Serbia: in Serbia the "Jewish Question and Gypsy Question have been solved"; in consequence, the gassing van employed there may be returned to Berlin.

September 18, 1942
Agreement between Reich Minister of Justice Thierack and Himmler about the transfer of all "asocial elements" from legal detention to the *Reichsführer-SS* for "extermination through labor." Besides Jews, Russians, Ukrainians and others, Gypsies are effected as well.

January 29, 1943
Implementing regulations by the Reich Security Main Office to Himmler's so-called "Auschwitz Directive" of December 16, 1942: "Gypsies of mixed blood, Romany Gypsies and Balkan Gypsies" are to be taken to Auschwitz Concentration Camp. – Gypsies from all over Europe are being deported to the "Gypsy camp" which has been established in Auschwitz-Birkenau.

May 1945
The number of European Gypsies murdered by the National Socialists has been estimated as at least 220,000; other estimates run as high as half a million or more.

Text 36

Circular Directive of December 8, 1938 by the Reichsführer-SS and Chief of German Police, pertaining to the "Settlement of the Gypsy Question"

Combating the Gypsy Plague
Circular Directive of December 8, 1938 by the *Reichsführer-SS* and Chief of German Police in the Reich Ministry of the Interior
S-Kr. 1 No. 557 VIII/38–2026–6

A. General Directives
I. Domestic Gypsies

1. (1) The experiences collected so far in combating the Gypsy plague, and the knowledge gained from racial-biological research would make it seem advisable to tackle the settlement of the Gypsy Question with the nature of this race in mind. According to experience, individuals of mixed race contribute the largest share to Gypsy criminality. Conversely, it has been shown that all attempts to settle Gypsies in a permanent place of residence failed in particular with pure-blooded Gypsies because of their strong urge to roam. Thus, it will be necessary to deal separately with the pure-blooded Gypsies and those of mixed blood when it comes to the final solution of the Gypsy Question.
[...]

(3) I therefore direct that all Gypsies, whether sedentary or not, as well as all persons roaming in Gypsy fashion must be rounded up [*erfaßt*] by the Reich Criminal Police Office – Central Reich Administration for Combating Gypsy Malefaction.
[...]

2. (1) Prior to submitting a report, all Gypsies, Gypsies of mixed blood and persons roaming in Gypsy fashion who have completed their sixth year of life must be registered with the Criminal Identification Department [*erkennungsdienstlich zu behandeln*].

147   Deportation of Gypsies. Exhibition halls in Cologne, May 1940.

148   A Sinto survivor with the concentration camp number tattooed into the skin of his forearm.

(2) Furthermore, also prior to submitting a report, the normal procedure for person identification [*Personenfeststellungsverfahren*] must be applied. For this purpose [...] preventive detention may be imposed by the police in accordance with preventive crime fighting by the police.
[...]

3. (1) The ultimate determination as to whether one deals with a Gypsy, a Gypsy of mixed blood, or some person roaming in Gypsy fashion will be made by the Reich Criminal Police Office based on the testimony of an expert.
(2) I therefore direct [...] that all Gypsies, Gypsies of mixed blood, and persons roaming in Gypsy fashion be compelled to submit to a racial-biological examination required for the presentation of a testimony by an expert, and to provide the necessary information about their descent. The implementation of this directive is to be ensured by means of forceful police measures.
[...]

4. (3) It must be clearly marked in the identification papers that the person making the application is a Gypsy, a Gypsy of mixed blood or a person roaming in Gypsy fashion.
[...]

8. (1) Gypsies, Gypsies of mixed blood and persons roaming in Gypsy fashion who travel in hordes must be dispersed.
[...]

9. (1) In all cases involving Gypsies or persons roaming in Gypsy fashion it must be checked whether the prerequisite provision [...] concerning preventive crime fighting by the police is applicable. (Endangering the public through asocial behavior). In this connection, particularly severe standards must be applied.
[...]

II. Foreign Gypsies
1. Foreign gypsies must be prevented from entering German territory. Refusal to grant entry permits and to move them back is required procedure even if foreign Gypsies are in possession of passports entitling them to immigrate, of substitute documents in lieu of passports, or of visa.

2. Bans on residence for the entire territory of the Reich must be promulgated with regard to all foreign Gypsies encountered on German territory; in accordance with the Directive of August 22, 1938 (*Reichsgesetzblatt* I p. 1953) issued by the Alien Police. They are to be expelled across the frontier of the Reich.
[...]

Text 37

Express Letter of August 17, 1939 from the Reich Security Main Office, pertaining to the "rounding up" ["Erfassung"] of Gypsies

Berlin, October 10,1939
Reich Security Main Office
Tgb. No. RKPA. 149/1939 -g

Express Letter

To the State Criminal Police – Regional and Local Commands of the Criminal Police [...]

Subject: Rounding Up of Gypsies
By order of the *Reichsführer-SS* and Chief of German Police the Gypsy Question will be fundamentally settled before long within the entire German territory by a uniform standard applied throughout the Reich. I therefore ask you to initiate the following measures at once:
1. The local police stations and the Rural Police must be instructed immediately to notify all Gypsies and Gypsies of mixed blood within their respective districts that effective immediately they may not leave their residence or their present whereabouts until further notice. Anybody in violation of this injunction will be threatened with dispatch to a concentration camp.
[...]

Addendum for the Regional Commands [*Leitstellen*]
Those Gypsies to be subsequently apprehended are to be kept in special assembly camps until their final deportation.

The Regional Commands of the Criminal Police must proceed at once to see to the manner of accomodation and the setting up of such assembly camps. The number of assembly camps to be established will have to depend on local conditions and the number of Gypsies that will be apprehended. Thus it will depend on these factors whether only one such camp is to be established within the district of any Regional Command of the Criminal Police, or whether the establishment of camps must also be considered for the region of the subordinate Criminal Police stations. The necessary decision is up to the Regional Commands of the Criminal Police.
[...]

Text 38

Guidelines of April 27, 1940 by the Reichsführer-SS and Chief of German Police, pertaining to the deportation of Gypsies

Berlin, April 27, 1940

Reichsführer-SS
and Chief of German Police
in the Reich Ministry of the Interior
to V B No. 95/40

Guidelines for resettling Gypsies (First transport from the western and northwestern border zone)

1. Determination of persons affected
1. To be deported [*abgeschoben*]:
a) All Gypsies and Gypsies of mixed blood who have been rounded up and registered in accordance with the express letter of October 17, 1939 from the Reich Security Main Office.
b) Under no circumstances may the maximum of 2,500 be exceeded.
[...]

III. Treatment in the assembly camps
1. To begin with, all Gypsies are to be registered alphabetically according to their separate local police districts. All Gypsies above 14 years of age will have a serial number affixed to their left forearm in colored ink.
[...]

Text 39

Express letter of January 29, 1943 from the Reich Security Main Office, pertaining to the confinement of "Gypsies of Mixed Blood", "Romany Gypsies" and "Balkan Gypsies" to a concentration camp

Berlin, January 29, 1943

Reich Security Main Office
VA No. 59/43 g

Express Letter
[...]

Subject: Confinement of Gypsies of mixed blood, Romany Gypsies and Balkan Gypsies in a concentration camp
[...]
I. By order of the *Reichsführer-SS* dated December 16, 1942 [...], Gypsies of mixed blood, Romany Gypsies and members of Gypsy clans of non-German blood and of Balkan origins are to be selected according to fixed guidelines, and in the course of an operation lasting only a few weeks are to be confined in a concentration camp. People affected [*Personenkreis*] will henceforth briefly be referred to as "Persons of Gypsy origin."
Confinement will take place by families, regardless of the degree of mixed blood, in Concentration Camp (Gypsy Camp) Auschwitz.
[...]

(III) 1. Attempts should be made to obtain consent for sterilization from persons of Gypsy origin above 12 years of age and not yet sterilized;
[...]
4. In case of refusal, the Reich Criminal Police Office, after having ascertained the reasons, will decide what steps are to be taken.
[...]

Text 40

Statement of Findings ["Feststellung"] by the Reich Minister of the Interior in a notarized copy of the Reich Security Main Office dated January 26, 1943, pertaining to the confiscation of Gypsy property

Notarized Copy
Reich Minister of the Interior
Pol S II A 5 No. 38/43–212–

Berlin SW 11, January 26, 1943
Prinz-Albrecht- Strasse 8
Tel.: 12 00 40

Statement of Findings

In accordance with the Law of July 14, 1933 – *Reichsgesetzblatt* I, p. 479 – pertaining to the confiscation of property [of persons] hostile to people and state, it is herewith established that the intentions of persons of Gypsy origins to be confined in a concentration camp by order of the *Reichsführer-SS*, dated December 16, 1942, have been hostile to the people or the Reich, respectively.

4.4. Nazi Rule in Europe: Poland

While under German rule, occupied Poland became a laboratory for National Socialist racial and population politics. After the outbreak of war, Jews and non-Jews, in particular members of the Polish leadership and intellectual strata, became victims of Special Units of the Security Police who subsequently continued their activities of repression after becoming stationary agencies of the Security Police and Security Service. The *Generalgouvernement* Poland was intended as a manpower reservoir for the German war economy while the country as such served as an object of exploitation for military and civilian purposes. *Gauleiter* [regional Nazi leader] Greiser attempted, in cooperation with the administrative agencies of the *Reichsführer-SS* in the "*Warthegau*," to create a German model *Gau*. Hundreds of thousands of Poles were "resettled" into the *Generalgouvernement* between 1939 and 1941, with loss of their property. Similar expulsions in the Lublin district likewise resulted in destitution and misery for the population. "Germanization" and the quest for "German blood" were characteristic features of German population policy. Poles were to be "racially crushed."

Deprivation of rights and ghettoization of the Jewish population ran parallel to this. Poland became the center of mass extermination for Europe's Jews. In the extermination camps Chelmno (*Warthegau*), Belzec, Sobibor, Treblinka and Auschwitz-Birkenau, millions of Jews from all of Europe were murdered. The extermination operations in the Polish ghettos and the deportation of the Jewish population were events that could not be kept secret. Not only the Security Police and Security Service but also the police battalions of the General Police left their bloody traces throughout the country. At the same time, the concentration camps Auschwitz, Majdanek and Stutthof were likewise places of terror and death for non-Jewish Poles who were dragged there by the thousands.

In no other European country except for the Soviet Union did so many human beings become victims of National Socialist terror as in Poland.

Text 41

Express Letter of September 21, 1939, from Heydrich to the Commanders of Special Units of Security Police, pertaining to the "Jewish Question" in the occupied territories of Poland

Berlin, September 21, 1939
To the Commanders of all Special Units of Security Police

Subject: Jewish Question in occupied territory.

I refer to the meeting that took place today in Berlin and want to point out once again that the overall measures planned (thus, the final objective) must be kept strictly secret.
Distinctions must be drawn between
1. the final objective (which will require more extensive time periods), and

2. the phases toward fulfillment of the final objective (which will be carried out on a short-term basis).
It is obvious that the tasks ahead cannot be determined from here in every detail. The following instructions and guidelines will simultaneously serve the purpose of prompting the commanders of Special Units to do some practical thinking.

I. The first prerequisite for the final objective will be, for one, the concentration of Jews from the countryside into the larger cities.
This must be carried out expeditiously ...
Attention must be paid to the requirement that only such cities may be designated as areas of concentration which are either railway junctions or are at least situated on a railway line.
One prevailing basic rule will be that Jewish congregations of less than 500 members will be dis-

solved and moved to the nearest city of concentration.

...

II. Jewish Councils of Elders.

1. Each Jewish congregation must set up a Jewish Council of Elders ...

It will be fully responsible, in the truest sense of the word, for an exact and prompt execution of all past or future directives.

2. In case of sabotage of such directives, the councils will be advised that most severe measures will be taken.

3. The Jewish Councils must take a provisional census of Jews within their respective localities — if possible, arranged on a generational basis (by age groups), a) up to 16 years, b) from 16 to 20 years and c) beyond, as well as on an occupational basis — and must report the results without delay.

4. The Councils of Elders must be informed of the deadlines for and times of departure, the means of departure and, finally, the routes of departure. They must then be held personally responsible for the departure of the Jews from the countryside.

The explanation of why Jews are being concentrated in cities shall be that Jews have prominently participated in guerilla raids and looting activities. [...]

III.

As a matter of principle, all necessary measures must always be taken in closest agreement and cooperation with the German civilian administrative authorities and the appropriate local military authorities ...

IV.

Commanders of Special Units will report to me routinely on the following matters:

1. A numerical overall account of Jews within their respective regions (if possible by the arrangement listed above) ...

2. Names of cities that have been designated as areas of concentration.

3. Deadlines given to the Jews for departure into the cities.

4. An overall account of all Jewish foodstuffs [?] and wartime [German version garbled] as well as of all industrial branches and factories important for the Four Year Plan within their respective regions ...

V.

To accomplish the objectives outlined I expect the fullest commitment of all forces of Security Police and Security Service.

Commanders of Special Units in adjoining positions must establish contact with each other at once in order to make sure that all affected regions will be completely covered.

VI.

The Supreme Command of the Army, the Plenipotentiary for the Four Year Plan (Att. Undersecretary Neumann), the Reich Ministry of the Interior (Att. Undersecretary Stuckart), [Reich Ministry] of Food Supplies and the Economy (Att. Undersecretary Landfried) and the heads of the civilian administration of the occupied territory have received copies of this directive.

Text 42

"Führer Decree" of October 7, 1939, pertaining to "Strengthening Germanism" and the appointment of the Reichsführer-SS as "Reich Commissioner for Strengthening Germanism"

Decree
of October 7, 1939,
by the *Führer* and Reich Chancellor on Strengthening Germanism

The consequences of [the peace treaty of] Versailles in Europe have been eliminated. This will enable Greater Germany to bring German people, who up to now were forced to live abroad, home into its territory, to settle them here, and to arrange within the sphere of its [territorial] interests the settlement of ethnic groups in such a way that better dividing lines will be drawn between them. I am entrusting the implementation of this task to the *Reichsführer-SS* with the following stipulations:

I.

The *Reichsführer-SS* will carry out the following tasks according to my guidelines:

1. The final return of all eligible German citizens and ethnic Germans still abroad back to their homeland,

2. The removal of all harmful influences on the part of those population groups alien to our people who constitute a threat to the Reich and to the German people's community,

3. The establishment of new German settlement areas through resettlement, in particular by making permanent residences available to German citizens and ethnic Germans returning from abroad.

[...]

To carry out the tasks entrusted to him in paragraph 1, No. 2, the *Reichsführer-SS* may assign to

A b s c h r i f t.

Der Chef der Sicherheitspolizei   Berlin, den 21. Dezember 1939.
     und des SD.

C.d.S. B.Nr. 12743/39. IV/R Ech/Br.

26

1.) An

den Befehlshaber der Sicherheitspolizei und des SD.
                    in K r a k a u,

an

die Inspekteure der Sicherheitspolizei und des SD
                    in B r e s l a u,
                       P o s e n,
                       D a n z i g,
                       Königsberg.

2.) Nachrichtlich

an die
Höheren ⚡⚡- und Polizeiführer

                    in Krakau,
                       Posen,
                       Breslau,
                       Danzig,
                       Königsberg.

Betr.: Räumung in den Ostprovinzen.
Vorg.: Dienstbesprechung v. 19.12.1939.

     Sachdienliche Gründe machen die zentrale Bearbei-
tung der sicherheitspolizeilichen Angelegenheiten bei
der Durchführung der Räumung im Ostraum notwendig.

Zu meinem Sonderreferenten im Reichssicherheitshauptamt, Amt IV, habe ich den ⚡⚡-Hauptsturmführer E i c h -
m a n n (Vertreter ⚡⚡-Hauptsturmführer G ü n t h e r)
bestellt. Der Dienstsitz dieses Sonderreferates befin-
det sich in Berlin W 62, Kurfürstenstrasse 115-116,
Tel. Nr. 25 92 51.
Der Schriftverkehr ist über das Reichssicherheitshauptamt, Amt IV, Berlin SW 11, Prinz-Albrecht-Str. 8 zu
leiten.

          Der Chef der Sicherheitspolizei und des SD.
               gez. H e y d r i c h
               ⚡⚡-Gruppenführer.

- - - - - - - - - - - - - - - - - -

149   Letter of the Chief of Security Police and Security Service, dated December 21, 1939, appointing Adolf Eichmann
"Special Section Manager" ["*Sonderreferent*"] for all "Security Police matters involving the clearance of eastern territory."
(See Abstract 9 in Appendix).

the population groups in question special areas of residence.

[...]

Berlin, October 7, 1939

The *Führer* and Reich Chancellor
signed: Adolf Hitler

The Chairman of the Ministerial
Council for National Defense
signed: Göring
Field Marshal

Reich Minister and Director
of the Reich Chancellory
signed: Dr. Lammers

Chief of the Supreme Command of the Army
signed: Keitel

Text 43

Order of October 30, 1939, by the Reichs-führer-SS, pertaining to the deportation of Jews and Poles from the annexed Polish territory

Directive I/II

During the months of November and December 1939, and during the months of January and February 1940, the following resettlements are to be carried out:

150   **Adolf Eichmann** (1906–1962)
Born in Solingen, grew up in Linz. Through his acquaintance with Ernst Kaltenbrunner he joined the (Austrian) NSDAP and SS in 1932. In 1934 he became an employee in the Security Service Main Office in Berlin where he attended to "Jewish Affairs" in Section II 112. In 1938 he built up a "Central Office for Jewish Emigration" in Vienna, then in Prague, finally in Berlin. When the emigration of Jews was banned once war had broken out, Eichmann was put in charge of Section IV B 4 of the Reich Security Main Office, to which he had belonged since 1939, and from this position organized the "Final Solution of the Jewish Question." In 1961 he was sentenced to death by an Israeli court and was executed in 1962.

1) All Jews [must be removed] from the formerly Polish, now German provinces and regions.
2) From the Province Danzig/West Prussia all "Congress Poles."
3) From the Provinces Poznan, South and East Prussia and eastern Upper Silesia an as yet undetermined number of especially hostile elements of the Polish population.
4) The Higher SS and Police Leader East will make known how many of those to be resettled the *Generalgouvernement* can absorb, and he will do so by giving separate figures for administrative districts and larger towns.
5) The Higher SS and Police Leaders Vistula, Warthe, North East, South East and East [*Generalgouvernement*] or, respectively, the Inspectors and Commanders of Security Police will determine the resettlement plan jointly. For each province, a particular administrative district of the *Generalgouvernement* is to be designated as a resettlement area, [and] for each town within the German provinces a particular town on as the case may be, a particular subdistrict [*Landkreis*] within the larger administrative districts.
6) Each Higher SS and Police Leader will be responsible for departures and transports within his district; in the new residence areas the Polish administration or, respectively, self-administration will be responsible for assigning accomodations.

Reichsführer-SS
Himmler

Text 44

Table of December 1940 by the Reich Commissioner for Strengthening Germanism [Himmler] on deportations to the "Generalgouvernement" and unoccupied France put into effect until November 15, 1940

Table on evacuations put into effect
(Compiled by the Chief of Security Police and Security Service.)

Evacuations to the *Generalgouvernement* until November 15, 1940:
From *Reichsgau* [NS administrative districts(s)]
                          Wartheland: 234,620 Poles
From *Reichsgau*   East Prussia: 14,636 Poles
From *Reichsgau* Eastern Upper
                          Silesia: 14,322 Poles
From *Reichsgau*   West Prussia: 30,758 Poles

                          294,336 Poles
The evacuations were carried out in 303 special trains.

151   This building once housed the (Jewish) "Fraternal Lodge" at Kurfürstenstrasse 115–116; since 1939 it was the seat of the Reich Security Main Office's Section IV B 4, run by Eichmann.

On the initiative of the *Generalgouvernement*, the Poles received from May 14, 1940 on 1,401,774 kilograms of food as rations for two weeks; in addition, every Pole was given 20 zloties (altogether 5,947,780 zloties, i.e. 2,973,890 Reichsmarks).
The following number of Jews were evacuated to the *Generalgouvernement* by November 15, 1940
From Prague, Vienna, Mährisch
Ostrau and .... 5,035 Jews,
From Stettin .... 1,000 Jews,
From the western region of
Germany .... 2,800 Gypsies.
In the West, from Baden and the Palatinate, 6,504 Jews were deported into unoccupied France by November 15, 1940; from Lorraine, 47,187 French-speaking persons (final destination Lyon). Total number of persons evacuated by November 15, 1940:
into the *Generalgouvernement* 303,171
into unoccupied France 53,691

total 356,862

Text 45

Fundamental Declaration of December 1940 by the Reich Commissioner for Strengthening Germanism, pertaining to the "Re-Germanization of lost [verlorengegangenen] German Blood"

1. Utilization of those Poles who can be Germanized.

Purging all incorporated eastern territories of persons of alien race is one of the most important objectives to be attained in the German East. It will be a cardinal police task of a national nature which the *Reichsführer-SS*, Reich Commissioner for Strengthening Germanism, will have to accomplish in the incorporated eastern territories. In carrying out his assignment, which is most closely connected to the problem of national identity in the eastern territories, overriding and, purely and simply, decisive importance must be given, next to such aspects as language, education, and religion, to racial selection. As essential as it may be for a lasting union of the German eastern territories to prevent elements of alien blood now living there from remaining or becoming rooted there, it is equally imperative to reclaim German blood extant in these parts for Germanism, even if the bearers of such blood have become Polonized in attitude and language. Precisely from among these German blood-carriers [*Blutsträger*] came those born leaders of the former Polish state who in the last analysis — be it because they were struck with blindness or through conscious or unconscious misjudgement of their own blood ties — turned against their own Germanic heritage with the most pronounced antagonism.

Thus, it is an absolute necessity from a national-political perspective to "comb" the incorporated eastern territories as well as the *Generalgouvernement* in search of just such blood-bearers so as to restore again the blood that was lost to our own German people. What measures are to be taken against renegades may well be of secondary importance. Imperative is that at least their children must no longer remain hostages to Polish ways but shall be brought up within a German environment. However, re-Germanization cannot take place in the hitherto existing Polish environment, but solely in the *Altreich* (Germany with its 1937 borders) or in Austria [*Ostmark*].

The following two vital factors make a reclamation of lost German blood absolutely essential:
1. We must prevent Polish intellectual strata from gaining further increases at the cost of originally

152   Map of all "incorporated eastern territories" and of the
"*Generalgouvernement*", 1939–1945
Explanation of legend
Left:
German eastern frontier, 1914
German eastern frontier and Polish state frontier, 1937
German eastern frontier 1939–1945
(customs and administrative frontier)
German police frontier in the east, 1939–1945
German-Soviet demarcation line, 1939–1941
Borders between the provinces East Prussia, West Prussia and
Poznan, 1914

Right:
Borders of provinces or *Gaue*, respectively, 1939
Borders of the administrative districts within the "incorporated
territories"
Borders of the sub-districts within the "incorporated territo-
ries"
District borders within the *Generalgouvernement*
Administrative boundaries between the *Generalgouverne-
ment*, Bialystok District and the Reich Commissariates East
[*Ostland*] and Ukraine
Towns from which the administrative districts were run

German, albeit Polonized, kinship groups [*Sip-
pen*].
2. We must stimulate racially desirable population growth for the German people, and we must
obtain a work force that is unobjectionable from a
national-biological viewpoint for the German
buildup of agriculture and industry.

This task of re-Germanization of lost German
blood has already begun with the evacuation of
Poles from the Warthegau; they were forced to
yield their territory to Balts and ethnic Germans
from Volhynia who are to be settled there.
[...]

Text 46

Report of September 26, 1941 by the Commissioner of the Jewish Residential District in Warsaw, Heinz Auerswald, pertaining to the death toll in the Warsaw ghetto from January until August 1941

The increase of food supply deliveries referred to could not prevent the growing number of deaths which are due to the generally worsening misery of the Jews ever since the outbreak of war. The following numbers convey an impressive illustration of the death toll:

January 1941	898
February 1941	1,023
March 1941	1,608
April 1941	2,061
May 1941	3,821
June 1941	4,290
July 1941	5,550
August 1941	5,560

A second reason for the increasing mortality rate is the spread of typhus in the Jewish residential

153   At the Warsaw Ghetto wall.

154   Deportation of Polish Jews by the SS in 1942.

district. Despite rigorous efforts to fight the spread of typhus, the curve has steadily risen. Weekly reports on typhus cases have remained on a fairly even level since July. They vary between 320 and 450 new cases. The last monthly figure (August) of 1788 persons is only somewhat higher than in the previous month, with 1736 new cases.

Text 47

Excerpt from an editoral of August 20, 1942 in the SS weekly, "Das Schwarze Korps" (The Black Corps) pertaining to "Germanization" of the "East"

"It will not be our task to Germanize the East in the old sense, that is, by teaching people who live there the German language and German laws, but to take care that only people of truly German, of Germanic blood will live in the East."

Text 48

Himmler's Order of July 19, 1942 pertaining to the deadline of December 31, 1942 as the final date when the Jewish population must have been deported from the Generalgouvernement

I herewith direct that the resettlement of the entire Jewish population from the *Generalgouvernement* be carried out and concluded by December 31, 1942. On December 31, 1942 no persons of Jewish origin may be present in the *Generalgouvernement*, except for those now staying in the assembly camps in Warsaw, Cracow, Czenstochau, Radom or Lublin [all ghettos]. All other work projects utilizing Jewish labor must have been completed by then or, if this is not possible, must be moved to an assembly camp.

These measures are essential for accomplishing the required ethnic segregation of races and peoples in accordance with the pending New Order of Europe, but also with a view to the security and integrity of the German Reich and its spheres of interest. Any violation of this rule en-

155   Warsaw Ghetto uprising in May 1943. Survivors are taken into custody by the SS.

dangers peace and order in the entire territory that is of interest to Germany.

For all these reasons a complete clearing-up process is necessary and must be carried through. Anticipated failure to meet deadlines must be reported to me in time so that I can remedy the situation as soon as possible. All requests by other administrative agencies for changes or exemptions must be submitted to me personally.

H. Himmler

Text 49

Closing Account for "Operation Reinhard" of December 15, 1943 pertaining to the "Financial and Material Property Assets" from April 1, 1942 until December 15, 1943
[O.R. was the code name for a major (authorized) looting operation of Jewish property in the eastern territory]

Interim closing account of the Operation "Reinhard" Fund, Lublin, as of December 15, 1943.

In the course of Operation "Reinhard," Lublin, the following financial and material assets were sent to Greater Germany [Großdeutsches Reich] in the period between April 1, 1942 and December 15, 1943, inclusive:

156   Notification of measures of reprisals in Poland, 1942. (See Abstract 10 in Appendix).

Cash

		Income
Cash in hand	RM	17,470,796.66
To Reichsbank, Berlin, RM notes and coins	RM	3,979,523.50
To Reichsbank, Berlin, Zloty notes and coins	RM	5,000,466.00
SS Manager, Cracow	RM	50,416,181.37
Loans to SS economic enterprises	RM	8,218,878.35
Income from Title 21/E	RM	656,062.40
	RM	85,741,903.28

Expenses

Personal fees/charges, Title 21/7a	RM	96,207.28
Miscellaneous expenses [Sachausgaben] (of which approximately 40% were for J-[ewish] transports, Title 21/7b)	RM	11,756,552.62
Counterfeit money (Zloty notes)	RM	28,062.64
	RM	11,889,822.54

Tally:

Income	RM 85,741,903.28		
Expenses		RM	11,889,822.54
Clear Profit		RM	73,852,080.74
	RM 85,741,903.28		
		RM	85,741,903.28

Precious Metals:

236 gold bars – 2,909.68 kilograms at 2800 RM a piece	RM	8.147,104.00
2143 silver bars – 18,733.69 kilograms at 40 RM a piece	RM	749,347.60
Platinum – 15.44 kilograms at 5000 RM	RM	77,200.00
	RM	8,973,651.60

Woven Fabrics:

1901 freight cars with clothing, linens, downs and rags at an average value of	RM	26,000,000.00
stock supplies at an average value of	RM	20,000,000.00
	RM	46,000,000.00

Tally of the total:

Money delivered, Zloty and Reichsmark notes	RM	73,852,080.74
Precious metals	RM	8,973,651.60
Foreign currency, notes	RM	4,521,224.13
Foreign currency, in minted value	RM	1,736,554.12
Jewels and related assets	RM	43,662,450.00
Woven fabrics	RM	46,000,000.00
	RM	178,745,960.59

Rzepa	Wippern
SS Sergeant and Treasurer	SS Major and Head of Administration

Globocnik [Higher SS and Police Commander, in charge of operations].

4.5. Nazi Rule in Europe: Soviet Union

The *Reichsführer-SS* and Chief of German Police was entrusted with securing "police enforced order" in Soviet territory as well. Here, four Special Units of Security Police and Security Service, organized according to plans drawn up by the Reich Security Main Office, carried out the first phase of the "Final Solution of the Jewish Question." Hundreds of thousands of Jews in the Soviet Union became their victims through mass executions. The "Reports on Results" [*Erfolgsmeldungen*] sent by the Special Units to the Reich Security Main Office formed the basis for the "Reports by the Special Units" that were compiled by Department IV of the RSMO.

Commandos of Security Police and Security Service searched through prisoner of war camps for commissars, Communist functionaries and Jews. These were shot close to their respective camps or by means of special installations put up in German concentration camps, where they were shot through the neck. Millions of Soviet prisoners of war died under unspeakable conditions in the prisoner of war camps, in particular during the winter of 1941/42. When a policy was adopted in the spring of 1942 to use prisoners of war for forced labor in the German war economy, only a few hundred thousand prisoners capable of work were left. Units of police and combat SS [*Waffen-SS*] led by Higher SS and Police Leaders tried to curb the partisan movement by way of ambitiously arranged "operations to fight [partisan] gangs." These ventures were in fact killing operations whereby tens of thousands of civilians became victims. The rule of SS and police on Soviet territory was one of the bloodiest phases in the history of the Second World War.

Text 50

"Führer Decree" of July 17, 1941 pertaining to the "police protection of the newly occupied eastern territories"

Copy.
Decree by the *Führer* pertaining to police protection of the newly occupied eastern territories.
July 17, 1941

I.
Police protection of the newly occupied territories is the responsibility of the *Reichsführer-SS* and Head of German Police.

II.
After civilian administration has been instituted in these territories, the *Reichsführer-SS* and Head of German Police is authorized to give instructions to the Reich Commissioners in accordance with his duties listed under I.
Insofar as such instructions are of a general nature, or are politically of fundamental significance, they must be routed via the Reich Minister for the Occupied Eastern Territories unless it concerns a defensive action against immediate danger.

III.
To carry out such police protection, a Higher SS and Police Leader will be assigned to each Reich Commissioner; he will be directly and personally subordinate to the Reich Commissioner.
Officers of SS and police will be assigned to all General Commissioners, Chief Commissioners and Regional Commissioners; they will be directly and personally subordinate to them.

Führer Headquarters, July 17, 1941
The *Führer*
signed: Adolf Hitler

Chief of the Army High Command
signed: Keitel

Reich Minister and Head of the Reich Chancellory
signed: Dr. Lammers

157   Pogrom in Kaunas (Kovno), initiated by members of "Special Unit A," from June 25 through 29, 1941.

Text 51

Guidelines of July 17, 1941 issued by the Reich Security Main Office concerning "political scrutiny," "selection," and "further treatment" of prisoners of war by the Commandos of Security Police and Security Service

Top Secret!
Berlin, July 17, 1941
Department IV

Guidelines
for the Commandos of the Chief of Security Police and Security Service that will be assigned to prisoner of war camps.
[...]
The Commandos will work independently by virtue of special authority bestowed upon them and according to the general guidelines they were given within the framework of the camp rules. It is self-evident that the Commandos will keep in closest contact with the camp commander and with the intelligence officer assigned to him.
The task of the Commandos will be the political scrutiny of all camp inmates and the selection and further treatment.
a) of those among them who are unacceptable for political, criminal or other resons,
b) of those persons who can be utilized for the reconstruction of the occupied territories.
[...]

Most importantly, the following categories must be identified: all significant functionaries of the state and party, notably professional revolutionaries,
functionaries of the Comintern,
all significant party functionaries of the C. P. of the Soviet Union and their subordinate organizations in the central and regional committees,
all people's commissars and their deputies,
all former political commissars in the Red Army,
the leading personages of the central and intermediate echelons within the state agencies,
leading personages within the economic sphere,
Soviet Russian intellectuals,
all Jews,
all persons identified as agitators or fanatical communists.
As already mentioned, it will be no less important to identify all persons who may be put to use in the reconstruction, administration and management of the conquered Russian territories.
[...]
No executions may be carried out within the camp or in its immediate vicinity. If the camps are located in the *Generalgouvernement* very close to the border, prisoners singled out for special treatment are to be transported to formerly Soviet Russian territory. If executions should become necessary, for reasons of camp discipline, the commander of the Special Unit must contact the camp commander on the matter.

Text 52

Report of December 1, 1941 by Special Command 3 of Special Unit A, pertaining to mass murders in Lithuania

The Commander of Security Police and Security Service

Special Command 3   Kauen, December 1, 1941
Top Secret!

5 copies:
4 th copy

Complete list of all executions carried out within the sector of Special Command 3 up to December 1, 1941.

Special Command 3 assumend all Security Police tasks in Lithuania on July 2, 1941.
(The Vilna region was taken over by Special Command 3 on Aug. 9, 1941, the Schaulen region on Oct. 2, 1941. Until this juncture, Vilna was processed [*bearbeitet*] by Special command 9, and Shaulen y Special Command 2.)

The following is a list of all executuons carried out by Lithuanian partisans according to my instructions and by my orders:

July	4, 1941	Kauen-Fort VII:	416 Jews, 47 Jewesses	463
July	6, 1941	Kauen-Fort VII:	Jews	2,514

After the formation of a raiding squad led by SS First Lieutennt Hamann and eight to ten proven man of Special Command 3, the following operations were carried out in cooperation with Lithuanian partisans:

July	7, 1941	Mariampole	Jews	32
July	8, 1941	Mariampole	14 Jews and 5 Communist functionaries	19
July	8, 1941	Cirkalinei	Communist functionaries	6
July	9, 1941	Wendziogals	32 Jews, 2 Jewesses, 1 Lithuanian woman, 2 Lithuanien Communists, 1 Russian Communist	38
July	9, 1941	Kauen-Fort VIII	21 Jews, 3 Jewesses	24
July	14, 1941	Mariampole	21 Jews, 1 Russian, 9 Lithuanian Communists	31
July	17, 1941	Babtei	8 Communist functionaries (6 of them Jews)	8
July	18, 1941	Mariampole	39 Jews, 14 Jewesses	53
July	19, 1941	Kauen-Fort VIII	17 Jews, 2 Jewesses, 4 Lithuanian Communists, 2 Comm. Lith. Women, 1 German Comm.	26
July	21, 1941	Panevezys	59 Jews, 11 Jewesses, 1 Lith. woman, 1 Pole, 22 Lith. Comm., 9 Russ. Comm.	103
July	22, 1941	Panevezys	1 Jew	1
July	23, 1941	Kedsiniai	83 Jews, 12 Jewesses, 14 Russ. Comm., 15 Lith. Comm., 1 Russ. Commissar	125
July	25, 1941	Mariampole	90 Jews, 13 Jewesses	103
July	28, 1941	Panevezys	234 Jews, 15 jewesses, 19 Russ. comm., 20 Lith. Comm.	288

carry over 3,834

[...]

page 5
− carry over: 66159

Month of October:

Oct. 2, 1941	Zagare	633 Jews, 1107 Jewesses, 496 Jewish children	2236

(while these Jews were being taken away, a mutiny ensued. however, it was quelled at once. In the process, 150 Jews were shot at once, 7 partisans were injured)

Oct. 4, 1941	Kauen-Ft. IX	315 jews, 712 Jewesses, 818 Jew. ch[ildren] (punitive action because a German policeman had been shot at in the ghetto)	1845
Oct. 29, 1941	Kauen-Ft. IX	2007 Jews, 2920 Jewesses, 4273 Jew children (clearing the ghetto of superfluous Jews)	9200

Month of November:

Nov. 3, 1941	Lazdijai	485 Jewes, 511 Jewesses, 539 Jew children.	1535
Nov. 15, 1941	Wilkowiski	36 Jews, 48 Jewesses, 31 Jew children	115
Nov. 25, 1941	Kauen-Ft. IX	1159 Jews, 1600 Jewesses, 175 Jew children (Resettlers from Berlin, Munich and Frankfurt/Main)	2934
Nov. 29, 1941	Kauen-Ft. IX	17 Jews, 1 Jewess who had violated ghetto laws. 1 German who had converted to Judaism and had attended a rabbinical training seminary, then 15 terrorists from the Kalinin Gang.	34

Sub-Commando of Special Commando 3 in Dünaburg during the period

from July 13 – August 21, 1941	9012 Jews, Jewesses and Jew children, 573 active Communists	9585

Sub-Commando of Special Commando 3 in Vilna:

Aug. 12–

Sept. 1, 1941	Vilna-City	425 Jews, 19 Jewesses, 8 Communists, 9 femle Communists	461
Sept. 2, 1941	Vilna-City	864 Jews, 2019 Jewesses, 817 Jew children (Special operation, because Jews fired on German soldiers)	3700

carry over:	99804

[...]

Today I can state that the objective of solving the Jewish problem in Lithuania has been accomplished by Special Commando 3. There are no more jews in Lithuania, except for the labor Jews, including their families.

Those are:

in Schaulen	approximately	4 500
in Kauen	approximately	15 000
in Vilna	approximately	15 000

These labor Jews, including their families, I wanted to bump off as well, but I ran into stiff opposition from the civilian administration (the Reich Commissioner [*Reichskommissar*]) and the army. This resulted in the injunction: these Jews and their families are not to be shot!

The objective to make Lithuania free of Jews [*judenrein*] could only be achieved by the establishment of a raiding squad with picked men led by SS First Lieutenant Hamann. He made all my objectives thoroughly his own and was able to ensure the cooperation of the Lithuanian partisans and the appropriate civilian agencies.

The execution of such operations is first and foremost a matter of organization. The decision to make each district systematically free of Jews required thorough preparation for each individual operation as well as the investigation of the prevailing circumstance within each district concerned.

The Jews had to be concentrated in one place, or in several ones. On the basis of how many there were, the location for the required graves [*Gruben*] had to be found and the graves dug. The length of the marching route from the collecting point to the graves was on an average 4 to 5 kilometers. The Jews were transported to the place of execution in groups of 500, with at least 2 kilometers distance between groups. [...]

Only by skillful use of time has it been possible to carry out five operations a week while at the same time coping with the routine work at Kauen in such a way that there would be no interruption of duties within the department.

The operations in Kauen proper, where sufficient reasonably well-trained partisans are at our disposal, can be considered a piece of cake compared to the often unbelievable difficulties that had to be overcome outside. [...]

It is my opinion that sterilization of the male labor Jews should begin at once in order to prevent reproduction. Should a Jewess become pregnant anyway, she is to be liquidated.

Aside from the Jew operations [*Judenaktionen*], Special Commando 3 saw one of its most important tasks in checking the — mostly overcrowded — prisuans in the individul localities and towns. On an average, 600 persons of Lithuanian nationality were kept in jail in each district town although a valid reason for imprisonment was missing. [...] Nobody paid them any attention. One must have been inside these prisons and must have spent a moment in one of these overcrowded cells which defy any description as far as hygiene is concerned [to appreciate their plight]. In Jonava [...] 16 men were kept for five weeks in a dark basement cell 3 meters wide and 1,65 meters long; all of them could be released as there were no charges held against them. [...] Those about to be released were taken by train to the market place and there, after a brief address, were discharged in the presence of many local residents. The address contained the following:

"If we were Bolsheviks we would have shot you. Because we are Germans we return you to liberty." [...] It is difficult to convey the joy, gratefulness, and enthusiasm which this measure of ours generated among those freed, and among the population at large. It was necessary to fend off the enthusiasm with sharp words as women, children and men tried, with tears in their eyes, to kiss our hands and feet.

(stamp) Jäger
SS-Colonel

Text 53

Table of deportation transports that arrived in Minsk between May and October 1941, and the [number of] persons killed immediately upon arrival

The following transports of Jews arriving in Minsk during the period between May and October 1942 fell victim to the measures of extermintion:

Consecutive Number	Train No.	Origin	No. of Occupants	Date of Arrival	Place of Arrival	of these, killed (minimum)	
1.	Da 201	Vienna	1,000	May 11, 1942	Minsk	(minimum)	900
2.	Da 203	Vienna	1,000	May 26, 1942	Minsk	(minimum)	900
3.	Da 204	Vienna	998	Jun 1, 1942	Minsk	(minimum)	900
4.	Da 205	Vienna	999	Jun 5–9, 1942	Minsk	(minimum)	900
5.	Da 206	Vienna	1,000	Jun 15, 1942	Minsk	(minimum)	900
6.	Da 40	Königsberg	465	Jun 26, 1942	Minsk	(minimum)	400
7.	Da 220	Theresienstadt	1,000	Jul 18, 1942	Minsk	(minimum)	900
8.	Da 219	Cologne	1,000	Jul 24, 1942	Minsk	(minimum)	900
9.	Da 222	Theresienstadt	993	Aug 10, 1942	Trostinez	(minimum)	900
10.	Da 223	Vienna	1,000	Aug 21, 1942	Trostinez	(minimum)	900
11.	Da 224	Theresienstadt	1,000	Aug 28, 1942	Trostinez	(minimum)	900
12.	Da 225	Vienna	1,000	Sep 4, 1942	Trostinez	(minimum)	900
13.	Da 226	Theresienstadt	1,000	Sep 12, 1942	Trostinez	(minimum)	900
14.	Da 227	Vienna	1,000	Sep 18, 1942	Trostinez	(minimum)	900
15.	Da 228	Theresienstadt	1,000	Sep 25, 1942	Trostinez	(minimum)	900
16.	Da 230	Vienna	547	Oct 9, 1942	Trostinez	(minimum)	500

Persons deported: 15,002; of these, killed immediately after arrival: 13,500

In connection with this table it should be noted that those transports initially destined for Minsk carried the identification numbers Da 201 – Da 218. But the trains Da 202 and Da 207 – Da 218 were cancelled. In their place ran the trains Da 40 and Da 219 – DA 230. Of these, Da 221 was unloaded in Baranovicz while Da 229 was cancelled.

Text 54

Report of early summer 1942 by a district farmer [Kreislandwirt] commissioned with the registration of livestock and agricultural products in the occupied territories, pertaining to the devastation of villages and the murder of their inhabitants in Belo-Russia

Report about the operation in the Begomel district.

It was my task during the operation to register livestock and other agricultural products. In the process I passed through many villages. Everybody knows that wherever there is fighting there will also be devastation and destruction. It is incomprehensible, however, that after villages have been conquered and the inhabitants are gradually returning from the forests full of trust and offer their services to the [military] units, they are shot and burned a few days later.

On May 25 and 26 I was in the village of Osinivik. There a staff unit of the Security Service (SD) was billeted. The people were either out working or sat in front of their houses. When I returned to the place on June 2, I found instead of the village a huge pyre. The village had been burnt down. According to the testimony of other comrades, men, women, and children had been shot. In one house I found a partly charred corpse which bore out the testimony of the comrades. The following villages that I saw were destroyed in this fashion: Novosiolky, Osinoviknna Pijany-Sas. Furthermore, according to official statements, Vitunicz, Budilovka, Beresnievka and Begomel.

On May 24 I found at the far end of the village of Niebyczyno a burnt barn containing six charred corpses. That happened immediately after the village was taken. The population cannot help but come to the conclusion that these people were burned alive.

Together with the district farmers Wortmann and Hartmann I have registered
727 head of cattle
575 head of sheep
and more than one wagonload of hides and pelt.

Bölt District Farmer

Text 55

Order of February 5, 1943 by the Commander of the Security Police and the Security Service at Minsk, pertaining to the "resettlement" of Jews in Sluzk

Minsk, February 5, 1943
The Commander of Security Police and Security Service in White Ruthenia

Order to the Commando

On February 8 and 9, 1943, the local commando unit will carry out the resettlement of the Jews of the town of Sluzk. Those members of the commando listed below as well as roughly 110 members of the Latvian volunteer company will participate in the operation. The operation will be led by SS First Lieutenant Müller. On February 7, 1943 at 11:15 a.m., participating members will report for departure — which will be at 11:30 a.m. — in the lower corridor of the service building. Lunch will be served at 10:30 a.m. SS Major Br. will be in command of the motor convoy. [...]

Execution of the operation in Sluzk:

Ghetto
The General Police [Ordnungspolizei] will take care of securing and guarding the ghetto.
Evaluation of all Jewish property that will accrue will be handled by SS Capitain Mad. who will have at his disposal for this task two [police] officers (Kru., Buch.), two interpreters (Michelsen, Natarow) and ten Latvians. The roundup of the Jews in the ghetto will take place under the command of SS Major Gra. who will have at his disposal six commandos composed of one [police] officer and nine Latvians each. The following noncoms [Unterführer] have been designated for the commandos:
Krause, Nikol, Gen., Ehrig, Wel., Ze. The transport of the Jews to the place of resettlement will be carried out by means of six trucks, each of them accompanied by four Latvians.

Resettlement Terrain:
On the resettlement terrain are two pits. At each pit a group of ten leaders and men will be working who will relieve each other every two hours. The time periods are: 8–10 a.m., 10–12 a.m., 12 noon to 2 p.m., 2 to 4 p.m.

Pit No 1:
First group:
SS Major Br. (in command)
SS First Lieutenants Kaul, Merbach; SS Captain Schneider; SS Lieutenant Wertholz; SS Lieutenant Müller; SS Lieutenant Ju.; SS Sergeant Major

Fritz; SS Lance Corporals [Privates First Class] Gei. and Gröner.

Second group:
SS Captain Schlegel; SS Sergeants Bur.; Seckinger, Brandlmeier; SS Master Sergeant Hüttner; SS Master Sergeant Wel.; SS Corporal v. Toll; *SS-Scharführer* [no Brit. or U.S. equiv.; between corporal and sergeant] Rex.; Police Corporal Exner and SS Corporal Hör.

Pit No. 2:
First group:
SS First Lieutenant Müller; SS Lieutenant Müller; SS Lieutenant Eck; SS Captain Fr.; Police Private First Class Krahnke; SS Master Sergeant v.d. Go.; SS Privates First Class Schr., Str., Egger, Zehmann, Fi.

Second group:
SS First Lieutenant Oswald; SS Captain Rü.; SS Lieutenant Schmidt; SS Master Sergeant Kreimann; SS Sergeants Schu., Gersberger, Fockler; SS Corporal Strathmann and SS Sergeant Kramer; SS Corporal Get.

SS Lieutenant Pierre and ten Latvians will secure the resettlement terrain.

signed: Strauch
SS First Lieutenant

Text 56

Verdict of May 21, 1963 handed down by a special court at the Regional Superior Court in Koblenz against former members of the commando that had murdered the Jews of the town of Sluzk on February 8/9, 1943

In the name of the People

The criminal case against:

1. Senior Chief Detective Superintendent [*Kriminaloberrat*] Georg Albert Wilhelm Heuser, born February, 1913 in Berlin, residing in Koblenz, presently in pretrial detention in Koblenz prison, married;
2. Bookkeeper and former Police Inspector Karl Robert Dalheimer, born November 5, 1907 in Geestemünde, residing in Bremen, married;
3. *Kriminalmeister* [no precise equivalent in English] Johannes Hugo Otto Feder, born May 21, 1911 in Liegnitz/Silesia, residing in Cologne-Braunsfeld, married;
4. Commercial Clerk Arthur Alexander Harder, born September 19, 1910 in Frankfurt/Main, married;
5. Chief Customs Inspector Wilhelm Kaul, born

May 10, 1906 in Lippstadt, residing in Münster/Westphalia, married;
6. Office Employee Friedrich Merbach, born April 27, 1912 in Gotha/Thuringia, residing in Ludwigshafen-Mundenheim, presently in pretrial detention in Koblenz prison, married;
7. Electrician Jakob Herbert Oswald, born March 1, 1900 in Marburg/Lahn, residing in Lübeck, married;
8. Commercial Clerk Rudolf Schlegel, born July 11, 1913 in Chemnitz, residing in Stuttgart-Bad Cannstatt, presently in pretrial detention in Koblenz prison, married;
9. Unskilled Worker Franz Stark, born October 7, 1907 in St. Louis [Missouri]/USA, residing in Munich, widowed, presently in pretrial detention in Koblenz prison;
10. Employee Eberhard Richard Ernst von Toll, born January 15, 1906 in Piddul/Estonia, residing in Stadthagen, married;
11. Former Teacher Artur Fritz Wilke, born February 1, 1910 in Hohensalza/Poznan Region, residing in Stederdorf, District Peine, presently in pretrial detention in Koblenz prison, married;

Because of murder having been committed, the jury at the Regional Superior Court in Koblenz has adjudged, decreed and determined during a session held on May 21, 1963:

I.
1. The defendant Heuser, having committed in conjunction with others nine crimes of aiding and abetting murder, and one crime of aiding and abetting manslaughter, is herewith sentenced to serve a total of fifteen years in a penitentiary.
He will be deprived of his civil rights for a period of five years.
2. The defendant Dalheimer, having committed in conjunction with others one crime of aiding and abetting murder, is herewith sentenced to serve four years in a penitentiary.
3. The defendant Feder, having committed in conjunction with others two crimes of aiding and abetting murder, is herewith sentenced to serve a total of four years and six months in a penitentiary.
4. The defendant Harder, having committed in conjunction with others one crime of aiding and abetting murder, is herewith sentenced to serve three years and six months in a penitentiary.
5. The defendant Kaul, having committed in conjunction with others two crimes of aiding and abetting murder, is herewith sentenced to serve a total of four years and six months in a penitentiary.

6. The defendant Merbach, having committed in conjunction with others five crimes of aiding and abetting murder, is herewith sentenced to serve a total of seven years in a penitentiary.

He will be deprived of his civil rights for a period of three years.

7. The defendant Oswald, having committed in conjunction with others one crime of aiding and abetting murder, is herewith sentenced to serve four years in a penitentiary.

8. The defendant Schlegel, having comitted in conjunction with others five crimes of aiding and abetting murder, is herewith sentenced to serve eight years in a penitentiary.

9. The defendant Stark, having committed three crimes of murder, is herewith sentenced to serve a life term in a penitentiary. Furthermore, having commited in conjunction with others five crimes of aiding and abetting murder, he is herewith sentenced to serve a total of eight years in a penitentiary.

He will be deprived of his civil rights for life.

10. The defendant von Toll, having committed in conjunction with others four crimes of aiding and abetting murder is herewith sentenced to serve a total of four years and six months in a penitentiary.

11. The defendant Wilke, having committed in conjunction with others six crimes of aiding and abetting murder, is herewith sentenced to serve a total of ten years in a penitentiary.

He will be deprived of his civil rights for a period of three years.

II.
Where no verdict has been given, the defendants stand acquitted.

III.
All defendants will have their time served in pre-trial detention taken into account; for the defendant Stark this will apply to his second penitentiary term.

IV.
Where sentences have been passed, the costs of legal proceedings will have to be born by the defendants, and any remaining balance by the state.

158   Himmler (third from the right) and Higher SS and Police Leader (HSSPF [German abbreviation]) Central Russia, Erich von dem Bach-Zelewski (sixth from the right, partly hidden) inspect a prisoner of war camp near Minsk in July/August 1941.

159   Murder of civilians, probably in Lithuania, in 1941.

Text 57

Internal memorandum of June 1, 1943 by the General Commissioner for White Ruthenia pertaining to the execution of an "operation against gangs" [Bandenaktion] in the Borissow region

Minsk, June 1, 1943

The General Commissioner
in Minsk
Department I, Political,

To the
Chief Department Head I,
here in residence.

Subject: Operation against gangs in the Borissow region
Reference: none

The — so far oral — report of the official in Borissow responsible for political matters about incidents that have occurred during the ongoing operation is less than edifying. In the municipality of Vitonicz in the Borissow region the inhabitants were driven into a barn, moved down, and the building burned to the ground. As the corpses were not completely burned, the now ownerless pigs drag body parts of the corpses through the village. Those [persons] who were shot were simply left lying where they were.

It is said, by way of example, that days later people reported to the hospital because the men carrying out the operation had believed them to be dead when in fact they were only wounded and had fainted. They then got up from among those shot to death and sought help.

A thoroughgoing official report from Borissow will follow.

By order:
signed: Lange

4.6. Nazi Rule in Europe: Other Countries

As in Poland and the Soviet Russian territories, the *Reichsführer-SS* and the SS and police forces under his command were also assigned police related safeguarding tasks in all other countries occupied by Germany. In agreement with the military and civilian administrative agencies, anti-Jewish measures were carried out everywhere, and the Jewish population, at times with the assistance of local collaborators, was carried off into the extermination camps. On January 20, 1942 at the "Wannsee Conference" in Berlin, Reinhard Heydrich had announced the extermination program to the participating representatives of ministries and departments.

The organizational center of all deportation measures was the "Jewish Section" IV B 4 of the Reich Security Main Office whose director was Adolf Eichmann. His representatives did not only sit in the administrative agencies of the Security Police in the occupied territories, but so-called "Advisors on Jewish Affairs" [*Judenberater*] negotiated also with all allied countries about the extradition of their Jewish populations. Despite all the difficulties caused by wartime conditions, deportation trains went to Auschwitz until the fall of 1944.

The representatives of the departments of the Reich Security Main Office, the *Gestapo*, the Criminal Police and the Security Service fought bloody battles against the various native resistance movements throughout Europe. Thousands of civilians fell victim to it. Lidice, Marzabotto, the Ardeatini Caves and Oradour are symbols of these events. Prisoners from all over Europe suffered and died as a result of *Gestapo* torture and in German concentration camps. With the aid of the "Night and Fog Decree" the Security Police tried to maintain order under German domination.

Text 58

Protocol of the conference held on January 20, 1942 in Berlin-Wannsee where the organizational execution of the "Final Solution of the Jewish Question" was coordinated according to plan ("Wannsee Conference")

Top Secret!

30 copies
16th copy

Protocol.

I.
The following persons participated in the conference of January 20, 1942 held in Berlin, Am Großen Wannsee 56−58, on the final solution of the Jewish question:

Gauleiter Dr. Meyer and Reichadministrative Direktor [*Reichsamtsleiter*] Dr. Leibbrandt	Reich Ministry for the Occupied Territories
Undersecretary Dr. Stuckart	Reich Ministry of the Interior
Undersecretary Neumann	Office of Plenipotentiary of the Four Year Plan
Undersecretary Dr. Freisler	Reich Ministry of Justice
Undersecretary Dr. Bühler	Office of the *Generalgouvernment* [Poland]
Assistant Undersecretary Luther	Foreign Office
SS-Oberführer [no English equivalent; rank between colonel and brigadier general] Klopfer	Party Chancellory
Ministerial Department Head Dr. Kritzinger	Reich Chancellory
SS Major General Hofmann	Race and Resettlement Main Office

SS Major General Müller	Reich Security Main Office
SS Lieutenant Colonel Eichmann	
SS-Oberführer [see above] Dr. Schöngarth, Commanding Officer of Security Police and Security Service in the General-gouvernement [Poland]	Security Police and Security Service
SS Major Dr. Lange, Commander of Security Police and Security Service for the General-District of Lettland, as deputy of the Commander of Security Police and Security Service for the Reich Commissariat in the East [Ostland]	Security Police and Security Service

160   The villa Am Großen Wannsee No. 56–58, the place where the "Wannsee Conference" was held on January 20, 1942.

II.

SS Lieutenant General Heydrich, Chief of Security Police and Security Service, opened the meeting by informing everyone that the Reich Marshal [Göring] had put him in charge of preparations for the final solution of the Jewish question. The invitations of this conference had been issued to clarify fundamental questions. The Reich Marshal's request that a draft be submitted to him with regard to the organizational, functional and material considerations in connection with the final solution of the European Jewish question requires that all central agencies directly concerned with these problems first meet together in order to coordinate their lines of action.

The authority for processing the final solution of the Jewish question lies centralized in the hands of the Reichsführer-SS, head of German Police (Head of Security Police and Security Service), regardless of geographic boundaries.

The Chief of Security Police and Security Service (SD) then gave a brief review of the struggle fought thus far against this foe. The most important stages had been:

a) forcing the Jews out of the various spheres of life [Lebensgebiete] of the German people,
b) forcing the Jews out of the German people's living space [Lebensraum].

In pursuance of these endeavors, an accelerated emigration of the Jews from the territory of the Reich was seen as the only temporary solution that was accordingly embarked upon in an intensified and systematic manner.

On instructions of the Reich Marshal, a Reich Central Office for Jewish Emigration was established in January 1939; its direction was entrusted to the Chief of Security Police and Security Service (SD).
a) Its special tasks were to take measures for the preparation of increased Jewish emigration,
b) to direct the flow of emigration,
c) to speed up the emigration process in individual cases.

The goal of the task was to purge German living space of Jews by legal means.

The disadvantages of such forced emigration were evident to all agencies concerned. Yet in the absence of other feasible solutions they had to put up with them for the time being.

The problems connected with emigration were subsequently not merely German ones but also problems that concerned the relevant agencies of the countries of destination or, as it were, immigration. Financial difficulties such as increased surety to be presented upon landing and higher landing fees that different foreign countries demanded, insufficient berths on the ships, constantly increasing immigration restrictions and suspensions, all of these made emigration efforts exceedingly more difficult. Yet despite these difficulties, roughly 537,000 Jews were made to emigrate from the day of seizure of power on until October 31, 1941.
Of these,

ca. 360,000 left after January 30, 1933 from the *Altreich* [Germany with its 1937 borders]
ca. 147,000 left after March 15, 1938 from the *Ostmark* [Austria after March 1938]
ca. 30,000 left after March 15, 1939 from the Protectorate of Bohemia and Moravia.

Emigration was financed by the Jews themselves or, as the case may be, the Jewish political organizations. In order to make sure that the proletarianized Jews would not stay behind, a rule was applied by which affluent Jews had to finance the emigration of Jews without means; based on assessments of means, an appropriate apportionment or an emigration tax was prescribed which was used to pay for all financial obligations impecunious Jews had incurred in the course of their emigration.

In addition to this levy in Reichsmarks, foreign currencies were required for surety to be presented upon landing and also for landing fees. In order to spare German currency reserves, Jewish financial institutions abroad were called upon by the Jewish organizations in Germany to make sure that the required sums in foreign currency were supplied. In this manner, up to October 30, 1941 a total of about $ 9,500,000 altogether was made available as gifts by these foreign Jews.

Meanwhile, in view of the dangers posed by emigration in wartime, and in view of the possibilities in the east, the *Reichsführer-SS* and Head of German Police has forbidden the [further] emigration of Jews.

III.

In lieu of emigration, the evacuation of the Jews to the east has emerged as an additional possible solution, now that the appropriate prior authorization by the Führer has been obtained. But although these operations are to be regarded solely as temporary measures, practical experiences are already being gathered here and will be of major importance for the upcoming solution of the Jewish question.

Roughly eleven million Jews will probably be involved in the solution of the European Jewish question. They are distributed as follows among the individual countries:

Country	Numbers
A.	
Altreich [Germany with its 1937 borders]	131,800
Ostmark [formerly Austria]	43,700
Eastern territories	420,000
Generalgouvernement	2,284,000
Bialystok	400,000
Protectorate of Bohemia and Moravia	74,200
Estonia- free of Jews Latvia	3,500
Lithuania	34,000
Belgium	43,000
Denmark	5,600
France/occupied territory	165,000
unoccupied territory	700,000
Greece	69,600
Netherlands	160,800
Norway	1,300

B.	
Bulgaria	48,000
England	330,000
Finland	2,300
Ireland	4,000
Italy, including Sardinia	58,000
Albania	200
Croatia	40,000
Portugal	3,000
Rumania, incl. Besarabia	342,000
Sweden	8,000
Switzerland	18,000
Serbia	10,000
Slovakia	88,000
Spain	6,000
Turkey (European part)	55,500
Hungary	742,800
USSR	5,000,000
Ukraine	2,994,684
White Russia,[except for Bialystok]	446,484

Altogether: over   11,000,000

The figures of Jews in the different countries listed here pertain only to those who are of the Jewish faith, however, as definitions of Jews along racial lines are in part still lacking. Given the prevailing attitudes and conceptions in Hungary and Rumania particularly, the handling of the problem in the individual countries will encounter certain difficulties. For example, a Jew in Rumania even today can buy for cash the appropriate documents that certify him as possessing a foreign nationality.

The influence that Jews in the USSR exert everywhere is known. In the European part live approximately five million, in the Asian part barely a quarter million Jews.

The occupational distribution of Jews living in the European part of the USSR was approximately as follows:

Agriculture	9.1%
Urban workers	14.8%
Trade	20.9%
State employees	23.4%
Private professions — medical, press, theater, etc.	32.0%

In the course of the final solution the Jews are to be sent in a suitable manner and under appropriate direction to do labor in the east. Separated by sexes, those Jews able to work will be led in large labor columns into these areas while building roads. In the process, large numbers will undoubtedly drop away through natural attrition. The final remainder that conceivably will still be around and that undoubtedly constitutes the sturdiest segment will have to be dealt with accordingly as it represents a natural selection which, when left at liberty, has to be seen as a germ cell of new Jewish development. (See the lesson history teaches).

In the course of the practical implementation of the final solution, Europe will be combed through from west to east. Priority will have to be given to the area of the Reich, including the Protectorate of Bohemia and Moravia, if only because of housing shortages and other socio-political needs.

The evacuated Jews will initially be brought without delay into so-called transit ghettos, and from there will be transported further to the east.

As SS Lieutenant General Heydrich pointed out in addition, one important prerequisite for carrying out the evacuation at all will be the precise designation of all persons to be involved.

It is intended not to evacuate Jews over 65 years of age but to send them to an old people's ghetto; Theresienstadt is earmarked for this purpose.

In addition to these age groups — and of the 280,000 Jews who lived in the *Altreich* and Austria on October 1, 1941, some 30% are over 65 — the old people's ghetto will also receive Jews who are badly war-disabled, and Jews with war decorations (Iron Cross First Class). With this convenient solution the many intercessions will be eliminated at one blow.

The beginning of the various major evacuation operations will largely depend on military developments. With regard to the treatment of the final solution in those European regions occupied or influenced by us, it was suggested that the appropriate specialists of the Foreign Office get together with whoever is the official handling this matter for the Security Police and Security Service (SD).

In Slovakia and Croatia the situation is no longer all that difficult since the essential key questions there have already been resolved. Meanwhile the Rumanian government has likewise appointed a plenipotentiary for Jewish affairs. In order to settle the matter in Hungary it will be necessary before long to impose upon the Hungarian government an advisor on Jewish questions.

With regard to the beginning of preparations for a settlement of this problem in Italy, SS Lieutenant General Heydrich considers it advisable to establish contact about these concerns with the head of police.

In occupied and unoccupied France, the collection of Jews for evacuation will in all probability proceed without major difficulties.

Assistant Under Secretary Luther [Foreign Office] commented in this connection that the far-reaching treatment of this problem will cause difficulties in some countries, notably the nordic countries. For this reason he would recommend deferring the

matter for the time being in these countries. In view of the insignificant number of Jews involved there, such a postponement would not amount to a substantial restriction.

On the other hand, the Foreign Office visualizes no major difficulties in southeastern and western Europe.

SS Major General Hofmann voiced his intention to send along a specialist from the Race and Resettlement Main Office for general orientation purposes to Hungary when the Chief of Security Police and Security Service (SD) gets ready to tackle the matter over there. It was decided that this specialist of the Race and Resettlement Main Office — who was not to become actively involved — be officially attached, on a temporary basis, as an assistant to the Police Attaché.

IV.

During the progress of the final solution project, its basis, as it were, should be the Nuremberg Laws, whereby the solution of mixed marriages and mixed parentage [racially speaking] must likewise be a prerequisite for the definitive settlement of the problem.

[...]

With regard to the question of how much the evacuation of the Jews would be affecting economic life, Undersecretary Neumann stated that Jews presently working in enterprises essential to the war effort could not be evacuated until they could be replaced.

SS Lieutenant General Heydrich pointed out that in accordance with directives for current evacuations authorized by him, these Jews were not being evacuated anyway.

Undersecretary Dr. Bühler noted that the *Generalgouvernement* would be gratified if the final solution of this question began in the *Generalgouvernement* because the transportation problem was no overriding factor there, and because considerations of work utilization would not impede the course of action. Jews should be removed from the territory of the *Generalgouvernement* as speedily as possible because precisely there the Jews constitute a significant danger as carriers of epidemics; furthermore, they were upsetting the economic structure of the region through ceaseless black market activities. Moreover, the majority of the $2^1/_2$ million Jews involved were not capable of work.

Undersecretary Dr. Bühler noted further that the Chief of Security Police and Security Service was in charge of the final solution of the Jewish question in the *Generalgouvernement* and that the administrative agencies of the *Generalgouverne-*

ment would assist him in his work. He had only one favor to ask: that the Jewish question in this territory be solved as fast as possible.

In conclusion there was a discussion about the various types of possible solutions. Here both *Gauleiter* Dr. Meyer and Undersecretary Dr. Bühler took the position that in connection with the final solution certain preparatory measures be carried out at once in the occupied territories, but in such a way as to avoid that the population [of non-Jews] there become apprehensive.

The Chief of Security Police and Security Service (SD) terminated the conference with the request that all participants in today's deliberations give him their cooperation in implementing the tasks connected with the [final] solution.

Text 59

Telegram of June 28, 1942 from Assistant Undersecretary in the Foreign Office, Luther, pertaining to the deportation of Belgian, French and Dutch Jews to Auschwitz

The Chief of Security Police and Security Service has imparted the following:

"Beginning in mid-July or early August, as the case may be, it has been planned to transport initially about 40,000 Jews from French occupied territory, 40,000 Jews from the Netherlands, and 10,000 Jews from Belgium to Camp Auschwitz to perform labor. This is to be accomplished by means of daily special trains with a capacity of 1000 persons.

The persons to be affected will be initially Jews able to work, as long as they do not live in mixed marriages and are not nationals of the British Empire, the USA, Mexico, enemy countries in central and south America or neutral and allied countries."

Comments at everybody's earliest convenience are requested.

Luther

Text 60

Memorandum of July 8, 1942 by the Specialist for Jewish Affairs with the Commanding Officer of Security Police and Security Service (SD) in Paris, pertaining to the deportation of Jews

Paris, July 8, 1942

IV J SA 24

Subject: Additional transports of Jews leaving France – First meeting of the operations committee

1.) Memorandum:
Participants in the deliberations:
A) SS Captain Dannecker,
    SS Corporal Heinrichsohn
B) Darquier de Pellepoix,
    Mr. Leguay, Deputy of the Chief of Police,
    Director Francois, Chief of Prison Camps,
    Director Hannequin, Chief of Urban Police,
    Director Tulard, Chief of the Jewish index file at the Paris Préfecture,
    Director Garnier, Deputy of the Prefect Seine [district],
    Director Schweblin, Anti-Jewish Police,
    Mr. Gallien, Chief of Cabinet with Darquier,
    Mr. Guidot, Staff Officer of the Urban Police.

Darquier pointed out by way of introduction that the occupying authorities had indicated their willingness to relieve the French state of its Jews, and that one had now gathered here in order to discuss the technical process of this expulsion. [...]

Thereupon began the actual meeting, and SS Captain Dannecker ascertained:

1.) Whether all gentlemen present were authorized representatives of their respective administrative agencies so that all decisions arrived at today would be binding, and no requests for further particulars or changes would be forthcoming. All gentlemen present thereupon stated that they had been given the necessary authority [to make decisions].

In the course of the meeting
2.) the discussion turned to the number of Jews to be reckoned with within Greater Paris.
Accordingly, roughly 28,000 Jews are to be arrested in Paris on the basis of the special guidelines (stateless, etc.). To these must be added Russian Jews (white or red), so that after the deduction of Jews who are sick, unfit for transport or too old, one may count on a figure of 22,000 Jews for Paris.

161   The village of Oradour-sur-Glane in southern France
which, together with its inhabitants, was annihilated by the SS
on June 10, 1944 in retaliation for an anti-German action on
the part of the French *Résistance*.

Subsequently the topic of

3.) the actual arrest procedure was discussed.

Accordingly, all inspectors of the Préfecture, the Anti-Jewish Police and female auxiliary forces will pull the requisite index cards and sort them according to *arrondissement*. Then Director Hennequin (*Police Municipale*) will receive these cards and will distribute them to the police commissioners of the *arrondissements*. These will carry out the arrests on the basis of those cards and will return all cards of Jews who were not at home.

The sorting of cards must be finished by Friday, July 10, 1942, and on Monday morning (July 13, 1942) the operation can take place simultaneously in all *arrondissements*.

The Jews will then be assembled at the various mayors' offices and subsequently transported to the main collection point (Vel d'hiver). Their transport into the individual camps will be carried out by the French themselves.

The designated age limit was from "16–50".

Children left behind will likewise be assembled at some communal place and will subsequently be taken over by the Union of Jews in France and brought to children's homes. All Jews within the appropriate age groups are to be arrested if they are in good enough shape to be transported (but not those living in mixed marriages!).

In the *départements* Seine et Oise and Seine et Marne, the operation will be carried out following that in Paris, and with the assistance of the Paris Police.

In this connection the

4.) capacities of the individual prison camps were discussed. Thereupon the following figures were established by SS Captain Dannecker:

Drancy: 6,000 Jews (women and men)
Compiègne: 6,000 Jews (women and men)
Pithiviers: 5,000 Jews (women and men)
Beaune-la-Rolande:
                    5,000 Jews (women and men)

5.) The actual transport of the Jews to the east.
It was determined that every week a transport will leave each camp. This solution was reached because every transport requires thorough preparations (searching the Jews, provisions, lists, etc).
Thus every week, four trains with 1000 Jews each will leave the occupied territory in an easterly direction.
French *gendarmerie* will guard the trains; the guards will be supervised by a lieutenant and eight men of a command of German Military Police.
[...]

The representative of the *préfecture de la Seine* anticipated no difficulties.

2.) Submitted to BdS [Chief of Security Police and Security Service in occupied countries] with the request to take note.

3.) Submitted to SS Lieutenant Colonel Lischka with the request to take note.
[...]

Signed: Dannecker
SS Captain

Text 61

Dutch protest leaflet against the deportation of Jews, July 1942

FELLOW CITIZENS [*Volksgenossen*]!
THE TIME HAS COME!
After a long line of inhumane decrees during the past weeks: the yellow star; the surrender of bicycles; the prohibition to enter houses of non-Jews; the prohibition to use the telephone, streetcars or trains; the prohibition to shop in non-Jewish stores except during specified hours, etc., now the crowning blow has been struck:
THE DEPORTATION OF ALL JEWS BETWEEN THE AGES OF 16 AND 42!
During the night of July 15, 1942 around 1:50 a.m., the first group had to report at Amsterdam's Central Station. Thereafter, every day 1,200 Jews will have to do likewise. From Westerbork in Drenthe where the unfortunate people are being screened, approximately 4,000 Jews altogether are being deported each time. The trains for this purpose stand ready. Specialists from Prague

162   Deportation of Dutch Jews in 1942.

well versed as executioners have gone there in order to expedite the deportations as much as possible. In this manner, a total of approximately 120,000 Jewish Dutch citizens will be taken away.

Such are the sober facts. They compare in brutality and matter-of-factness only with the instructions of the Egyptian Pharaoh who had all Jewish male children killed, and with Herod, that anti-Semite, who had all infants in Bethlehem killed in order to kill Jesus. Now, several thousand years later, Hitler and his henchmen have found their place in this company. Official Polish reports name the figure of 700,000 Jews who have already perished in the clutches of the Germans. Our Jewish fellow citizens will suffer a like fate. True, the lot of the non-Jewish workers (Dutch) in Germany is hard; but when it comes to the Jews, we are dealing with the realization of threats which the Nazis have hurled at the Jews again and again — their destruction and annihilation.

FELLOW CITIZENS!

The Dutch people have taken note of the anti-Jewish measure with disgust and outrage. To be sure, our people must pay heavily for the fact that they did not refuse to sign the Declaration on Jews [Judenerklärung] so ingenuously presented to them. It is our joint guilt — that of the Jewish Council not excepted — that our enemies now dispose over a complete Jewish administration.

All prior German measures had aimed at isolating the Jews from the rest of the Dutch, to make contact impossible, and to kill our sentiments concerning living side by side and in solidarity. They [the Germans] have succeeded much better than we know ourselves or are probably willing to admit. The Jews have to be killed in secrecy and we, the witnesses, must remain deaf, blind, and silent. We may not listen to their moans, may not watch their misery, may not voice our abhorrence and our pity. God and history will condemn us and hold us partly responsible for this mass murder if we now remain silent and simply look on.

Holland has been hit hard and is deeply humiliated. Now we must bring proof that even under pressure we have not lost our honor, that our conscience has not been struck dumb, that our faith has not been paralyzed. For this reason we expect that every citizen will sabotage preparations and executions of this deportation. Remember the February strikes of 1941, when a nation, provoked to the utmost limit, showed what it can do if it only wants to do it. We expect general secretaries, mayors, [and] high officials to lay their job on the line and not to cooperate any longer with the German occupation power. Whoever remains glued to his office chair will have a tough time after the liberation to justify his attitude. We are counting on it that all who are in a position to do so, notably public officials, police, railway officials etc., will sabotage these inhumane Nazi measures.

One final word: We urge all Dutch citizens to protest to the address of the Commander in Chief of the German Army in the Netherlands, Lieutenant General of the Air Force Christiansen.

[...]

Text 62

Report of June 25, 1943 from the representative of the Foreign Office with the Reich Commissioner for the Occupied Territories of the Netherlands, pertaining to the deportation of Jews

The Hague, June 25, 1943

The Reich Commissioner
for the Occupied Territories of the Netherlands
The Representative of the Foreign Office
D Pol 3 No. 8 No. 70 g

To the Foreign Office, Berlin

Subject: Jews

In his secret report to the Reich Commissioner, the Chief of Security Police and Security Service (SD) [in the Netherlands] writes as follows:

"Of those 140,000 *Volljuden* [Jews with two Jewish parents] originally registered with the police in the Netherlands, 100,000 Jews have now been removed from the body of the nation [*Volkskörper*] (the exact figure is 102,000). Of these, 72,000 have been deported to do labor in the east. An additional 10,000 have left the country in other ways (deportation to concentration camps in Germany proper, internment camps, resettlement in Theresienstadt, emigration, fleeing the country). Nearly 20,000 Jews are presently concentrated in the camps at Westerbork, Vught and Barneveld. Thus, within eleven months the Netherlands have been cleared of nearly 3/4 of the original number of Jews.

The last great increase of Jews to be deported was achieved on Sunday, June 20, 1943 by means of a second mammoth operation [*Großaktion*] in Amsterdam. In the course of it, 5500 Jews were rounded up during a search operation lasting 24 hours. All of Amsterdam's city districts in the south, including the Transvaal district (approximately 1/3 of Amsterdam's total area), were sealed off, and Security Police together with General Police searched apartment after apartment.

The Jews found (except for mixed marriages, Jews of foreign nationality, those able to prove that they were not fully Jewish, and a few special cases) were prepared for departure and transported to Westerbork [camp] the same night. Although, in view of the hitherto obviously unsatisfactory results of ridding Amsterdam of Jews, the lot of them [*Judenschaft*] might have expected such an operation to occur soon again, success was this time secured because the preparations for this huge operation could be kept secret until the last moment. Despite many rumors, the Jewish lot was taken by complete surprise and is now depressed, one reason why only few Jews are presently showing their faces in public. – There were no incidents. The Dutch population is thoroughly opposed to the deportations but outwardly displays for the most part an air of impassivity. Large numbers of people were angry because they could only leave the sealed off districts with difficulty. – Jewish auxiliary police from Camp Westerbork were used to help with the carting off process.

In the course of the operation we also succeeded in catching and carting off the core of the former Jewish Council. Those Jews already in Westerbork, especially emigrants from Germany, reacted to this circumstance by gloating openly. They voiced their general regret, though, that the top echelon, in particular the Jews Asscher and Cohen and their retinue had not been brought in as well.

By this time the Jews have also been removed from all armament plants (except for those involved in diamond processing). The transfer of a portion of skilled workers to Camp Vlught is in progress."

[...]

Text 63

Telegram of June 19, 1944 from Special Representative Veesenmayer to Ambassador Ritter, pertaining to a report from the Higher SS and Police Leader in Budapest

Telegram
from Budapest, No. 1830 of June 17.
Received: June 19, 1944, 7 p.m.
Secret!

163   Selection of Hungarian Jews at the ramp in Auschwitz-Birkenau in 1944.

To Ambassador Ritter.
Subsequent to today's Wire No. 261.
The Higher SS and Police Leader reported to me on June 16th:

1) Communism.
According to a report from KdS [Commander of Security Police and Security Service] in Szeged, altogether 18 persons were arrested during the night of June 13, 1943 by a special detachment of Hungarian Rural Police on account of Communist activities.

2) Bandits, Parachutist Agents.
In the sector of the KdS in Stuhlweissenburg, a parachutist was taken prisoner between Veszprem and Gyula-Viratot.

3) The total number of Jews deported to the Reich amounts to 340,124. Therewith the transport from Zone 3 has been completed. Those Jews who are presently working in industry as free laborers will be incorporated before long into the Jewish labor service. The Honved Ministry has now issued a decree by which the Jewish labor service is to be guarded more strictly.

As already commented upon in the daily report of June 8, 1944, the game with Jews who tried to flee illegally abroad continues, linked to the German Air Force. In this connection, another six Jews were arrested. They had offered 300,000 Pengös to members of the Air Force for transport to Switzerland.

IV) National Treason.
According to a confidential report, adverse propaganda to stir up the population against operations of the Combat-SS is said to be going on in Pußtavan with the assistance of Pastor Gustav Weinberger. Allegedly, signatures are being collected. The petition is to bear the inscription: "We do not serve a foreign country." Allegedly, ethnic Germans have signed as well.
Farmer Josef Hohmann who is a Hungarian citizen could be arrested while he collected signatures at the homes of opponents of the People's League [*Volksbundgegner*] against the third SS operation.

V) Enemy Propaganda.
In the sector of the KdS in Miskolc, a leaflet with the inscription "National Committee for a Free

164   Children of a deportation train from Hungary, Auschwitz, October 1944.

165   Shooting of Yugoslav hostages in Panžewo near Belgrade in 1942.

Germany" could be secured for the first time during the night of June 11, 1944 in the vicinity of Munkacs.

Veesenmayer

Text 64

Memorandum of December 3, 1941 about a meeting held in the Reich Criminal Police Office and chaired by Heydrich, pertaining to the use of foreign workers in the German Reich

Memorandum

Subject: Use of foreign workers in the Reich.

A meeting concerning the above subject was held at 11 a.m. on December 3, 1941 in the Reich Criminal Police Office under the chairmanship of SS Lieutenant General and General of Police Heydrich. Approximately 45 to 50 representatives of different administrative agencies were present, among them [those of] the Party Chancellory, Ministry East, Foreign Office, Reich Ministry of Economics, Reich Ministry of Labor, the counterin-

telligence and armament departments of the Army Supreme Command, the Main Office of General Police, the Reich Security Main Office, the offices of the Reich Commissioner for Strengthening Germanism, and the Reich Governor [*Reichsstatthalter*] of Hamburg, the German Labor Front and the Association of Farmers and Agricultural Workers [*Reichsnährstand*] (Department Head Dr. Hatesaul, Councillor Dr. Wittern, Councillor Schwarz).

H. pointed out that roughly 9 million foreign people (among them ca. 6.5 million prisoners of war) are living on German territory. They constitute a danger in many respects and require special attention, given our present nerve-wracking times. Special mention was made of the economic aspects (increasing production and defense against sabotage) as well as the danger of infiltration. While there is no doubt that the economic concerns are entirely relevant we must at the same time firmly reject all attempts to postpone questions of race and ethnic identity [*Volkstum*] until after the war, as the duration of the war is uncertain, and danger increases as time passes.

Unfortunately, deployment of foreigners [for labor] has been started without any guidelines regarding their recruitment, deployment, treatment, etc., with the result that it has become increasingly more difficult to intervene subsequently with a guiding hand. The deployment of Russians now in progress does offer such an opportunity, however, and must and will be utilized in view of the special dangers which these peoples pose.

One will have to distinguish between the following groups of foreigners:

1. Foreigners living inside the Reich: Poles and Czechs.

The Polish problem has been solved. The Czechs have not been screened. H. considers 40% to 60% of them suitable to be Germanized. Conceivably, some screening and separation can be achieved by means of their deployment for labor.

3. [= 2.] Recruited labor forces from the occupied territories of the same ethnic origins: Flemings, Dutch, Danes, Norwegians.

3. Ethnically alien nationals from friendly countries (Italians, Spaniards, Croats, Slovaks, Hungarians, Bulgarians).

4. Other nationals who are ethnically alien.

Since it has been established that most difficulties in the way of their treatment and deployment are caused precisely by persons from friendly nations, we must try, according to the Führer's views, to replace them as far as possible with personnel from the territory we have occupied and, since these people will then be within reach of the executive, keep and deploy them on the prisoner of war level (low wages, housing in barracks). This will also be the easiest method to reduce racial [*völkische*] dangers, as they will have to spend their leisure time in the barracks as well. H. mentioned in this context a private deal with the Italian Head of Police and an appeal, now in the stage of preparation, to the sense of honor of our brothers in arms to keep their distance from the wives of absent [German] frontline soldiers.

There are quite a number of measures which in part will have to become effective upon short notice if the deployment of Russians [for labor] is to proceed with the least possible danger and difficulty. The barrack camps for the Russians must be ready for occupancy the minute they arrive; otherwise the workers will scatter and will be lost. The camp regulations must also be ready in clear language, above all because of the hygenic aspects that must be taken into consideration. During deployment [for labor], a separation between Russians and German workers, male and female, will hardly be possible, even at the risk of thereby losing some valuable German workers. Thus, the inner defenses at the place of work must be strengthened in order to undercut by all available means any possible feelings of solidarity with the Russians that may arise on the German side, and to prevent sabotage and espionage. Racial dangers will likewise increase, since working together in groups cannot be avoided, and since most enterprises employ many female workers. Distinguishing marks for peoples from the east must be clarified, whereby certain differentiations

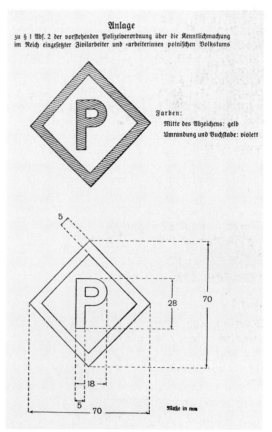

166   Stipulation for the distinguishing patch that Polish "civilian male and female workers" were forced to wear, 1940. The text above reads: Appendix to article 1, paragraph 2, concerning police ordinance about marking civilian male and female workers of Polish ethnicity deployed in the Reich. Next to the large P is this inscription:
Colors:
Background of patch: yellow
Border and letter: violet
Below, next to graph:
Scale in millimeters.

must be observed; for instance, "east" will be the general marking, with a supplementary one for the old-Russian territories. At the same time, though, all impulses aiming at independence [e.g., the Ukrainians] must thereby be neither supported nor advanced. The sole criterion on which decisions should be based proceeds from the viewpoint that the greatest possible advantages must be attained for the German war economy. [...]

Text 65

Police Ordinance of March 8, 1940 pertaining to the wearing of a distinguishing patch by all civilian male and female workers of Polish ethnicity who are deployed in the Reich

By authority of the ordinance relating to the police ordinances of the Reich Ministers of November 14, 1938 (*Reichsgesetzblatt* I, p. 1582), it is decreed:

§ 1
(1) Male and female workers of Polish ethnicity who are or will be deployed on German territory for rendering civilian labor services must wear at all times on the right side of each article of their clothing and firmly affixed to it at chest height a distinguishing patch that must be visible at all times.
(2) The distinguishing patch consists of a tilted square, pointing downward, with sides of five centimeters in length, that displays on a yellow background a violet letter "P", two and a half centimeters high, surrounded by a violet border one half centimeter wide.

§ 2
(1) Whoever violates the regulation of § 1 either intentionally or through carelessness will be penalized by a fine of up to 150 Reichsmarks or a prison term of up to six weeks.
(2) Any provisons of the penal code that call for a heavier punishment as well as security measures by the police remain unchanged.

§ 3
All legal and administrative provisions essential for the execution and realization of this police ordinance will be issued by the *Reichsführer-SS* and Head of German Police in the Reich Ministry of the Interior.

§ 4
The ordinance applies to the territory of the Greater German Reich except for those eastern territories that have been annexed by the Reich.

§ 5
The ordinance will become effective three weeks after it has been promulgated.

Berlin, March 8, 1940.
Reich Minister of the Interior
Acting as Deputy H. Himmler

Text 66

It is one of our most dangerous self-delusions that we, as adults, consider ourselves immune to inhumane actions, and this only because we are living on the whole under average social conditions and are not, for instance, being seduced to resort to massive destructive activities. It has been shown that under exceptional social conditions or even in connection with laboratory experiments, a majority of people of all social strata can be diverted from following such significant moral principles with which the persons concerned had always believed to identify. The extent to which human behavior in the moral sphere can be influenced is so extreme that it is obviously no longer compatible with our general sense of self-worth and, for this reason, will commonly be flatly denied.

Horst Eberhard Richter

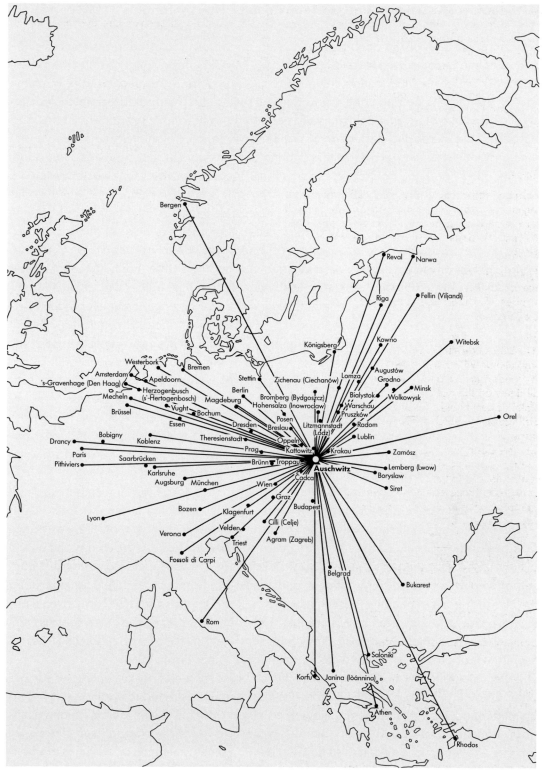

167   General map of cities from which prisoner transports
went to Auschwitz.

4.7. Political Resistance and Gestapo Prison ["Hausgefängnis"] (1939–45)

With the outbreak of the Second World War, conditions for offering resistance to the Nazi Regime became even more difficult. Many Germans stood solidly behind the system [of state], under the intoxicating influence of military victories as much as later on in the face of threatening defeat. Others considered it their duty to support the political leadership in times of war, even though they did not belong to its fanatic supporters. To this must be added the increasing perfection of police surveillance, heightened persecution, and the constantly mounting excessiveness of penalties for oppositional behavior of any kind. On the other hand, the political spectrum of the Resistance Movement was broadening. During the inital years [of National Socialist rule] it had been comprised nearly exclusively of members of the working class and a few clergymen, the latter having been driven by their conscience into an oppositional stance to the official policies of the established churches. Yet opposition had gradually developed also within various circles of the national-conservative power elites who initially had followed Hitler but had changed their minds as a result of his war policies and the crimes that the regime was committing increasingly more brazenly. Thus, one finds during the war among the enemies of the Nazi system martyrs of conscience, based on either Christian or Socialist conviction; militant democrats as well as opponents of a nationalist bent; and, at the very end of the spectrum, opportunists who tried to switch sides in the face of the predictable denouement. Under the impact of existing developments, the Resistance Movement was forced to draw consequences that for many of its members came only at the end of a long process of disenchantment. Some came down on the side of tyrannicide, hoping by this means to save the state and to create a new beginning in the inner political sphere. Others opted for sabotage and military treason after having reached the conclusion that liberation from the Nazi yoke was only possible at the price of military defeat.

Since the outbreak of war, many individual fighters like Georg Elser or members of small resistance groups like Robert Havemann were held in detention in the *Gestapo* Prison ["*Hausgefängnis*"]. Most prominently represented were members of the Resistance Group Harnack/Schulze-Boysen ("Red Orchestra") and the various groupings of the 20th of July, 1944, that ranged from the Socialists and the "Kreisau Circle" to nationalist-conservative public officials, high officers, and specialists from Counterintelligence. During the investigations, especially those involving the "Red Orchestra" in 1942, and even more so those that followed after the 20th of July, 1944, the *Gestapo* Prison ["*Hausgefängnis*"] proved much too small. As a result, many prisoners were taken to Prinz-Albrecht-Strasse 8 for interrogation only, but were held in detention in other Berlin jails.

This documentation of political prisoners which presents a number of "witnesses for another Germany" by means of brief portraits must remain restricted to examples. It should be mentioned, though, that during the war prisoners from the Soviet Union, Poland, Hungary, Czechoslovakia and other countries were held in the *Gestapo* Prison ["Hausgefängnis"] as well, but any personal data as to their names, numbers, or destinies are nonexistent.

168 **Johann Georg Elser** (1903—1945), on November 13—14, 1939, during an interrogation by the "Special Commission Assassination Attempt Bürgerbräu" [the attempt made on Hitler's life in said beer hall a few days earlier].

He was a cabinetmaker and carpenter of artistic furniture who at the end of the 1920s sympathized with the German Communist Party and was a member of the League of Red Frontline Fighters [*Roter Frontkämpferbund*]. During the "Sudeten Crisis" in 1938 he decided to make an assassination attempt on Hitler's life. On November 8, 1939, a time bomb which he had built and installed exploded in the Bürgerbräu beer hall in Munich. It killed eight people; Hitler had left the room a few minutes before the explosion. Elser was arrested the same evening and was first interrogated by a special commission of *Gestapo* and Criminal Police officials in Munich. Then the *Gestapo* alone took charge of the inquiry and interrogated Elser from November 19 through 23, 1939 at Prinz-Albrecht-Strasse 8. At the conclusion of the interrogations he was sent to Concentration Camp Sachsenhausen, subsequently to Dachau. There he was murdered on April 9, 1945, according to instructions from the Secret State Police Office.

In 1940 Braune was Vice President of the Central Committee for the Inner Mission of the German Protestant Church. He was arrested on August 12, 1940, because of his open opposition to the murder of the mentally handicapped of which he had learned as Director of the Hoffnungstal Institutions near Berlin. He was kept for three months at Prinz-Albrecht-Strasse 8 by the *Gestapo*, but was subsequently released on probation. After the war, Braune remained until his death director of the Hoffnungstal Institutions, Canon of Brandenburg, and a member of the presidium of the German Protestant Church.

170 **Rudolf Breitscheid** (1874—1944), 1943 in Concentration Camp Buchenwald.

Doctor of philosophy, he was a member of the SPD from 1912 on; 1917—1922 member of the USPD; 1918—1919 Prussian Minister of the Interior; 1929—1933 Reichstag delegate, 1928—1933 chairman of the SPD delegation. While in exile in Paris, Breitscheid advocated the creation of a popular front against Hitler.

He was arrested end of 1940 in southern France and handed over to the *Gestapo*. He was kept imprisoned at Prinz-Albrecht-Strasse 8 from February 13, 1941 until January 9, 1942. From there he was transferred to Concentration Camp Sachsenhausen, subsequently to Buchenwald, where he perished on August 24, 1944 during an aerial attack.

169 **Paul Gerhard Braune** (1887—1954), after 1945

171 **Kurt Lehmann** (born 1906), around 1944. Prior to

1933 he was a functionary of the merchant marine union [*See-leute-Gewerkschaft*] in Hamburg. Went into exile in Holland in May 1933 and together with his brother Werner (1904–1941) was active in union-based resistance against the Nazi Regime – with the support of the Federation of International Transport Workers (ITF). Both fought in the Spanish Civil War in 1936.

In 1939, both Kurt and Werner Lehmann were interned in France, and in 1941 were handed over to the *Gestapo*. On August 20 they were taken to Prinz-Albrecht-Strasse 8. Werner Lehmann died there on September 21, 1941 under circumstances that so far have not been completely cleared up, probably by way of suicide. Kurt Lehmann remained in the basement prison until July 1943. Thereafter he was held in pretrial detention at Moabit, in Plötzensee Prison, and in the penitentiaries at Amberg and Straubing. After 1945 Kurt Lehmann was a public service employee.

172 Harro Schulze-Boysen (1904–1942) and **Libertas Schulze-Boysen**, née Haas-Heye (1913–1942), end of the 1930s.

H.Schulze-Boysen:

He was a member of the "Young German Order" [*Jungdeutscher Orden*] and from 1932 on publisher of the journal *Der Gegner* which was banned in April 1933. He was temporarily arrested in 1933 and brutally maltreated by Stormtroopers while in detention. In a resistance group which the *Gestapo* had named "Red Orchestra" [*Rote Kapelle*] he and Arvid Harnack occupied key positions. Since 1941, while a first lieutenant in the Reich Air Force Ministry, he transmitted military information to the Soviet Union. He also wrote articles for the underground newspaper *Die Innere Front* and organized illegal operations of distributing leaflets and putting up anti-Nazi posters.

After his arrest on August 30, 1942 he was taken to Prinz-Albrecht-Strasse 8 where he was interrogated and tortured by the *Gestapo*, as were Arvid and Mildred Harnack, Adam Kuckhoff, and other members of the group. He remained in the *Gestapo* Prison (*Hausgefängnis*) until he was sentenced on December 19; he was executed in Plötzensee Prison on December 22, 1942.

L. Schulze-Boysen:

Until 1935 she worked in the press section of Metro-Goldwyn-Mayer in Berlin as an assistant, then as a freelancing journalist, and subsequently as a staff member of the Berlin Cultural Film Center. In 1936 she married Harro Schulze-Boysen and, together with her husband and Arvid Harnack, was one of the most important members of their resistance group. After her arrest on September 3, 1942 she was interrogated at Prinz-Albrecht-Strasse 8 by the *Gestapo*. She was condemned to death, together with her husband, and was executed in Plötzensee Prison on December 22, 1942.

173   **Arvid Harnack** (1901–1942), in 1942 while in *Gestapo* detention.

Doctor of Law. Worked from 1935 on in the Reich Ministry of Economics, eventually as Senior Executive Officer [*Oberregierungsrat*]. Prior to 1933, Harnack was a co-founder and general secretary of a "work study group for investigating Soviet Russia's planned economy". Next to Harro Schulze-Boysen, he was a central figure in the resistance group "Red Orchestra". Together with his wife, Mildred Harnack-Fish, he was arrested on September 7, 1942, and imprisoned at Prinz-Albrecht-Strasse 8. Arvid Harnack was also one of the members of this resistance group who was tortured by the *Gestapo*. He was sentenced to death on December 19, and executed in Plötzensee Prison on December 22, 1942.

174   **Mildred Harnack-Fish**, née Fish (1902–1943) in 1942 while in *Gestapo* detention.

Doctor of philosophy, she grew up in USA. Taught modern American literature at the University of Wisconsin, in Madison. After she had moved to Berlin she worked as a translator, as a reader for a publishing house, and taught at Berlin University. Like her husband she belonged to the resistance group of Harro Schulze-Boysen.

On September 7, 1942 she and her husband were arrested and imprisoned at Prinz-Albrecht-Strasse 8. Like many members of the group, she was tortured during interrogations. The sentence of six years of penitentiary imprisonment which the Reich War Tribunal handed down was set aside on Hitler's order. In new proceedings another division of the Reich War Tribunal sentenced her to death on January 16, and she was executed in Plötzensee Prison on February 16, 1943.

175   **Greta Kuckhoff**, née Lorke (1902–1981), around 1946.

Teacher. In 1924, she began a supplementary study of national economy. Study trip to USA where she met Arvid Harnack and Mildred Fish. Worked from 1933 on as a translator and interpreter. In 1937 she married Adam Kuckhoff. Greta Kuckhoff was aware of the activities of the resistance group "Red Orchestra" and supported them. She was arrested on September 12, 1942 and was interrogated at Prinz-Albrecht-Strasse 8. But, like most women in this group, she was held in detention in the prison of police headquarters on Alexanderplatz. The death sentence that the Reich War Tribunal handed to her was commuted in May 1943 into a sentence of ten years in a penitentiary. She remained in the penitentiary of Cottbus until her liberation.

After 1945 Greta Kuckhoff joined the Socialist Unity Party [*Sozialistische Einheitspartei*, or SED], was a delegate to the parliament of the German Democratic Republic from 1949 to 1958, and from 1950 to 1958 President of the GDR's Central Bank [*Notenbank*].

176   **Adam Kuckhoff** (1887–1943), in 1934
Doctor of philosophy. In 1927 he founded the Theater of Artists in Frankfurt am Main. 1928 to 1929 chief editor of the journal *Die Tat*. From 1930–1932 director [*Spielleiter*] at the National Theater [*Staatstheater*] in Berlin, later working for the most part as a reader for publishing houses and as an author. He had close contacts with Arvid and Mildred Harnack as well as with Harro Schulze-Boysen. Actively involved in resistance, he was, among others, editor of the underground newspaper *Die Innere Front*. Kuckhoff was arrested in Prague on September 12, 1942 and was subsequently held in detention at Prinz-Albrecht-Strasse 8. He was sentenced to death by the Reich War Tribunal and executed in Plötzensee Prison on August 5, 1943.

Sculptor. Senior pupil [*Meisterschüler*] of Ludwig Gies. Won the Prussian State Award in 1931. Until the building was taken over by the *Gestapo*, he worked in a studio of the former School of Industrial Arts and Crafts at Prinz-Albrecht-Strasse 8. Schumacher and his wife Elisabeth, née Hohenemser (1904–1942) participated in the resistance activities of "Red Orchestra". Kurt and Elisabeth Schumacher were arrested in September 1942. He was taken to the *Gestapo* Prison ("*Hausgefängnis*") at Prinz-Albrecht-Strasse 8, she to the Police Prison on Alexanderplatz. Both were sentenced to death on December 19 and executed in Plötzensee Prison on December 22, 1942.

Text 67

Because I got nabbed when I was trying to deliver a note for Harro to a Frenchman by slipping it into the slot through which we get our food, I was deprived of everything – my own books from here, all writing material, even the picture my beloved Elisabeth drew of our two faces. It is so good that its destruction would be a real pity. Even the poor little walk I can no longer take; I cannot get any mail or packages. All this started ten days ago. At times it is nearly unbearable and I think at times with horror of the women, of Elisabeth, at the Alex (i. g. Alexanderplatz). She is not allowed any reading material, as she wrote me, and for reasons of economy has no light, either ... We are fighting for our cause.
In fetters, November 2, 1942   Kurt Schumacher

177   **Kurt Schumacher** (1905–1942), 1931 as recipient of the Prussian State Award.

178   **Günther Weisenborn** (1902–1969), around 1950.
Dramatist and novelist. In 1922 study of medicine, German lit-

erature and philosophy. In 1928 opening night of "Submarine S 4" at the Berlin *Volksbühne*. From 1930 on he worked with Brecht and Eisler, among others. In 1937 his first encounter with Harro Schulze-Boysen. Worked for Metro-Goldwyn-Mayer. In 1941 senior dramatic adviser at the Schiller Theater in Berlin. Resistance activities with the "Red Orchestra" group. Weisenborn, together with his wife, was arrested on September 26, 1942 and was initially imprisoned at Prinz-Albrecht-Strasse 8 where he stayed until October 20th. After a brief interlude in Spandau Prison he was returned there and remained for several months in solitary confinement, except for another brief stay in Spandau in February 1943. He was sentenced to three years in a penitentiary by the Reich War Tribunal and remained in the penitentiary of Luckau, Lower Lusatia, until his liberation in 1945.

After 1945 he did theater work in Berlin and Hamburg. He had numerous literary publications. In 1953 he published a book about the German Resistance Movement (The Silent Rebellion [*Der lautlose Aufstand*]).

Text 68

When one must spend one's day sitting on a footstool, in fetters, in a completely unheated basement cell, without a book, hungry, virtually in the dark, one is almost embarrassed to think about the progress that mankind has made. Everything that once constituted the world has been eliminated with cunning meticulousness. You can hardly discern anything because the light in the hall reaches only through a miniscule frosted glass plane. You hear nothing but the deadly silence of those perilous basements. You are weak from hunger, nearly senseless from having frozen for months, miserable, filthy, alone. And you analyze with the precision of what still remains of your brain that this is a deadly method indeed, leading after all this misery to the disintegration of one's personality. Entire sections collapse without a sound. This system of justice is perfect in its complex desire to destroy. Its three stages are: first, the destruction of the circumstances under which you have lived. Second, the obliteration of your personality and, finally, your physical annihilation by the cheapest possible means. [...] At 4 p.m. the slot at my door drops open. The SS guard shouts: "You'll be picked up shortly..." and then follow the terrible words: ... "for interrogation."

I sit as if I were paralyzed. My heart starts pounding. Then I begin feverishly to review my strategy once again. And if he asks this, and that? And if he wants to know this, and wants to know that? Quick. You'll be picked up in a moment. It is 5 p.m. I sit there, my teeth clenched in an iron grip, determined, sparked with energy, tense, and ready for battle. Again and again my thoughts race through all the possibilities. Now it is 6 p.m., time for the evening soup. After supper a hasty walk within the

179   **Adolf Grimme** (1889–1963), around 1930.
A member of the SPD from 1918 on he was Prussian Minister for Advanced Knowledge [*Wissenschaft*], Art and National Education from 1930–1932, and a delegate to the Prussian diet from 1932 to 1933.
In the course of the *Gestapo*'s investigations of the resistance group "Red Orchestra", Grimme, a friend of Adam Kuckhoff, was arrested on October 11, 1942. Until his trial on Febrary 1 and 2, 1943 he remained in the *Gestapo* Prison ("*Hausgefängnis*") at Prinz-Albrecht-Strasse 8. He was sentenced to three years in a penitentiary on February 3, 1943 and was imprisoned consecutively in Spandau, Luckau/Lusatia, and Fuhlsbüttel.
From 1946 to 1948 Grimme was Minister for Cultural Affairs in the Land Hanover/Lower Saxony. From 1948 to 1956 he chaired the governing board of the Northwest German Broadcasting Station was also its managing director.

cell. My thoughts race, spin in circles. I am getting tired. It is 8 p.m.

I am lying on my cot, ready to jump up at once. My thoughts begin to get muddled. The cell is cold and I am freezing like a dog. From the outside I can hear the clock strike 10 p.m. I've had it.

I no longer know what to do. Everything seems so senseless! The clock strikes 11 p.m. I am nearly paralyzed from wasted energy. Nothing matters anymore. I am lying with my eyes open. The clock strikes midnight. They won't come anymore, and if they do, it won't matter. Tired, I am tired. Finally, around 1:30 a.m., I hear keys rattling, the door opens. A pale, nasty looking SS guard:

"Let's go, come along, interrogation!"

I get up, completely bushed, go with him.

An alert, well-rested man is of no use to the interrogator. He wants one who has lost his nerve before it even starts.

Günther Weisenborn

180   John Sieg (1903–1942), 1942 in *Gestapo* detention. Born and grew up in USA where he was an active union member between 1923 and 1928. From 1928 on in Germany where he joined the KPD in 1929. Wrote for *Berliner Tageblatt, Vossische Zeitung, Die Tat* and *Der Gegner.* He also worked on *Die Rote Fahne,* central organ of the German Communist Party, shortly before that paper was banned. He was imprisoned from March to June 1933. Joined the resistance group "Red Orchestra" and wrote for its underground newspaper, *Die Innere Front.*

Sieg was arrest by the *Gestapo* on October 11, 1942. After the first interrogations he committed suicide on October 15, 1942 at Prinz-Albrecht-Straße 8.

181   Max Josef Metzger (1887–1944), around 1940. Doctor of Divinity, Catholic theologian and pacifist. In 1917 he founded the "World Peace League of the White Cross" [*Weltfriedensbund vom Weißen Kreuz*] whose German affiliate became the "Peace League of German Catholics" [*Friedensbund deutscher Katholiken*]. In 1919 he founded the "Mission Society of the White Cross" [*Missionsgesellschaft vom Weißen Kreuz*] (since 1927 "Christ is King Society" [*Christkönigsgesellschaft*] and 1939 the unitary brotherhood *Una Sancta.* Metzger, who had already been arrested in January 1934 because of his publication "The Church and the new Germany" and who had spent a second period in prison, from November 9 until December 12, 1943, was arrested again by the *Gestapo* in Berlin on June 29, 1934 and was taken to Prinz-Albrecht-Strasse 8 where he stayed until September 11, 1943. Because of his political contacts to the Archbishop of Uppsala he was sentenced to death on October 14, 1943, and executed in Brandenburg Penitentiary on April 17, 1944.

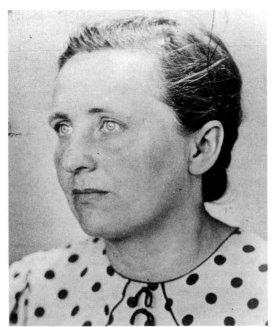

182   Charlotte Hundt, née Thiele (1900–1943). This stenographer from Berlin-Wittenau was arrested by the *Gestapo* on March 17, 1943 because she had helped a former Berlin Communist, Ernst Beuthke, who had emigrated to the Soviet Union in 1933 and who had parachuted into Germany around the turn of the year 1942/1943. On Himmler's orders she and fourteen other persons who had been arrested in this connection were murdered in September 1943 in Concentration Camp Sachsenhausen without the benefit of a trial.

183   **Robert Havemann** (1910—1982), around 1947. Doctor of Philosophy. In 1932 he joined the German Communist Party; from 1933 on he was active in the Resistance Movement, and in 1939 joined the "European Union," a group that developed on the initiative of Dr. Georg Groscurth.
Havemann was arrested on September 5, 1943 and — like Dr. Groscurth as well — was taken to the *Gestapo* Prison ("*Hausgefängnis*") at Prinz-Albrecht-Strasse 8. On December 16, 1943 the People's Court sentenced him to death. The execution was postponed twice so as to enable him to continue with his scholarly research that was deemed important for the war effort. Havemann was in Brandenburg Penitentiary when he was liberated. From 1945 to 1950 he was Director of the Kaiser-Wilhelm-Institut in Berlin-Dahlem and Professor of Physiochemical Science at Humboldt University. From 1950 until 1963 he was a delegate to the parliament [*Volkskammer*] of the German Democratic Republic. In 1966 he was expelled from the Academy of Sciences. When troops of the Warsaw Pact marched into Czechoslovakia in 1968, he sharply criticized this move, among others. He was then deprived of all job opportunities and was stripped of his official posts. He remained under "house arrest" until his death in 1982.

Text 69

The interrogations were held on Prinz-Albrecht-Strasse where I, too, was imprisoned, in cell no. 24, in the basement. They lasted until mid-November, thus roughly two and a half months. I knew, of course, from the outset that there could be only one particular penalty. That's why I was able to behave in a relatively simple manner. The *Gestapo* tried continuously to keep my hopes up. The interrogator always said: "Why act as if you were running around here sort of carrying your head under your arm," to which I would reply: "Well, you have sentenced people to death for

merely listening to enemy broadcasts. You can imagine that I, for one, won't deny that I have listened very eagerly to the so-called 'enemy' broadcasting stations." Initially we were mistreated of course; they always started out that way. I believed from the start that it would be a mistake to react to maltreatment [i.e. torture] in any way whatsoever. Later on I heard from others that those who reacted to maltreatment were subsequently manhandled to an even worse degree. However, I told the people who beat and tortured me that their efforts to inflict pain were ridiculous; that under certain psychological conditions people do not feel the pain inflicted upon them; that a soldier may have a leg torn off in battle by a cannon ball, but he would only notice this while trying to walk — and similar chitchat. Anyway, I believe that it was vitally important to adopt such an attitude vis-a-vis the *Gestapo* interrogators: I had to have them believe that I was fearless, had to impress them somehow. In such situations it is essential that people who treat someone unjustly gain tremendous respect for him. This way one can keep such people at arm's length.

Robert Havemann

184   **Max Sievers** (1887—1944), probably in exile. Member of the SPD, then of the USPD. 1920—1921 he was a member of the German Communist Party and editor of the *Rote Fahne*. In March 1921 he rejoined the SPD. From 1922 to 1936 he was Secretary of the Association of Freethinkers [Atheists], and from 1930 to 1933 its chairman and also editor of the journal *Der Freidenker*. In 1933, Sievers spent three

Monat _Jan._ 19 44   Dienſtſtelle _IV A 5 b_

Am ____ von ____ in bar zur Verfügung geſtellt: ____ RM.

Lfd. Nr.	Akten- zeichen	Kurze Sachbezeichnung:	Tag der Aus- gabe	Verausgabender Beamter:	Betrag: Überpauſchalen Bewegungsgeld RM Pf	für*)	Beſondere Fahndunge- hoſten RM Pf	Grund der Ausgabe und Erfolg:	Erſtattet am: Quittung:	Bemerkungen:
				Übertrag:	266 85					
34	699/44	Herm. Romanowski	2/2	Kos Neundorf	8 84			Fahndung	Neundorf	
35	402/33	Sondersache	24/2	Kos Wenmann	5 60			Ermittlungen	Wenmann	
36		Erich Müller	2/2	Kos Ast	2 80			Ermittlungen	Ast	
37	391/44	Egon	2/2	Kos Knuth	5 70			Ermittlungen	Knuth	
38		Hasslaub	24/2	Kr. Müller	9 30			Ermittlungen	Müller	
39	310/43	Alfred Hoffmann	19/2	K7 Fende	10 60			Vertrauliche Ermittlungen	Fende	
40	446/00	Caroline Oslage	17/2	Kos Knuth	5 10			Ermittlungen	Knuth	
41	200/44	Sonderauftrag	17/2	K.R. Sanders	19 90			Ermittlungen	Sanders	
42	"	Sondersache "20 Juli"	2/2	Kos Fene	7 20			Vorbereitung zur Festnahme	Fene	
43	"	Sondersache "20 Juli"	24/2	Kos Vatteroth	10 10			Vorbereitung zur Festnahme	Vatteroth	
44	396/00	Herm. Schmitz	24/2	Kos Knuth	6 20			Ermittlungen	Knuth	
45	721/44	Erna Linden	24/2	Kos Ast	4 60			Ermittlungen	Ast	
46	1530/44	Mäbring		KR Müller	5 80			Ermittlungen	Müller	
47	446/44	Walter Deoth	24/2	Kos Knuth	3 80			Ermittlungen	Knuth	
48	"	Sondersache "20 Juli"	24/7	RA Ratte	7 40			Vorbereitung zur Festnahme	Müller	
49	773/44	Paul Wickerle	18/2	Kos Ast	4 50			Vorbereitung zur Festnahme	Ast	
				Übertrag:	384, 05					

185   An account of expenses incurred by *Gestapo* Section IV A 5 b, in connection with investigations (among others, "Special Case July 20th").

„weeks in "protective custody" and went into exile in April 1933. From 1933 to 1934 he was director of "Freethinkers International" in Brussels. After 1933 he financed various exile publications which were illegally distributed inside the German Reich. From May 1940 on, Sievers was interned consecutively in Belgium and France. Subsequently, while on his way to escape, he was arrested by the *Gestapo* in June 1943 and taken to Prinz-Albrecht-Strasse 8. On November 17 he was sentenced to death and executed in Brandenburg Penitentiary on January 17, 1944.

186 Dietrich Bonhoeffer (1906–1945), 1944 in Tegel Prison.

Doctor of Philosophy and Protestant theologian. Spent from 1933 to 1935 in England, and in 1935 became director of the Theological Seminary of the Confessional Church in Finkenwalde/Pomerania. In 1936, as a leading member of the Confessional Church, he was forbidden to teach. In 1940 he was forbidden to lecture or publish. Bonhoeffer proceeded to move from religious to political resistance and worked together with groups of the military opposition. In May 1942, as a representative of the German Resistance Movement, he met with the Bishop of Chichester in Sweden.

Bonhoeffer was arrested by the *Gestapo* on April 5, 1943. Until October 8, 1944 he remained imprisoned in Berlin-Tegel and was then transferred to Prinz-Albrecht-Strasse 8. On February 7, 1945 he was taken to Concentration Camp Buchenwald, from there to Schönberg, finally to Flossenbürg. There he was murdered on April 9, 1945, together with Canaris, Oster, and others.

187 Count Helmuth James von Moltke (1907–1945), on January 9/11, 1945, before the People's Court.

Member of the legal profession. Lived abroad frequently. From 1935 to 1939 he practiced law in Berlin. In 1939 he became a councillor for war administration [*Kriegsverwaltungsrat*] in the Department "Foreign Countries/Counterintelligence" at the Supreme Command of the Armed Forces. There he was also active as an expert for the law of war and international law. Moltke was a decided opponent of the Nazi Regime. From 1940 on he assembled numerous younger opponents of various political origins and views who met repeatedly on his Silesian estate Kreisau (thus, "Kreisau Circle") where they worked on plans for reforms and reorganization in a Germany after Hitler. Manifold ties to other resistance groups existed as well.

Moltke was arrested on January 19, 1944, and taken to Prinz-Albrecht-Strasse 8. On February 7 he was imprisoned in Concentration Camp Ravensbrück, and subsequently was transferred to Tegel Prison. Sentenced to death by the People's Court he was executed in Plötzensee Prison on January 23, 1945.

189   **Adolf Reichwein** (1898–1944), on October 20, 1944, before the People's Court.
Doctor of Philosophy. After 1930 member of the SPD. 1929/1930 personal assistant to the Prussian Minister of Culture, Becker. From 1930 to 1933 Professor of History and Civics at the Teacher's Academy in Halle/Saale. In 1933 teacher at a village school in Tiefensee, near Berlin. Reichwein had very close contacts to Helmuth von Moltke and other members of the "Kreisau Circle;" in case of a successful coup, he was slated to become Minister of Culture.
In a joint attempt with Julius Leber to establish contact with the Communist Resistance, he was arrested on July 4, 1944 and initially confined in Brandenburg Penitentiary. From there he was taken to Berlin for interrogation, probably to Prinz-Albrecht-Strasse 8. After August 15, 1944 he was held in detention in the Lehrter Strasse Prison, and from October 14, 1944 on he was in the *Gestapo* Prison ("*Hausgefängnis*") at Prinz-Albrecht-Strasse 8. On October 20, 1944 the People's Court sentenced him to death and he was executed the same day in Plötzensee Prison.

188   **Julius Leber** (1891–1945), on October 20, 1944, before the People's Court.
Doctor of Political Science. From 1913 on member of the SPD. From 1921 until 1933 member of Lübeck's city parliament [*Bürgerschaft*] and Chief Editor of the Social Democratic newspaper *Lübecker Volksbote*. Also Reichstag delegate from 1924 to 1933. As early as 1933 Leber was repeatedly being arrested and spent from June 1933 until May 1937 in various prisons and concentration camps. He was one of the leading figures in the German Resistance Movement and worked together with the military opposition, the group around Goerdeler and with the "Kreisau Circle." In case of a successful coup, Leber was slated to head the Ministry of the Interior.
On July 5, 1944 he was arrested once again. After confinement in Brandenburg Penitentiary, in the Security Police Academy in Drögen/Mecklenburg, in Concentration Camp Ravensbrück (in the so-called "*Zellenbau*"), and in the Lehrter Strasse Prison in Berlin, he was presumably confined from October 14, 1944 on at Prinz-Albrecht-Strasse 8. On October 20, 1944 he was sentenced to death, and executed in Plötzensee Prison on January 5, 1945.

190   **Gustav Dahrendorf** (1901–1954), on October 20, 1944, before the People's Court.
Member of the SPD from 1918 on. From 1928–1933 member of the Hamburg city government, 1932–1933 delegate to the Reichstag. From 1921 to 1933 he was a member of the Social Democratic executive board of Hamburg.
From May to July 1933, Dahrendorf was in Concentration Camp Fuhlsbüttel. After 1934 he lived in Berlin where he sub-

sequently worked in a leading capacity, at the Preussag. He had close contacts to Leber, Leuschner, and other Social Democrats and labor unions connected with what was to become the "20th of July conspiracy."

He was arrested on July 23, 1944 and, after having stayed in detention in Concentration Camp Ravensbrück and the Lehrter Strasse Prison, he was taken to Prinz-Albrecht-Strasse 8 on October 14, 1944. On October 20, 1944, he was sentenced to serve seven years in a penitentiary and was confined to Brandenburg Penitentiary, where he was liberated in April 1945.

In 1945 he became a member of the Central Committee of the SPD in Berlin. From 1947 to 1949 he served as Vice President of the Economic Council for the three western zones.

191   Count Peter Yorck von Wartenburg (1904—1944), on August 7/8, 1944, before the People's Court.

Doctor of Law. After the completion of his studies he worked at first with a Berlin law firm. From 1931 to 1933 he was a Commissioner for Aid to the (German) East. In 1935 he became a senior executive officer at the Silesian chief administrative office in Breslau. From 1937 on he was in charge of a section on fundamental rules with the Reich Commissioner for Price Control, ultimately as chief executive officer. In 1942 he joined the Office of Defense Economy and Armaments at the Army High Command.

Next to Helmuth von Moltke, Count Peter Yorck von Wartenburg was the second leading figure in the "Kreisau Circle". In his and Countess Marion Yorck's apartment at Hortensienstrasse 50, in Lichterfelde, most of the meetings of the Circle took place. He was in close contact with Count Claus Schenk von Stauffenberg.

On July 20, 1944 he was arrested in a building on Bendlerstrasse where the Commandant of the Reserve Army had his office. Together with other arrestees he was taken to the *Gestapo* Prison ("*Hausgefängnis*") at Prinz-Albrecht-Strasse 8 where he was subsequently repeatedly interrogated. Thereafter he was kept imprisoned in various places of detention and in concentration camps, among others in Sachsenhausen, Ravensbrück, and the Police Prison on Lehrter Strasse. On August 8, 1944, the People's Court sentenced him to death. He was executed at Plötzensee Prison the same day.

192   Countess Marion Yorck von Wartenburg, née Winter (born 1904), around 1940. Doctor of Law.

After the completion of her studies she lived in Berlin and in 1930 married Count Peter Yorck von Wartenburg. She was a regular participant of all major conferences held by the "Kreisau Circle" and of the recurrent meetings at Hortensienstrasse 50 in Berlin.

After failure of the coup on July 20, 1944 and the arrest of her husband she tried in vain to obtain visiting rights which the *Gestapo* refused to grant her. She herself was arrested on August 10, 1944. The night from August 10 to August 11 she spent in a cell of the *Gestapo* Prison ("*Hausgefängnis*") at Prinz-Albrecht-Strasse 8 and was then transferred to the pretrial prison in Moabit where she was held for nearly three months.

In 1946 Countess Marion Yorck became a judge at Lichterfelde's lower district court. She became ultimately a presiding judge at Berlin's Superior Court in charge of the 9th Major Criminal Court for juveniles. She lives today in West Berlin.

193   Adam von Trott zu Solz (1909–1944), on August 15, 1944 before the People's Court.

Doctor of Law. After completion of his studies (including as a Cecil Rhodes Scholar at Oxford University) he spent time abroad, both in the United States and East Asia. In 1940 he was taken on as an "assistant research employee" [*wissenschaftlicher Hilfsarbeiter*] by the information department of the Foreign Office. In 1943 he became a Legation Secretary, then Legation Councillor in the Foreign Office.

Next to Moltke and Yorck, Trott was the third most important figure of the "Kreisau Circle". He participated in its conferences and meetings from the beginning on. His professional position enabled him to travel into both neutral and (German) occupied European countries. Especially during the late phase of resistance activities on the part of the "Kreisau Circle" he was for all practical purposes its foreign political expert. In the event of a successful coup on July 20, 1944 Trott was slated to become undersecretary of state in the Foreign Office. He was arrested on July 25, 1944 and taken to the *Gestapo* Prison ("*Hausgefängnis*") at Prinz-Albrecht-Strasse 8; thereafter he was held at Oranienburg Concentration Camp and the Police Prison on Lehrter Strasse. After three weeks of interrogations, for the most part held at *Gestapo* headquarters Prinz-Albrecht-Strasse 8, the People's Court sentenced him to death on August 15, 1944. After he had been sentenced, the *Gestapo* continued to interrogate him. Adam von Trott zu Solz was executed on August 26, 1944 at Plötzensee Prison.

194   Eugen Gerstenmaier (1906–1986), on January 9/11, 1945, before the People's Court.

Doctor of Divinity and from 1936 on a staff member of the Ecclesiastical Office for External Affairs of the Protestant Church; from 1939 on Director of the Ecumenical Section. From 1939 to 1942 he worked in the cultural-political department of the Foreign Office. Starting in 1942 he participated in the deliberations of the "Kreisau Circle" and had contacts, among others, to the resistance group around Oster und von Dohnanyi. Gerstenmaier was arrested on July 20, 1944, and taken to Prinz-Albrecht-Strasse 8. On July 22 he was transferred to the Lehrter Strasse Prison, subsequently to the Tegel Prison. The People's Court sentenced him on January 1, 1945 to seven years in a penitentiary. He was liberated in April 1945 while imprisoned in Bayreuth Penitentiary.

From 1945 until 1951 he directed the relief organization of the Protestant Church in Stuttgart. From 1949 until 1969 he was a CDU delegate in the parliament of the German Federal Republic. He was president of the *Bundestag* from 1954 to 1969, and Deputy Chairman of the CDU from 1956–1964.

195   Erwin Planck (1893–1945), on October 23, 1944, before the People's Court.

Son of the physicist Max Planck. Embarked upon an administrative career. 1932–1933 he was undersecretary in the Reich Chancellory but left state service in 1933 and worked next for the steel corporation Otto Wolff. Together with Goerdeler, Popitz, and others he prepared drafts of a constitution for a Germany after Hitler, and was also a contact and courier to frontline officers known to be in opposition.

He was arrested on July 23, 1944 and held prisoner at Prinz-Albrecht-Strasse 8. On October 23, 1944 he was sentenced to death and was executed in Plötzensee Prison on January 23, 1945.

196   Count Friedrich Werner von der Schulenburg
(1875—1944), on October 23, 1944, before the People's
Court.
A diplomat from 1901 on. Envoy in Teheran and Bucharest,
from 1934—1941 Ambassador in Moscow. He participated
prominently in the preparation of the German-Soviet Russian
Nonaggression Pact of 1939, and after the German invasion
of Russia in 1941 he worked hard for a separate peace and
negotiations with the Soviet Union. Schulenburg belonged to
the circle of "20th of July" conspirators and was slated to become foreign minister in a new government.
After his arrest he was imprisoned at Prinz-Albrecht-Strasse 8.
On October 23 he was sentenced to death and was executed
in Plötzensee Prison on November 10, 1944.

197   Ulrich von Hassell (1881—1944), on September 8,
1944, before the People's Court.
Diplomat. From 1918 to 1933 member of the German Nationalist Party [*Deutschnationale Volkspartei*]. From 1919—1921
Ambassador in Rome. Until 1926 Consul General in Barce-
lona. 1926—1930 Ambassador in Copenhagen. 1930—1932
Ambassador in Belgrade. 1932—1938 again Ambassador in

Rome. In 1938 he was retired from diplomatic service. Became
a member of the board of the influential "Central European
Economic Society" [*Mitteleuropäischer Wirtschaftstag*].
Hassel joined the resistance group around Beck and Goerdeler. In 1940 he negotiated in Switzerland as a spokesman
of the German Opposition. In Berlin he had close contacts with
the American chargé d'affaires, Kirk.
The *Gestapo* kept him under surveillance starting in 1942. A
few days after the abortive coup of July 20, 1944, he was arrested and taken to Prinz-Albrecht-Strasse 8. He was sentenced to death on September 8, 1944 and executed the same
day.

198   Eugen Bolz (1881—1945), on December 21, 1944 before the People's Court.
Doctor of Law (honorary degree), lawyer. Politically active in
the Center Party. Member of the Reichstag from 1912 to 1933
and delegate to the Württemberg diet from 1913 to 1933.
Minister of Justice in Württemberg from 1919 to 1923. Minister of the Interior in Württemberg from 1923 to 1933. From
1928 to 1933 he was simultaneously President of the State of
Württemberg (*Staatspräsident*).
The first time Eugen Bolz was held in protective custody was
from June 19 until July 12, 1933. Since the end of 1941/begin-
ning of 1942, he had several meetings with Carl Friedrich
Goerdeler. In the event of a successful coup, Bolz was slated
to become minister of culture, at times also minister of the interior. He was in contact with other active members of the Resistance from the former Center Party, such as Hermes, Kaiser,
Wirmer, Ersing, Helene Weber and Christine Teusch.
He was arrested on August 12, 1944, was taken to Berlin on
August 27, 1944 and for several days was held prisoner in the
Gestapo Prison ("*Hausgefängnis*") at Prinz-Albrecht-Strasse
8. Thereafter he was held in a cell at Ravensbrück Concentration Camp and was tortured during interrogations at the Security Police Academy in Drögen. From November 2, 1944 on
he was imprisoned in the Police Prison on Lehrter Strasse. The
People's Court sentenced Eugen Bolz to death on December
21, 1944. He was executed in Plötzensee Prison on January
23, 1945.

200   Carl Friedrich Goerdeler (1884–1945), on September 8, 1944, before the People's Court.
Jurist and professional administrator. Member of the German Nationalist Party. From 1920 to 1930 Second Mayor of Königsberg. 1930–1937 Lord Mayor of Leipzig. In 1931, and from 1934 to 1935 Reich Commissioner of Price Control. Member of the Board of the Association of German Municipalities [Gemeindetag] and co-author of the German Municipal Code of 1935. He resigned as Lord Mayor in April 1937 in protest against the removal of a statue of Felix Mendelssohn-Bartholdy.
From 1937 to 1939 he travelled abroad repeatedly for the firms of Krupp and Bosch. Goerdeler was a leading member of the German Resistance Movement and was slated to become chancellor of a new national government.
After his arrest had already been ordered on July 17, 1944, he was not apprehended until August 12, 1944, after a search of several weeks, and was sentenced to death on September 8, 1944. He remained in detention at Prinz-Albrecht-Strasse 8 until his execution on February 2, 1945 in Plötzensee Prison.

199   Theodor Strünck (1895–1945), on October 10, 1944, before the People's court.
Doctor of Law. Director of an insurance firm. At the outbreak of war he was assigned as a reserve captain to the Department „Foreign Countries/Counterintelligence" at the Supreme Command of the Armed Forces. Strünck belonged to the inner circle of the resistance group around Oster and von Dohnanyi. After his arrest on August 1, 1944, he was kept prisoner at Prinz-Albrecht-Strasse 8. The People's Court sentenced him to death on October 10, 1944. Together with Oster, Canaris, Thomas, Schacht, and others he was taken to Concentration Camp Flossenbürg on February 7, 1945, and was murdered there on April 9, 1945.

Text 70

One night I was taken out of my cell for interrogation. In the interrogation room were the following persons: Criminal Police Commissioner Habecker, his female secretary, a uniformed lance corporal of Security Service, and a detective ser-

201 **Johannes Popitz** (right, 1884–1945) and **Carl Lang-behn** (left, 1901–1944), on October 3, 1944, before the People's Court.

J. Popitz:
Doctor of Philosophy. He began in 1919 in the Reich Finance Ministry, from 1925–1929 as undersecretary [of state]. 1932/1933 Reich Minister without portfolio in the cabinet of General Schleicher. Prussian minister of finance from April 1933 to July 1944. He offered his resignation in 1938 but was allowed to stay in office. After that time he worked with the resistance groups around Goerdeler and Beck. In case of a successful coup d'etat, he was slated to become minister of finance.
Popitz was arrested on July 21, 1944 and taken to Prinz-Albrecht-Strasse 8. He was sentenced to death on October 3, 1944 and executed in Plötzensee Prison on February 2, 1945.

C. Langbehn:
Lawyer and notary public in Berlin. Close confidant of Popitz. Contacts to conservative resistance groups. Commissioned to do so by high ranking SS leaders, he tried to explore the possibilities of a separate peace with the western powers.
As a co-conspirator of the "20th of July," Langbehn was kept prisoner at Prinz-Albrecht-Strasse 8. Sentenced to death on October 3, 1944, he was executed on October 20, 1944.

202 **Fabian von Schlabrendorff** (1907–1980), around 1942.
Jurist. Adjutant to the Chief of Staff Second Army, Brigadier General Henning von Tresckow. Together they made preparations for two attempts on Hitler's life which both failed but remained undetected. In the military resistance he was responsible for contacts between frontline officers and the Counterintelligence people around Oster.
Schlabrendorff was arrested on August 17, 1944, in connection with the inquiries conducted by the "Special Commission July 20th," and was taken the following day to Prinz-Albrecht-Strasse 8 where he was brutally tortured. Proceedings against

geant in mufti. I was informed that this would be my last chance to make a confession. When I persisted in my previous denials they decided to apply torture. This torture proceeded in four stages.
During the first stage my hands were tied behind my back. Then some contraption was affixed over

him were delayed by the death of the President of the People's Court, Freisler. He was acquitted on March 16, 1945, and the warrant for his arrest cancelled. The *Gestapo* nevertheless continued to keep Schlabrendorff in detention at Prinz-Albrecht-Strasse 8 before they sent him a few days later, together with other prisoners, first to Concentration Camp Flossenbürg, subsequently to Dachau and to southern Tyrol where he was liberated on May 4, 1945.

After 1945, Schlabrendorff worked as a lawyer and from 1967–1975 was a judge at the Federal Constitutional Court in Karlsruhe.

prison doctor was called, and I endured his medical treatment with a good deal of suspicion. I remained in bed for several days before I was able to get up again and move about. As a consequence of my recovery, the torture procedure was repeated following the same four stages as the first time. The actual results, however, remained once again zero.

Fabian von Schlabrendorff

both of my hands in such a way that it enclosed each of my fingers separately. On the inside of the contraption were iron spines that pressed upon the base of the fingers. The entire machinery could be tightened by means of a screw in such a way that the spines dug into my fingers.

The second stage was like this: I was tied down on top of a contraption that resembled a bedstead, but with my face down. A blanket was thrown over my head and then a sort of stovepipe was put around each of my bare legs. On the inside of these two pipes were nails, and here, too, the walls of the pipes could be screwed tight by means of a special mechanism so that the nails were pressed into my thighs and shanks.

The "bedstead" served also as the main contraption for the third stage. I was tied to it, as before, with my head covered by a blanket. Then the bedstead, by means of some mechanism, was pulled apart either joltingly or gradually so that my body – tied up as it was – was forced to keep up with the movements of this procrustean bed.

In the fourth stage I was tied up in a twisted fashion by means of a special manacling process; as a result my body could not bend either forward or backward. Then the detective sergeant and the lance corporal beat me with heavy clubs from behind so that I fell forward with each blow; and as my hands were tied behind my back, my face and head hit the ground with full force. While this procedure went on, all participants displayed their enjoyment with derisive shouts. The first torture ended in a fainting spell.

None of these violent measures here described induced me either to confess anything, or to betray any of my likeminded friends. After I regained consciousness I was led back to my cell. The guards received me with unconcealed expressions of pity and horror. The next day I was unable to get up, so I could not even change my underwear, which was soaked with blood. Although I had been very healthy up to then I suffered a heart attack during the course of the day. The

203   **Hans Oster** (1887–1945), around 1942.
General Staff Officer in the First World War. After 1918 he served in the newly created *Reichswehr*. Quit active service in 1932 and starting October 1933 worked in the counterintelligence section of the *Reichswehr* Ministry. From 1938 on he headed the central section of the Department "Foreign Countries/Counterintelligence" at Supreme Command of the Armed Forces. In 1939/1940 Oster handed over to the Dutch military attaché the plans for attack and the timetable of the planned German offensive in the west. He was among the central figures of the military resistance against the Nazi Regime. After his close co-worker Hans von Dohnanyi had been arrested on April 5, 1943 Oster was suspended from his duties while court-martial proceedings were instituted against him on suspicion of favoritism.

On July 21, 1944 the *Gestapo* arrested him and shortly thereafter took him to Prinz-AlbrechtStrasse 8. Here he was interrogated for the next several months. On February 7, 1945 Oster and other prominent prisoners were taken to Concentration Camp Flossenbürg where they were murdered on April 9, 1945.

204   **Hans von Dohnanyi** (1902–1945), around 1940.
Doctor of Law. From 1925 to 1919 he worked in the Institute
for Foreign Policy at Hamburg University. From 1929 on he
was personal assistant to the Reich Minister of Justice, ultimately as senior executive officer under Gürtner. 1931/1932
on and off prosecuting attorney in Hamburg. In 1938 councillor at the Reich Supreme Court in Leipzig. From August 25,
1939 on he was in the office "Foreign Countries/Counterintel-
ligence" at the Army High Command. His function was group
leader ("ZB-foreign political reporting") in the central department ("Z") which was headed by Brigadier General Oster.
Von Dohnanyi, brother-in-law of the theologian Dietrich Bonhoeffer, was next to Hans Oster the principal figure in the
small resistance group within Counterintelligence.
He was arrested on April 5, 1943. Stations of imprisonment
were first the Army Prison on Lehrter Strasse. Subsequently,
after he fell seriously ill while in detention, he was in the Berlin
Charité hospital, then the prison hospital in Buch and the isolation hospital in Potsdam. On August 22, 1944 he was taken
to Sachsenhausen Concentration Camp and on February 1,
1945 to the *Gestapo* Prison ("*Hausgefängnis*") at Prinz-Albrecht-Strasse 8 where he remained imprisoned until the middle of March. On April 6, 1945, after a temporary stay in the
prisoner ward of Berlin's state hospital, the *Gestapo* took him
again to Sachsenhausen Concentration Camp. An SS drum-
head court-martial sentenced him to death the same day. On
April 9, 1945 Hans von Dohnanyi was executed in Sachsenhausen Concentration Camp.

Text 71

As for the rest, I found that what Admiral Canaris
had whispered to me on one of the first days on
our way to the wash room was true: "This is hell."
From my cell I frequently heard awful screams that
came from some floor above mine and often
lasted a long time, then turned into a whimper,
then grew loud again, so that there could be no

doubt as far as I was concerned: up there, people
were being badly mistreated. The screams were
so awful that I could not help but think of torture. I
myself did not experience this increase of violence until I was taken to Concentration Camp
Flossenbürg. But my hands were continuously
tied, and the surface of the manacles was rough;
everytime I made a rash movement, the fine hairs
at my wrists were rubbed away. This I found particularly painful whenever I was trying to get some
sleep. I had to remain tied up during meals, during
interrogations, and also throughout the night.
Although I myself never revealed a single name, I
can at least understand that one or the other of my
fellow prisoners lost his nerve. That perpetual
sensation of being hungry, being tied up day and
night, the light that was focused in such a way that
it flashed throughout the night directly into the prisoner's face – all these factors created constant
pressure which was further increased by the interrogations that lasted for hours, and by fears of
physical abuse. Needless to say, the Security Service people have generally denied, since the war,
that "torture" was ever applied. But shortly after I
was put into the basement prison of the RSMO, I
saw Julius Leber's bruised back, and the back of
one of the generals I saw in the wash room was
likewise covered with welts.

Josef Müller

205   **Josef Müller** (1898–1979), around 1946.
Doctor of Law, lawyer. Prior to 1933 he was active in the Bavarian People's Party and Center Party. Until 1939 he was legal adviser to clerical institutions. As a staff member of

counterintelligence during the war he acted as a link between the military and conservative-political opposition movements, and also between the German Resistance as a whole and clerical authorities at home and abroad.

Müller was arrested for the first time as early as 1933. He was arrested again in April 1943 and confined to the Lehrter Strasse Prison. Although the Reich War Tribunal acquitted him of the charge of high treason, he remained imprisoned at Prinz-Albrecht-Strasse 8 from September 26, 1944 until February 7, 1945. In February 1945 he was transferred via the concentration camps Buchenwald and Flossenbürg to Dachau, and subsequently to southern Tyrol, where he was liberated in May 1945. Müller was among the co-founders of the CSU [Christian Social Union] and from 1946 to 1949 its chairman. From 1946 until 1962 he was a member of the Bavarian Diet, from 1947 to 1950 Deputy Bavarian Minister President, and from 1947 to 1952 Bavarian Minister of Justice.

206   **Wilhelm Canaris** (1887—1945), around 1940.
Naval cadet in 1905. In the First World War he was commander of a submarine. Organized homeguards and citizens' militias in 1919—1920. From 1924—1928 active with the naval command, thereafter various assignments. From 1935 to 1944 Chief of the military Counterintelligence of the Army ["*Abwehr*"], ultimately with an admiral's rank. After the "Fritsch Crisis" in the spring of 1938, he established contact to the military resistance group around Beck and Halder. He was at least partly informed of resistance work carried out by staff members within the Counterintelligence section, such as Oster and von Dohnanyi. However, up to now his precise position within the military opposition has not been unequivocally established.

Canaris was arrested on July 23, 1944 and after a brief stay at the Border Police Academy Fürstenberg/Havel was taken to Prinz-Albrecht-Strasse 8. There was never a trial. On February 7, 1945 he was transferred to Concentration Camp Flossenbürg where he was murdered on April 9, 1945.

Text 72

The lower ranking officials specially assigned to guard political prisoners varied widely. Some behaved correctly and even groused about the system. Others were out and out sadists and tormentors of human beings. Harassment was vilest when

207   **Georg Thomas** (1890—1946), around 1940.
General. Until the beginning of 1943 he was Chief of the Department of Defense Economy and Armaments. From 1938 on he had contacts with the various military resistance groups formed around Beck, Witzleben, and Oster. Thomas was arrested on October 11, 1944 in the course of investigations by the *Gestapo* on the 20th of July plot, and taken to Prinz-Albrecht-Strasse 8. On February 7, 1945 he was transferred to Concentration Camp Flossenbürg. Via Concentration Camp Dachau and a transit camp near Innsbruck he ended up in southern Tyrol where he was liberated by American troops.

it came to trifling matters. To deprive us as much as possible of our human dignity was of utmost importance to them. All of those who had been sentenced to death were manacled day and night; the same was true of prisoners who were still being interrogated. I was only tied up once, when the building was on fire after an air raid. During air raids the "most interesting" prisoners were taken to the bunker; others were locked into their cells, hands and feet tied; and still others were locked up in a large basement room. Leisure time such as getting a breath of fresh air did not exist as far as the *Gestapo* was concerned. Torture was the order of the day. Planck, too, was tortured, in order to obtain by force some information involving me. The lawyer Dr. von Schlabrendorff was repeatedly brought back to his cell unconscious after he had been tortured.

Georg Thomas

208   **Hans Speidel** (1897–1984), around 1944.
Major General. In the summer of 1944 Chief of Staff of Army Group B under General Field Marshal Rommel. Speidel had contacts with the military resistance but was not involved in any concrete preparations for a coup.

He was arrested on September 7, 1944, and on September 8 was taken from the military stockade on Lehrter Strasse to Prinz-Albrecht-Strasse 8, where he was interrogated until October 11. He was kept imprisoned at various localities until the end of the war, and in December, January, and February was taken repeatedly to Prinz-Albrecht-Strasse 8 for further interrogations.

Speidel became one of the leading military advisers to Adenauer in connection with preparations for the creation of the Federal Army [*Bundeswehr*].

In 1955 he was appointed Chief of the Department "Combined Armed Forces" in the Federal Ministry of Defense. He was Supreme Commander of the NATO land forces in Central Europe from 1957 to 1963.

209   **Franz Lange** (1904–1985), around 1946.
He joined the German Communist Party in 1926. In March 1933 he was arrested and confined in Concentration Camp Sonnenburg. Released in September 1933, he was again arrested on February 20, 1934 and taken to Camp V (Neusustrum) of the "Emsland" camps [in the Ems region]. In June 1937 he was free again. Did resistance work in connection with the Saefkow Group [a Communist resistance group].

Lange was once again arrested on April 9, 1945 and taken to Prinz-Albrecht-Strasse 8. He remained there until he was liberated on May 2, 1945. Ultimately he worked in the Ministry of Foreign Trade in the GDR.

Text 73

Around noon of May 1 [1945] we heard noises at the cell door. All of us inside posted ourselves facing the door. The door was yanked open, and we were pounced upon with a shout: "Out with you!" and were chased down the stairs. A German corporal who had been with us in the communal cell was bumped off by the SS on the stairs, and the other prisoners were locked up inside the former SS accomodations. Everybody was lost in his own thoughts. I myself was convinced that our liberation could only come with the Red Army. Pastor Reinecke, in contrast, found the strength to carry on through prayers which I, who had left the church at age 16, shall never forget. Unrest within the building increased during the course of the afternoon. We listened to the noises and noticed that the SS was assembling. When an SS man asked his major what was to be done about the prisoners who were locked up in there, the major replied: "We are letting them live as proof that we are not shooting prisoners." And then they took off. We were all by ourselves, alone in this giant building, a building almost completely wrecked. And then we waited, waited, waited. We waited throughout the evening, throughout the night, and it got light again and then, early in the morning of May 2 – it could have been around 6 a.m. – we heard Russian sounds. The Red Army entered the building. Steps were approaching. We hammered against the door. Then the folding slot in the door was opened from the outside and we were met by a Russian sound: "*Ključ.*" ["Key"]. My reply was: "*Ključ netu* ["no key"] – we are prisoners." It took only a few minutes, then the axes crashed against the door till it flew open. I stood face to face with a young Red Army soldier. We were liberated.

Franz Lange

5. From Destruction to Rediscovery

5.1. Bombs and Ruins

The saturation bombings which began in November 1943 caused heavy damages to Berlin's inner city. In April and May 1944 the government sector became the target of severe air raids. As the *Gestapo* and SS terrain was immediately to the south of it, it was likewise severely hit, so that most of the buildings had already been badly damaged by that time. The Prinz-Albrecht-Palais was largely destroyed, presumably by high-explosive bombs. The journalist Ursula von Kardorff, who was interrogated by the *Gestapo* on September 15, 1944, described the building on Prinz-Albrecht-Strasse as "partly burnt out," with cracks in the wall and windows boarded up in a makeshift fashion. She noticed concentration camp prisoners in the hallways who had to repaint the stairway. Concentration camp prisoners were also used on the *Gestapo* and SS terrain to remove rubble. Over 20 prisoners from a satellite camp of Concentration Camp Dachau perished on the morning of May 7, 1944 because during a bomb raid they were only allowed to seek shelter in an open slit trench.

Gestapo headquarters was hit by several bombs during an air raid on February 3, 1945. Further devastation was wrought during the last days of the war by artillery and tank fire in the fighting for the government sector. Starting from April 26, Soviet troops commanded by General Chuikov advanced from the Landwehrkanal and Hallesches Tor to the city center. After the defensive position on Köthener and Prinz-Albrecht-Strasse had been "moved back," heavy fighting flared up once more on Wilhelmstrasse until the City Commandant, Lieutenant General Weidling, capitulated on May 2, 1945.

The extent of damage to the terrain on Prinz-Albrecht-Strasse and Wilhelmstrasse varied. The former Hotel Prinz Albrecht and most buildings on Wilhelmstrasse were totally destroyed, most significantly the Prinz-Albrecht-Palais. Other buildings, among them *Gestapo* headquarters at Prinz-Albrecht-Strasse 8 and the neighboring Gropius mansion, although burned out inside, still retained their basic structure. A map drawn in 1945 shows the majority of buildings situated on Wilhelmstrasse as "thorougly damaged," whereas those on Saarlandstrasse (today: Stresemannstrasse) and on Prinz-Albrecht-Strasse (today: Niederkirchnerstrasse) are shown as "suitable for rebuilding."

Although the air raid of February 3, 1945 had knocked out the water supply and electric power supply throughout the entire building, the *Gestapo* Prison ("Hausgefängnis") remained in use until shortly before the capitulation. During the night from April 23 to 24, the majority of inmates still imprisoned at the time were shot by the *Gestapo* on a plot of ruins nearby. Only six prisoners were still alive at the time of liberation.

Nearly all important SS leaders, department heads of the Reich Security Main Office and *Gestapo* officials were no longer in Berlin during the last days of war. Himmler, together with Ohlendorf, Schellenberg and other members of the SS and RSMO leadership were in Slesvig-Holstein; Kaltenbrunner, Heydrich's successor as Head of the Reich Security Main Office, had moved his headquarters to Alt-Aussee in Styria, where Eichmann also showed up in April. Only *Gestapo* Chief Heinrich Müller was still seen at the end of April in the

Reich Chancellory. Himmler took poison after he had been caught by the British. Other SS leaders and officials of the RSMO were apprehended. A substantial number of these officials were able to escape retribution for what they had done for a brief or even extended period of time, while others got away for good.

210   After the air raid: Street scene on Askanischer Platz, February 3, 1945.

211   Aerial photograph of Friedrichstadt on February 3, 1945. Reconnaissance photo of the US Air Force (detail).
The photo shows the severe damages which the heavy bombing raid by the 8th US Army Air Force caused on the morning of February 3. The buildings along Wilhelmstrasse, notably the Prinz-Albrecht-Palais, were largely destroyed. *Gestapo* headquarters received several hits.
The two bright stripes recognizable directly below *Gestapo* headquarters are (left) the *Gestapo* auxiliary building, constructed 1943—1944, and (right) the air raid bunker to whose central hallway some of the inmates of the *Gestapo* Prison ("*Hausgefängnis*") were taken during air raids.

212   Prinz-Albrecht-Strasse 8 and environs, around 1947.
Gestapo headquarters and the seat of the Reich Security Main
Office; next to it on the right, the former Museum of Industrial
Arts and Crafts, behind it the Europahaus and Anhalter Bahn-
hof.

213   The ruins on Saarlandstrasse, spring 1945.
The Europahaus, next to it the Museum of Industrial Arts and
Crafts and the *Gestapo* headquarters.

Text 74

Hans Speidel's report on the bombing raid of February 3, 1945 on the Gestapo headquarters at Prinz-Albrecht-Strasse 8

At 11 a.m. on February 3 the heaviest air raid on Berlin so far started ... After an uninterrupted hail of bombs lasting 55 minutes, and with hits in the immediate vicinity, we were chased through bomb craters filled with rocks, wood, and glass back into our cells. The building had received several hits... Fires were still spreading, the heat mounted, and we soon noticed a decrease of oxygen. In order to breathe I climbed on a stool, then a table, and watched the sea of flames outside through the splintered pane. Water pipes had burst and water began to come in. The light in the cell no longer worked, but the cell remained locked.

Text 75

Heinz Hentschke's report on the conquest of the Reich Security Main Office terrain by the Red Army at the end of April 1945

On April 27 Red Army soldiers succeeded in reaching Hallesches Tor and even getting beyond it. One could already hear the firing of machine pistols and machine guns, and the artillery hammered away ceaselessly. The air was full of blazes and smoke. The *Gestapo* building had been included in the main line of resistance. Combat SS units had taken up positions in Prinz-Albrecht-Park and the adjoining ruins and piles of rubble. Now we were fired upon point-blank. The deafening noise rose at times to the roar of a hurricane. Through the windows of our cells we could see how hit after hit battered the Europahaus, which had been on fire for quite some time. Hit after hit struck our building as well, as we were lying helpless in our cells directly below the small barred cell windows. The building trembled and shook. It was impossible to get any sleep with all this excitement going on.

During the night of April 27/28: After a lull in the fighting, *Gestapo* officials raged and stormed through the cell block. They unlocked all the doors and rounded up us prisoners. Only ten of us were left. In a split-second the thought went through my head: they are going to bump you off yet, after all – and the Russians are over on Hedemannstrasse already, perhaps even at Anhalter Bahnhof. The six people of the 20th of July were taken back again into one of the cells and locked up.

214   View into one of the destroyed solitary cells of the *Gestapo* Prison ("*Hausgefängnis*") at Prinz-Albrecht-Strasse 8, in 1948.

215   The southern wing of the building at Prinz-Albrecht-Strasse 8, June 1951.
On the left the partly collapsed air raid bunker, behind it the former Museum of Industrial Arts and Crafts, in front of the east side the ruins of the canteen annex and the motor pool parking lot.

Text 76

General Chuikov's report on the conquest of the SS and Gestapo terrain by Soviet troops

General Bakanov, the commander of the 74th guards division, has told us the pleasant news that Potsdamer Bahnhof has been captured and that fighting is taking place in the 152nd District in front of the subway station on Saarlandstrasse. The Germans defended themselves desperately with bazookas. We responded with increased artillery fire of all calibers, mainly by firing point-blank, and also with bazookas.

The attack became more and more intense and massive. The 151st District where Wilhelmstrasse and Leipziger Strasse cross was occupied. The battle for the 150th and 153rd districts now raged. Here lay the center of the Tiergarten; here loomed the tall buildings which adjoin the Reich Chancellory to the south. The main thrust of the attack on May 1st was directed at the heart of the Third Reich.

The 152nd District was taken — the *Gestapo* lair! Our units had destroyed the cave of the most dangerous reptiles that tried to poison all living things with their venom...

As commander of the 8th guards army, General (subsequently Marshal) Chuikov, the "victor of Stalingrad," led those of the Soviets troops that conquered the inner city proceeding from Berlin's southern districts via Tempelhof Airport and Hallesches Tor, and then pushed forward via Saarlandstrasse and Wilhelmstrasse toward the north. — Prior to its offensive, the Red Army had divided the territory of Greater Berlin into districts.

Text 77

Excerpts from a letter by Pastor Reinicke (Menz/Brandenburg) to his former co-prisoner Bernhard Horstmann, dated January 6, 1947: The last days in the Gestapo Prison until liberation on May 2, 1945

After the prison was emptied — you probably do not know yet that a massacre took place during the night from April 23 to 24; the mass grave has been discovered; very valuable people, including clerics, perished — about ten people were retained; ultimately there were but seven of us, during the last few hours only six people. What I experienced by way of sadism during those last one and a half weeks I can hardly describe. It was horrible. The guard who behaved most vilely was Otto Runge of the Security Service. Very decent and, in fact, helpful proved to be little Eduard Koth. I still got hit by three shell fragments, one very close below the eye. For 44 hours they locked us into a communal cell that was under point-blank gun fire; we got neither food nor buckets as toilets, and all seven of us had stomach trouble, with nasty consequences. That's the way we were living, and under constant threats of being shot.

Suddenly, in the evening of May 1, we were taken — now only six of us — to a very secure cell where we found bread, jam, drinking water and buckets. They left us to our fate, whatever that might turn out to be. The Security Service then retreated. In the morning of May 2 the Russians arrived and liberated us. While we were in the kitchen, where we found marvelous things and began to supply ourselves, the man standing only a few centimeters away from me was accidently shot (the former *Gauleiter* Joseph Wagner, from Breslau).

The mass executions mentioned in the letter above took place on Puttkammerstaße, on a plot of land full of ruins, a few hundred meters away from *Gestapo* headquarters. — Josef Wagner (1899–1945), former *Gauleiter* of Silesia and Reich Commissioner for price control, fell out of favor with Hitler on account of his ties to the Catholic Church. In October 1942 he was relieved of his offices and expelled from the NSDAP. Although he was not part of the conspiracy, he was arrested by the *Gestapo* after July 20, 1944 and, after being taken to several in-between places, was brought to the prison at Prinz-Albrecht-Strasse 8.

216   Crossroads   Wilhelmstrasse/Prinz-Albrecht-Strasse, seen from Zimmerstrasse, in 1945.
The destroyed corner house Wilhelmstrasse 98/Prinz-Albrecht-Strasse 10; next to it the ruins of the former Hotel Prinz Albrecht; and on the right, the side facade of *Gestapo* headquarters.

217   View from Prinz-Albrecht-Park to the side wing of the former *Gestapo* headquarters, around 1946.
In front of the facade of the building are the air raid bunker and the prison yard.

218   View through the colonnades on Wilhelmstrasse on the
destroyed Prinz-Albrecht-Palais, in 1947.

219   The burnt-out Europahaus on Saarlandstrasse in 1945.

220   The Museum of Ethnology on Saarlandstrasse/Prinz-
Albrecht-Strasse in 1945.

221   Ruins of the former Museum of Industrial Arts and
Crafts, Prinz-Albrecht-Strasse 7, in 1946.

5.2. The First Postwar Years

Not long after the end of the "Third Reich," the building that once housed the *Gestapo* and the Reich Security Main Office attracted but little attention. The occupation troops were more interested in the Reichstag building and the new Reich Chancellory that symbolized – with Reichstag fire and Hitler's suicide – the beginning and end of the Nazi Regime.

A large segment of Berlin's population not only tried to forget the horrors of war as soon as possible, but also the crimes that had been committed while the Nazis were in power. In the midst of destruction and dire material needs, people concentrated on problems of survival. The few trees that had been left standing in Prinz-Albrecht-Park were cut down for heating fuel, and the bombed-out buildings were not ransacked for evidence of *Gestapo* and SS terror but for usable materials of all sorts.

Information about the crimes committed by the Nazi Regime that emerged via newspapers and journals, books, brochures and documentary films was not without its effect, but as elsewhere in Germany, it aroused defensive reactions among segments of Berlin's population. There was a great temptation not to face up to the past but to suppress it, and all too many people yielded to this. True, the fundamental anti-Fascist consensus of the immediate postwar period was impressively displayed in September 1945 and 1946 during huge commemorative ceremonies for the "victims of Fascist terror." It was sponsored by Berlin's municipal authorities, and united those persecuted and resistance fighters of all views. Soon thereafter, however, it was replaced by the new political constellations of the Cold War.

The International Military Tribunal at Nuremberg declared the *Gestapo*, SS, and Security Service to have been criminal organizations. One of the 24 defendants in the Trial of the Major War Criminals was Ernst Kaltenbrunner, last Head of the Reich Security Main Office. In the fall of 1946 he was sentenced to death and executed. During the trial of the commanders of Special Units ["*Einsatzgruppen*"], among whom were three former department heads of the Reich Security Main Office, only Ohlendorf was sentenced to death in 1948 and executed in 1951. Conversely, Jost and Six merely received prison sentences and were released from detention after only a few years. In subsequent years, criminal proceedings instituted by German judicial authorities against former officials of the Reich Security Main Office were the exception. Many, including leading members of the *Gestapo*, SS, and RSMO were spared any criminal prosecution.

During the course of years, the terrain of the Reich Security Main Office fell increasingly into oblivion. Only former prisoners of the *Gestapo* occasionally visited the site of their former sufferings. Best documented is the visit which Günther Weisenborn and Bertolt Brecht paid to the dilapidated prison cells in November 1950.

222   In 1945 a US patrol passes the main entrance of former
Gestapo headquarters on Prinz-Albrecht-Strasse.

223   „"Commemorative Rally for the Victims of Fascist Terror" at Werner-Seelenbinder-Arena in Neukölln on September 9, 1945.
The rally was organized by the municipal central committee "Victims of Fascism" and was the first public anti-fascist manifestation in Berlin. 35,000 people participated.

224   Election propaganda of the Socialist Union Party [SED] for the election to the municipal council of Berlin on October 20, 1946.
The streamer that reads: "Prinz-Albrecht-Strasse. Here was Himmler's headquarters of unrestrained murder; this ruin calls for socialist unity" was mounted at the building next to the former Prussian Chamber of Deputies, close to the junction of Stresemannstrasse. The ruins of *Gestapo* headquarters, though, were on the other side of the street.

SS And Gestapo Headquarters

Heinrich Himmler, who, as head of the Gestapo and SS troops, was the second most powerful man in National Socialist Germany, made his headquarters in this building. Deep beneath the structure was an elaborate air raid shelter. Although Himmler fled Berlin as Russian troops fought their way through the city, the building itself was defended by his SS troop followers against Red Army forces.

225   In a guide to Berlin, the American Army mistakenly depicts the Prussian Chamber of Deputies that faces the Martin-Gropius-Bau as the [former] SS and *Gestapo* headquarters. (*An Illustrated Introduction to the City of Berlin* [US headquarters, Berlin District], n.d.)

227   Ernst Kaltenbrunner before the International Military Tribunal at Nuremberg, December 10, 1945.
During the Nuremberg Trials of the Major War Criminals, the defendant Kaltenbrunner (standing), former Head of the Reich Security Main Office, pleaded "not guilty." To the left of Kaltenbrunner is Joachim von Ribbentrop, Hitler's last foreign minister. In front of the dock are the counsels for the defense.

226   Adolf Eichmann during interrogation in Jerusalem, in 1961.
In May 1945, Eichmann was picked up by an American patrol. While in prison he gave his identity as ""SS Lieutenant Otto Eckmann." Before his true identity could be established he succeeded, early in 1946, to escape from an internment camp run by the US Army. Thereafter he hid out in West Germany. In 1950 he fled via Italy to Argentina. In 1960 he was tracked down by the Israeli secret service and kidnapped to Jerusalem, where he was brought to trial. In December 1961, after a trial which aroused worldwide attention, he was sentenced to death and executed on June 1, 1962.

Text 78

From the testimony of witness Werner Best before the International Military Tribunal at Nuremberg on July 31, 1946

Dr. Merkel (defense counsel for the *Gestapo*): Did the appointments made in 1933 to the Political Police in the individual German states include party members?

Best: No. Appointments were made from the ranks of officials who had been with the previous police agencies. Only a few employees were newly appointed at that time.

Dr. Merkel: Were the ranking officials party members?

Best: That differed in the individual states. There were even officials who in the past had held quite different political views and had belonged to different parties ...

228   Otto Ohlendorf before the International Military Tribunal at Nuremberg ("Special Unit Trial"), February 13, 1948. Ohlendorf (at the microphone), former SS Major General, from 1939 to 1945 Head of Department III (Security Service, home country) in the Reich Security Main Office, delivering his closing statement in the Nuremberg Palace of Justice. Ohlendorf, as Commander of Special Unit D from June 1941 until June 1942, was responsible for the murder of roughly 90,000 civilians, most of them Jews. In the "Special Unit Trial" he and 23 other former members of Special Units were indicted for having committed crimes against humanity, war crimes, and for having been members of a criminal organization. He was sentenced to death on June 10, 1948, and executed on June 25, 1951.

Dr. Merkel: Why did these officials continue to carry out police duties under the National Socialist regime?

Best: Because even if there was a change of government, it was self-evident for any German official to continue serving the state as long as he was in a position to do so.

Dr. Merkel: Were these officials subsequently dismissed and replaced by National Socialists?

Best: No. Most of these gentlemen even worked their way up very well and were given top jobs.

Text 79

Adalbert Rückerl, for many years Director of the Central Office of the Länder Administrations of Justice for the Clarification of National Socialist Crimes in Ludwigsburg, on the "forgotten" legal proceedings in the case of the "Reich Security Main Office"

As a particularly striking example one may cite the case of the "Reich Security Main Office." It has been known ever since the Nuremberg Trials that the Reich Security Main Office ordered, organized and coordinated the mass murders carried out by the Special Units of Security Police and Security Service (SD) in the extermination camps; the selection and murder of so-called "unacceptable" Soviet prisoners of war; the "special treatment" (i.e., execution by hanging) of foreign forced laborers; and the administrative death sentences imposed on individual concentration camp inmates. The scene of crime in this respect was Berlin. After 1950 no further obstacles existed to prevent the prosecuting attorney's office in Berlin in charge of these matters from initiating legal proceedings against members of said office [i.e., the RSMO] — some of whose names were known — according to Article 7 of the Code of Criminal Procedure.

However, nothing was done at the time. As the Attorney General at Berlin's Superior Court of Justice openly admitted in 1967 at a professional conference of judges and public prosecutors, it had simply been forgotten. And when a reminder came in 1963 one was, so to speak, absolutely flabbergasted.

Amnesty by the back door — the complete failure of all legal proceedings instituted against former members of the RSMO

In 1963, Berlin's Attorney General Günther appointed a committee consisting of 11 prosecuting attorneys and 23 police officers to inquire into the case entitled "criminal offenses committed by members of the Reich Security Main Office." The suspects were divided into three categories according to their alleged crimes: 1) Participation in the "final solution of the Jewish question," 2) having exerted influence on the composition and actions of the "Special Units," [and] 3) participation in mass executions. With respect to the first two categories, criminal prosecution of National Socialist crimes would have been extended for the first time systematically to the "middle level" of the persecution machinery, i.e., to the administrative specialists of mass murder and the armchair killers. In 1967, the first 18 proceedings against roughly 300 accused were ready for prosecution, and in 1968 began the first trial of the case as a whole.

As a result of criminal law reform passed by the German Federal Parliament which took effect on October 1, 1968, the proceedings initiated so far were for all practical purposes rendered unfeasible, although unwittingly so. Since as a rule the charge was formulated as "aiding and abetting murder" rather than as "murder" pure and simple,

Die Ergebnisse sind:

Paul Blobel	Todesstrafe. Keine Umwandlung	
Ernst Biberstein	statt Todesstrafe	lebenslänglich
Walter Blume	statt Todesstrafe	25 Jahre Gefängnis
Werner Braune	Todesstrafe. Keine Umwandlung	
Walter Hänsch	statt Todesstrafe	15 Jahre
Waldemar Klingelhöfer	statt Todesstrafe	lebenslänglich
Erich Naumann	Todesstrafe. Keine Umwandlung	
Otto Ohlendorf	Todesstrafe. Keine Umwandlung	
Adolf Ott	statt Todesstrafe	lebenslänglich
Martin Sandberger	statt Todesstrafe	lebenslänglich
Heinz Hermann Schubert	statt Todesstrafe	10 Jahre
Willi Seibert	statt Todesstrafe	15 Jahre
Eugen Steimle	statt Todesstrafe	20 Jahre
Heinz Jost	statt lebenslänglichem Gefängnis	10 Jahre
Gustav Nosske	statt lebenslänglichem Gefängnis	10 Jahre
Waldemar von Radetzky	statt 20 Jahren die verbüßte Strafzeit	
Erwin Schulz	statt 20 Jahren	15 Jahre
Franz Six	statt 20 Jahren	10 Jahre
Lothar Fendler	statt 10 Jahren	8 Jahre
Felix Rühl	statt 10 Jahren die verbüßte Strafzeit	

Der Fall des Angeklagten Strauch, der an Belgien ausgeliefert und dort wegen begangener Morde zum Tode verurteilt worden ist, unterlag nicht dieser Überprüfung.

229   "Decisions of the American High Commissioner, John McCloy, and the Commander in Chief of the American forces in Europe, General Thomas T. Handy, pertaining to the petitions for mercy on the part of war criminals who had been sentenced at Nuremberg and Dachau."
In the "Special Unit Trial," 13 additional defendants aside from Ohlendorf had been sentenced to death in 1948; two defendants were given life sentences, and five defendants were given prison terms of 3 to 20 years. On January 31, 1951, McCloy confirmed only four death sentences, commuted the remaining ones by an act of pardon, and reduced some of the prison terms to a considerable degree. The commutation of sentences as well as the mitigation of the other penalties took place in an intensifying Cold War climate and against the background of the impending rearmament of the Federal Republic. Thus, Franz A. Six, former Head of Department VII in the Reich Security Main Office and Chief of the "Advance Party Moscow" of Special Unit B, had originally been sentenced to a 20 year prison term. Yet on September 30, 1952 he was released from prison. Thereafter, he was active as a consultant for advertisement and industry, for the most part in the car business. The other defendants were also prematurely released in the middle of the fifties.
The two lines underneath the list of names read: "The case of the defendant Strauch, who was turned over to Belgium where he was sentenced to death for murders he had committed, was not subject to this review process."

the crime, according to the revised article 50, paragraph 2 of the criminal code (today article 28) already fell under the statute of limitation after 15 years, i.e., on May 8, 1960. The revision proceeded from the premise that those who had merely "aided and abetted" murder were to be punished less severely as long as the "characteristic features of the physical elements of the offense," i.e., of being a criminal, were absent. "All burden of proof heretofore reserved for the perpetration of crimes – cruelty, perfidy, baseness – was now applied to the senior office clerks. Had they handled the card files on Jews in a cruel fashion? Had they ordered deportations in a perfidious manner?" (J. Friedrich, Die kalte Amnestie. [Frankfurt/Main, 1984] p. 411). The added burden of proof, that more often than not could not be provided, forced the prosecution either to supply proof of the defendants' guilt, or to move that the case be dismissed. "In effect, an amnesty by the back door has been enacted by this," complained a Berlin prosecuting attorney in 1969 in Moabit's jury courtroom. And, "I never imagined that such insidiousness existed," was the stunned reaction of Federal Minister of Justice Gustav Heinemann. If, for once, an indictment for murder could nevertheless be made, the defendants were inevitably "permanently incapable of standing trial." An example is the former acting chief of the Reich Security Main Office, Werner Best, who survived the suspension of his proceedings until his death in 1989.

230   Prinz-Albrecht-Strasse 8: prison courtyard.
In November 1950, Günther Weisenborn together with Bertolt Brecht and jounalist Max Schroeder visited the former Ge-

stapo and SS terrain. The snapshot, taken by Brecht, shows Weisenborn and Schröder in the courtyard of the *Gestapo* Prison ("*Hausgefängnis*").

Text 80

With Bertolt Brecht in the former Gestapo headquarters, November 1950. From a report by Günther Weisenborn

To reach the courtyard through a gap in the fence was very easy. In former times, a double sentry of statue-like SS men had been posted at the portal, but I had never passed through the portal at Prinz-Albrecht-Strasse. At the time I was transported to the courtyard and taken to the basement where the cells were located. If somebody closed the door forcefully from the outside, the air pressure affected one's ears. This was *Gestapo* headquarters. Now all this had fallen into decay. Within the ruins, the first story floor was sloping downward, curved like a tent. It was deathly silent. Brecht and I first turned into the small courtyard where we took at the time our so-called "strolls": six people, 20 minutes duration, no talking. Then we proceeded to the waiting room where once the brown benches that resembled pews had stood; their side panels were intended to make surreptitious talks with the person next to

you more difficult. I explained all this to him. I turned around and shall never forget the expression on Brecht's face, this nearly scientific interest mixed with suppressed anger. We walked along the passageway and looked at the cells. They were empty. On the floor was debris: broken bits of glass, military relics, gas mask containers, empty cigarette boxes, occasionally a snapshot, a grimy leaflet. — We entered my former cell where I had spent months. It was very dark. "Was it always that dark?"

"Yes."

"Was it cold?"

"Yes, but not as bad as in Spandau."

The door was gone — probably used for fuel. I could barely see Brecht in the dark. There he stood like a shadow, motionless, in my former cell which had become so dilapidated. For a long time we stood without moving. In width it [the cell] measured from the tip of the left hand to the right elbow, in length five paces. How many prisoners had still suffered here, after I was gone? I paced in the old way — five slow paces back and forth. The debris on the stone floor crunched underneath my shoes. When I stopped, it was deathly silent.

5.3. History Made Invisible

The split of Berlin's municipal administration at the end of 1948 was the first step on the way to a city divided into a western and eastern part. Southern Friedrichstrasse, rendered nearly unrecognizable by the war, lost all significance. A former section of the downtown area turned into a desolate wasteland, a "silent region" within the city. New municipal focal points developed both in the western and eastern sectors. The decline of southern Friedrichstrasse was — like its rise long ago — both an expression and a result of Berlin's development: at present it was the East-West conflict, structurally the "heritage" of the Nazi Regime.

As Prinz-Albrecht-Strasse belonged to the administrative district "Center" (Soviet Sector), but the buildings along its southern rim to the administrative district Kreuzberg (U.S. Sector), the terrain of the former Reich Security Main Office was now situated exactly at the point where East and West met. None of the buildings on Wilhelmstrasse that during the "Third Reich" had housed administrative offices of the *Gestapo* or Security Service was left in 1950. At the end of the forties, they were either blown up or torn down because of their "state of dilapidation." Whereas the demolition of the New Reich Chancellery, which began in February 1949, attracted much attention, the public took no notice when the ruined Prinz-Albrecht-Palais was blown up on April 27/28, 1949. The complete lack of consideration given to the preservation of monuments during the removal of what still remained of one of the last buildings designed by Schinkel contrasts markedly with the general outcry that was raised in the West when upon the initiative of the municipal administration of East Berlin the residential palace [*Schloss*] was blown up in 1950 and 1951. After Prinz-Albrecht-Strasse was renamed Niederkirchnerstrasse (in honor of a Communist resistance fighter executed by the SS), the partial demolition of the former *Gestapo* headquarters in 1953/1954 and the blowing-up of the remaining walls in 1956 came next; then followed the "removal" (rubble clearance and leveling) of the buildings on Wilhelmstrasse in 1958/1959. Finally, when in 1962/1963 the still relatively well preserved Museum of Ethnology was blown up nearly at the same time when the buildings at Niederkirchnerstrasse 8 and 9 as well as those at Wilhelmstrasse 98/99 were razed, the terrain where formerly a near solid block of houses had stood had been turned into a huge empty lot, except for the Europahaus and Martin-Gropius-Bau.

"Liberated" as it now was from all historic traces, the terrain became a veritable prey to city planners. In the mid-fifties, the Kreuzberg District Board came up with the proposal to turn the former Prinz-Albrecht-terrain into a heliport. More serious was a plan — emanating from a Senate sponsored contest entitled "Capital Berlin" — to turn Kochstrasse into an expressway, with an extension running west, across the terrain, toward the *Landwehrkanal*. This particular scheme, which in 1965 was also incorporated into a municipal land utilization plan, remained on the books until the early eighties.

The Wall that was built in August 1961, running in southern Friedrichstadt along Stresemannstrasse, Niederkirchnerstrasse, and Zimmermannstrasse, fixed the character of this part of the city as something marginal that had been ignored during the reconstruction boom. In the no-man's-land between Wall and *Landwehrkanal*, only a few isolated ruins

recalled the former significance of this quarter. The Gropius-Bau, more or less acciden-
tally spared, continued to decay from year to year. The fact that once upon a time this had
been the administrative center of the SS-State fell into oblivion, despite the fact that the
controversy about "coming to terms with the past" periodically flared up again, notably
on specific occasions such as the Auschwitz Trial at Frankfurt, the debate on the statute of
limitation held in the Federal Parliament, etc. The locality where the armchair killers of the
Gestapo and SS had done their work remained "a site of a rejected part of German History " (W. Scheffler).

231   View from the garden of the ruined Prinz-Albrecht-Palais, around 1948. The "Office for Supervision of Construction
Works" of the Kreuzberg District Board demolished the remains of the Prinz-Albrecht-Palais end of April 1949. The sal-
vaging of individual items that for architectural and art historical reasons would have been worth preserving was "forgotten" in the process. Neither curators of monuments nor art
historians were notified about the impending demolition. Four
years after the end of the war, as the art historian Johannes
Sievers wrote, "one faced, instead of a palais that even as a
ruin still retained impressive and noble features, such as the
beautiful vestibule and the elegant colonnade, a shapeless
pile of debris [...]. Thus, the history of the Albrecht Palais with
its abundant and constantly changing destinies ends on a dark
note: the demonstration of human thoughtlessness and defi-
cient sensibility for the proprietary possession of irretrievable
cultural values." (J. Sievers. *Bauten für die Prinzen August,
Friedrich und Albert von Preußen. [Karl Friedrich Schinkel Le-
benswerk]* Berlin 1954, p. 220.)

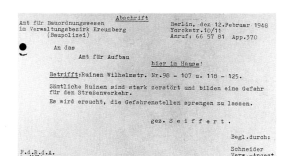

Amt für Bauordnungswesen   Abschrift
im Verwaltungsbezirk Kreuzberg   Berlin, den 12.Februar 1948
    (Baupolizei)   Yorckstr.10/11
                                                  Anruf: 66 57 81 App.370

      An das
            Amt für Aufbau
                      hier im Hause!

Betrifft:Ruinen Wilhelmstr. Nr.98 - 107 u. 118 - 125.

Sämtliche Ruinen sind stark zerstört und bilden eine Gefahr
für den Straßenverkehr.
Es wird ersucht, die Gefahrenstellen sprengen zu lassen.

                              gez. S e i f f e r t .

                                          Begl.durch:

F.d.R.d.A.   Schneider
                                           Verw.-Angest

232   Letter of February 12, 1948, from the Building Inspection Authority [*Baupolizei*] Kreuzberg to the Kreuzberg Office of Reconstruction. (See Abstract 11 in Appendix).

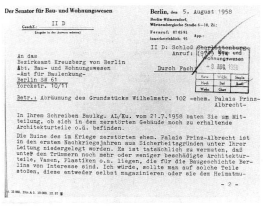

Der Senator für Bau- und Wohnungswesen   Berlin, den 5. August 1958

   GeschZ.:   II D   Berlin-Wilmersdorf,
   (Angabe in der Antwort erbeten)   Württembergische Straße 6–10, ZA:
                                                 Fernruf: 87 05 91
                                                 innerbetrieblich: 95   App.:

                                                 II D: Schloß Charlottenburg
An das   Anruf: (97th) 591 und
Bezirksamt Kreuzberg von Berlin   Wohnungswesen
-Amt für Bau- und Wohnungswesen   Durch Fach
Abt. Bau- und Wohnungswesen
-Amt für Baulenkung-
Berlin SW 61
Yorckstr. 10/11

Betr.: Abräumung des Grundstücks Wilhelmstr. 102 -ehem. Palais Prinz-Albrecht-

In Ihrem Schreiben Baulkg. AL/Ku. vom 21.7.1958 baten Sie um Mitteilung, ob sich in dem zerstörten Gebäude noch zu erhaltende Architekturteile o.ä. befinden.

Die Ruine des im Kriege zerstörten ehem. Palais Prinz-Albrecht ist in den ersten Nachkriegsjahren aus Sicherheitsgründen unter Ihrer Leitung niedergelegt worden. Es ist tatsächlich zu vermuten, daß unter den Trümmern noch mehr oder weniger beschädigte Architekturteile, Vasen, Plastiken o.a. liegen, die für die Baugeschichte Berlins von Interesse sind. Ich würde, sollte man auf solche Teile stoßen, diese entweder selbst magazinieren oder sie dem Heimatmu-

                                                          - 2 -

233   Excerpt of a letter of August 5, 1958, from the Senator for Construction and Housing to the Kreuzberg District Board. (See Abstract 11 in Appendix).

BOHR-UND SPRENG-GES.
P. H. RÖHLL KG.
Berlin - Augsburg - Bremen

An das
Bezirksamt Kreuzberg
von Gross-Berlin,   2.Ausfertigung
Amt für Aufbau,
B e r l i n SW 61
Yorckstr. 10-11

IHR ZEICHEN	IHR SCHREIBEN	UNSER ZEICHEN	BERLIN-FRIEDENAU BENNIGSENSTR. 11, DEN RUFNUMMER: 34 21 17
Aufbau II Sch.	8.5.48	4B/161/31/S	15.10.1948

BETRIFFT   Auftragsbestätigung.

Wir bestätigen dankend Ihren Auftrag auf Sprengung der
Gebäuderuine

                    Wilhelmstr. 102
             Auftrags-Nr. 6/633 vom 8.5.48
             Preis lt. Angebot DM 6.172,50

Wir erkennen als Vertragsbestandteile
    unser abgegebene Angebot vom 27.2.48,
    die besonderen Vertragsbedingungen der Stadt
    Berlin,
    die Verdingungsordnung für Bauleistungen,
    Ausgabe April 1943
als verbindlich an.

                              Hochachtungsvoll
                              BOHR- UND SPRENG-GES.
                              P. H. RÖHLL K.G.

2-fache Ausfertigung

DRAHTANSCHRIFT: BOHRSPRENG BERLIN   BANKKONTO: BEZIRKSBANK SCHÖNEBERG Nr. 71 684   POSTSCHECK: BERLIN Nr. 2124 60

234   Letter of October 15, 1948, from the Firm Röhl KG to the Kreuzberg District Board. (See Abstract 11 in Appendix).

235   The massive piles of debris of the blown-up Prinz-Albrecht-Palais and the adjacent building, Wilhelmstrasse 103/104, as viewed from the former park in 1953.

236   Ruins of the south wing of the former *Gestapo* headquarters, in 1951.

237   **Käthe "Katja" Niederkirchner**, around 1936.
In the process of a renaming operation by East Berlin's municipal administration that affected over 150 streets in April and
May 1951, Prinz-Albrecht-Strasse became Niederkirchnerstrasse.
Käthe Niederkirchner (1909–1944), a seamstress by profession, had joined the German Communist Party in 1929 and
emigrated in 1933 to the Soviet Union. In October 1943 she
parachuted from a Soviet Russian plane into Poland, was arrested on her way to Berlin, taken to Concentration Camp Ravensbrück in the summer of 1944, and there was murdered on
September 22, 1944.

238   The air raid bunker of the former Reich Security Main Office shortly before it was torn down, in 1954.
Of *Gestapo* headquarters, only a segment of the street front was still standing at this particular time. After the demolition of what had remained of *Gestapo* headquarters, when all build-ings once used as administrative offices by *Gestapo* and SS between 1933 and 1945 had disappeared in June 1956, the plots in question were "cleared," i.e., the rubble removed and the ground levelled, during a second phase between 1957 and 1963.

239   Detail from an aerial photo of southern Friedrichstadt in 1955. After the demolition work of the late forties, the eastern side of the terrain was turned into an empty lot covered with debris. The buildings that had lined Stresemannstrasse, the Museum of Ethnology, and the Europahaus Compound, how-ever, are still completely intact. On Niederkirchnerstrasse only a part of the former *Gestapo* headquarters' frontal wing and the garage section put up by the *Gestapo* are still standing next to the ruins of the Gropius-Bau. The building's south wing, where the *Gestapo* Prison ("*Hausgefängnis*") was, has been torn down already.

240   Facade of the former *Gestapo* headquarters, in 1953. This picture, taken three years prior to the demolition of the remainder of the building, belies press reports issued in connection with the demolition that after 1945 "only a high outer wall" towered "ghostlike into the sky."

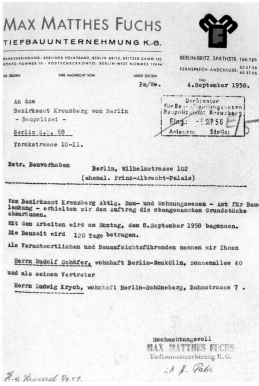

241   Blowing up the facade of the former *Gestapo* headquarters on June 15, 1956.

242   From the files of the Building Inspection Authority [*Baupolizei*] of the Kreuzberg District Board about the removal of
debris on the terrain between 1957 and 1963. (See Abstract
12 in Appendix).

243   With the exception of the plots along Niederkirchnerstrasse that have not yet been cleared of rubble, the terrain

between Anhalter Strasse and the Gropius-Bau has been
completely leveled.

244   The former Museum of Ethnology, corner Stresemann-
strasse/Niederkirchnerstrasse, in 1960.
During the first half of the fifties, the building was partly restored and was used after 1955 as the Museum for Prehistory
and Ancient History. It was demolished in 1963.

245   A drawing from the brochure "We are building a new
city," published around 1956 by the Kreuzberg District Board.
Under the heading "The future of urban development" the brochure reads: "A heliport is planned for the lot where formerly
Prinz-Albrecht-Park has been. Anhalter Bahnhof will be enlarged and will be given a new reception building [...]."

Contest "Capital Berlin" 1957

The Federal Republic and the Berlin Senate
shared the arrangement of an international urban
renewal contest of ideas, "Capital Berlin." The Federal Parliament had passed it in 1955, and in
1957 it was implemented. "The practical task of
the contest will be the rebuilding of Berlin's central part, so badly destroyed during the war; its
spiritual task will be to fashion the center in such a
way that it will become a visible expression of
Germany's capital and that of a modern metropolis." Thus reads the invitation to join the contest.
The area covered by the contest extended in a
west-easterly direction from the Tiergarten
(Großer Stern) to Jannowitzbrücke; the north-
south axis was formed by Friedrichstrasse in its
entire length. Thus, roughly one half of the area
covered by the contest was situated in the eastern
part of the city. The projected design included a
street network dominated by throughways (including four tangential *Autobahnen*) and a

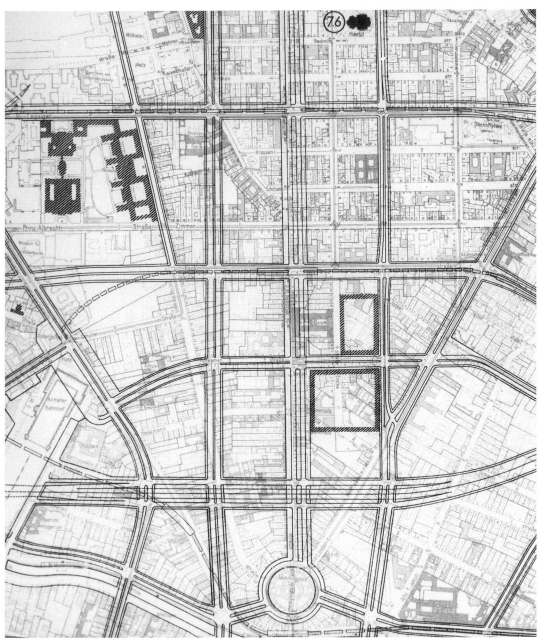

246   Planned design [*Planungsvorgabe*] by the Senate in connection with the contest "Capital Berlin" (1957).
The plan visualized by the Senate consisted of an integrated network of *Autobahnen* and expressways, a network that also would have included southern Friedrichstadt. Kochstrasse was to be widened and extended westward, across the terrain of the former Prinz-Albrecht-Palais. This project remained on the books until the beginning of the eighties and was only dropped at the initiative of the International Exhibition of Construction and Design, Berlin [*Internationale Bauausstellung Berlin*]. First prize at the time went to Spengelin/Eggeling/Pempelfort, a second prize was given to Hans Scharoun.

number of "fixed points." The latter were understood to be buildings that should be preserved either "because of their artistic or historical significance," or "because their preservation seemed desirable for financial or other reasons." Not included in either of these two categories were the Anhalter Bahnhof, the Europahaus, the Museum of Ethnology, or the Martin-Gropius-Bau.

247   Setting up anti-tank obstacles behind the Wall, at the
corner of Niederkirchnerstrasse, in November 1961.

248   "Studio at the barbed wire entanglement," fall of 1961.
The loudspeaker vans stand on the lot of the former School of
Industrial Arts and Crafts, until 1945 *Gestapo* headquarters.
The "wall behind the Wall" is all that remained of the building
up to that time. In the background are the burned-out ruins of
the Europahaus and the Martin-Gropius-Bau.

249   Aerial photograph of April 22, 1968.
In the center, that part of the Europahaus Compound which
was rebuilt in 1961 and named "House of the East German
Homeland" (today: "*Deutschlandhaus*"). It is situated at the
corner of Stresemannstrasse and Anhalter Strasse.

5.4. Return of a Repressed Past

The realization that the partition of Berlin had rendered invalid all plans that proceeded from the premise of a politically unified city gained ground only gradually in the years after the Wall was built. However, even as late as the seventies, the traffic projects for southern *Friedrichstadt* were not revised. Their execution was merely to be postponed, not abandoned. Thus, for nearly a decade and a half, the external appearance of the area bounded by Niederkirchnerstrasse, Wilhelmstrasse, and Anhalter Strasse was determined by such "interim usage" enterprises as a firm for the utilization of building materials and an "Autodrome" ("Driving without a license").

The first impetus for "rediscovering" the terrain's historic significance came at the end of the seventies from a historian of architecture, Dieter Hoffmann-Axthelm. When the attention of the "International Exhibition of Construction and Design, Berlin" [*Internationale Bauausstellung Berlin*, or *IBA*] was drawn by such information to the former use of the terrain, repeated opposition from this quarter against the projected beginning of work to widen Kochstrasse and to extend it westward, past the Martin-Gropius-Bau, was voiced in 1979/1980. Then, in 1980, various organizations began for the first time to demand that a memorial be erected on the terrain to honor the victims of Fascism. With the new utilization of the Martin-Gropius-Bau as an exhibition center, public attention was also directed to the neighboring terrain. The first exhibitions in the partly restored building were held in 1981. In August 1981, when the exhibition "Prussia — an attempt to take stock" opened, with a scenario adjacent to the Martin-Gropius-Bau right at the spot where the former *Gestapo* headquarters had been, this situation helped to recall facts to public consciousness that had lain dormant for decades. The then ongoing discussion of "how to deal with" the terrain was also influenced by the newly rekindled interest during the past years, particularly among young people, in the history of the National Socialist Regime. This led to a growing curiosity in the "history of everyday life" and local history, and with that an interest in research and documentation of the history of both the city and its various districts.

In 1982, after a debate over the subsequent form of the terrain in Berlin's parliament had occurred and a motion by the SPD to put up a memorial had been passed, preparations were made for a contest. Its sponsorship was assumed by Berlin's Lord Mayor, Richard von Weizsäcker; its execution was entrusted to the IBA. However, the task set by the contest which the City of Berlin had announced in June 1983 was problematic. For the contestants were expected to do justice to two contrasting demands; they were to come up with a creative solution which, as the invitation to the contest put it, "would reconcile the historic depth of a location with practical applications such as the establishment of parks, playgrounds, space for exercise, etc."

Whereas the contest aroused great interest, it met with strong criticism as to the way in which it was executed. In April 1984 the jury awarded a first price with the recommendation that the proposal be executed, and rewarded twelve additional entries. In December 1984 a letter from Lord Mayor Eberhard Diepgen informed the winners of the first prize that the Senate had resolved not to proceed with their contest proposal. Instead, the

Senator of Cultural Affairs assumed (temporarily) the responsibility for the terrain. The "provisional arrangement for the terrain by 1987" was entrusted to the authorized official in charge of Berlin's 750 Year Celebration and to the management of the central historical exhibition in the Martin-Gropius-Bau.

250   View from the Martin-Gropius-Bau in the direction of
Wilhelmstrasse, 1981.

251   Aerial photograph of the terrain between Stresemann-strasse, Niederkirchnerstrasse, Wilhelmstrasse, and Anhalter Strasse in 1984. Adjacent to the Gropius-Bau, at the right and along the Wall, a building material firm has been processing rubble from all over West Berlin since the early seventies. For the employees of the two telephone offices situated in the newly restored Europahaus, a parking lot was constructed behind the building.
The remainder of the former Prinz-Albrecht-terrain along Wilhelmstrasse and Anhalter Strasse was occupied by an "Autodrome" ("Driving without a license").

Text 81

Open Letter of January 24, 1980, from the International League for the Rights of Man to the Senator of Internal Affairs

Branch of the International League for the Rights of Man, New York,
accredited with the United Nations
Int. League for the Rights of Man, 1000 Berlin 12, Mommsenstrasse 27

Berlin, January 24, 1980

The ruins of the former Museum of Industrial Arts and Crafts on Niederkirchnerstrasse (formerly Prinz-Albrecht-Strasse 7) are presently being restored in view of the planned exhibit on Prussia. It is certainly the intention to refashion simultaneously the immediate environs (on this side of the Wall) within the framework of the projected construction — even if the result should merely be parking lots. It seems to have completely escaped the attention of those politicians responsible for our city that the building immediately next door, where prior to 1933 the School of Industrial Arts and Crafts had been (Prinz-Albrecht-Strasse 8), housed the infamous *Gestapo* headquarters during the period of Fascist dictatorship.

Prinz-Albrecht-Strasse No. 8 was a name that radiated fear and terror, since the *Gestapo* Center was known as a place where physical and mental brutality was practiced. After the Political Police had been turned into a terror weapon of the totalitarian state, men were systematically tormented and degraded in the torture basements at Prinz-Albrecht-Strasse 8. This was frequently followed by imprisonment in a German concentration camp.

When in 1981 old historic Prussia is commemorated with considerable public display, who will then remember those who were degraded and insulted and were made to suffer untold torments within the immediate neighborhood?

We do not know what plans the Senatorial Administration of Construction and Housing may have for the architectural design of the area in question. But regardless which project may ultimately be realized, THE INTERNATIONAL LEAGUE FOR THE RIGHTS OF MAN urges you, come what may, to remind people by way of a memorial or a commemorative plaque of this site where brown terror once held sway — and of its victims!

Wolfgang P. Schaar   E.M. Koneffke
                                        Anti-Fascist Committee

Text 82

Letter from the "Study Group of Persecuted Social Democrats" ["Arbeitsgemeinschaft Verfolgter Sozialdemokraten (AVS)"] of February 9, 1980, to the Senator of Construction and Housing

AVS Study Group of Persecuted Social Democrats
in the *Landesverband* [State Federation] Berlin of the SPD
Chairperson: Ruth Warnecke, 1000 Berlin 41,
Nordmannzeile 4   Tel: 885 5683

                              1 Berlin, February 9, 1980
To the Honorable
Senator of Construction and Housing
1000 Berlin 31
Württembergische Strasse 6

Subject: Reconstruction of a street connection to Potsdamer Strasse from Wilhelmstrasse to Stresemannstrasse

Sir:
Dear Senator,
In the matter indicated above, you have already heard the wishes of our study group during a personal conversation.
The Social Democratic resistance fighters and victims of the Nazi Regime expect that at the spot where the ruin of the Prinz-Albrecht-Palais once stood, i.e., the site where the *Gestapo* had its headquarters and tortured people, a dignified memorial be put up in remembrance of the National Socialist reign of terror. As your building administration is now collecting draft proposals required for commisssioning someone to construct and design such a memorial, the AVS Berlin requests participation in the appraisal of these draft proposals.
The former Prinz-Albrecht-Strasse should be renamed after the resistance fighter Carl von Ossietzky.
During a meeting that was held on January 28 by representatives of Central Study Groups of the Persecuted, a joint motion by our study group and the League of Politically and Racially Persecuted [*Bund politisch und rassisch Verfolgter* (PRV)] was unanimously adopted.
We ask you, Your Honor, to heed the wishes of the surviving victims of *Gestapo* persecution that a memorial become part of the road reconstruction project.
We are looking forward to your response.

With kind regards,
R. Warnecke

Text 83

Preface to Lord Mayor Richard von Weizsäcker's invitation to submit entries for the architectural contest; 1983

Reshaping the terrain where formerly the Prinz-Albrecht-Palais stood is one of the most important responsibilities our city faces, both for reasons of history and urban development. For better or for worse, Berlin is the custodian of German history, which here has left worse scars than anywhere else.
The terrain adjacent to the Marin-Gropius-Bau, which shall ultimately house a Museum of German History, contains visible and invisible traces of a heavy historic legacy: Invisible are the buildings from where the SS State operated its levers of terror. Visible is the Wall, cutting like a knife across the former Prinz-Albrecht-Strasse; and this we may well see as the nemesis of cynical power as it was practiced in this street during the National Socialist era.
As we go about reconstructing this area, it will be our task to proceed with contemporary history in mind while also providing a place for contemplation. Yet at the same time we must not miss the opportunity to give Kreuzberg District a terrain where life can unfold and leisure is possible. Moreover, the terrain must be integrated into the city at large. For it is not merely situated in Kreuzberg District and alongside the Wall; it also constitutes the central region as a part of southern Friedrichstadt with its enormous challenges to city planners.
Thus, the contest is of vital importance for our goal to attain Berlin's future without losing its past or repressing its evil features. It is not only as a sponsor that I take a lively personal interest in this remarkable contest.

The Contest "Berlin, southern Friedrichstadt, Reconstructing the terrain of the former Prinz-Albrecht-Palais" (1983)

194 entries were submitted. They showed in general the difficulties inherent in the objective to create a memorial which is to be used simultaneously as a city park. It also showed as a rule how problematic the proposed uses of symbolic and monumental solutions are in the reconstruction of a memorial site. While some of those who submitted entries have tried to deal with the contradictory demands by combining solutions, others decided to concentrate — at times in a rather

extreme way – on one of the objectives mentioned at the expense of all others.

Viewed as a whole, the entries submitted offered a remarkably wide range of solutions. Here, among others, are some of the suggestions:

- memorials as monuments, varying in their forms of expression,
- the creation of separate areas within the park, such as groves, public squares, lanes traversing the terrain, etc.,
- a reconstruction of history by means of a landscape of ruins, or by other ways of safeguarding traces (partly romanticizing, partly critically conceived),
- symbols and metaphors in the form of buildings or special landscaping (e.g., swastika/star of David, crater/eruption), either with or without water.
- preserving the terrain more or less as it is now, as a document of what has so far been repressed.

(From: Florian von Buttlar/Stefanie Endlich, Synopse zum Umgang mit dem Gestapo-Gelände [Synopsis of history and future of the Gestapo terrain], 1986).

Text 84

Some comments by Jürgen Wenzel and Nikolaus Lang, winners of the first prize, on the conception of their entry

If we proceed from a scenario of administered death as it was conceived, invented, planned, and organized on this terrain, then the site eludes all traditional, customary, "normal" criteria of design. [...] The draft design here submitted proceeds from this premise. The entire vacant site will be developed on the ground as a plane surface relief, consisting of cast-iron plates. Selected from a host of authentic documents [...], several thousands of them ... will be reproduced on such base plates [...]. These documents of anguish, inhumanity, injustice, and plain brutality will be mounted upon the foundations of the former *Gestapo* headquarters building, SS headquarters, and headquarters of the Security Service in such a way that there will be an outdoor document site suitable for walking and traversing. The ironclad, buried ground of this anti-site [*Ungelände*] will be set off by chestnut trees planted in double rows.

Text 85

Critical Comments on the Results of the Architectural Contest (1984–1986)
Ulrich Conrads (Editor-in-Chief of "Bauwelt")

The results of this contest can neither be described nor explained without revealing at the same time how it was achieved: everything was above board; the process was not accompanied by laxness or violation of rules; at times the discussions were intense and tough; the jury often worked close to the edge of exhaustion. But all this was simply not enough, because problems of communication, of language, of application were ignored in connection with a task where these aspects should have been the main focus.

Lore Ditzen (journalist)

The storm of ideas that swept across the terrain contained among currently fashionable methods of design also others which represented decidedly different approaches. Formalists shunning neither monumentality nor egocentric poetry have sounded off ... Sensitive skeptics of the younger generation pleaded against any formalist commitment and in favor of preserving what has so far been accomplished; this, they felt, would lead to open-mindedness in the future. Post-romantics want to seize the field in an effort to escape from reality into artificial metaphors ... Each individual idea, regardless of how absurd it may be, is an example of what is lurking in certain minds today ...

Ulrich Eckhardt (Director of Berliner Festspiele)

The result of the contest strongly reflects the dilemma inherent in the way it was posed. Whenever bad conscience is stirred up after a lengthy period of neglect and thoughtless repression, the reaction that follows is marked by overeagerness and mental contortions.

Gerhard Schoenberner (journalist, historian of the late modern period)

Whoever believed that mistakes made in the postwar era would be rectified in order to make up belatedly for what had been neglected earlier was wrong. It started with the text in which the invitation for the contest was phrased. It was formulated in vague and contradictory language and thus left many questions open ... There was no thorough and serious preparation. Those responsible failed to grasp – or grasped too late – that this was not a contest like any other; that routine alone would not do; that extraordinary efforts would be required ... It was indeed a very German tragedy that was performed here.

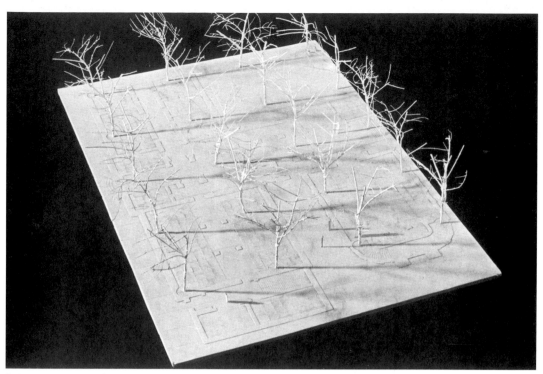

252

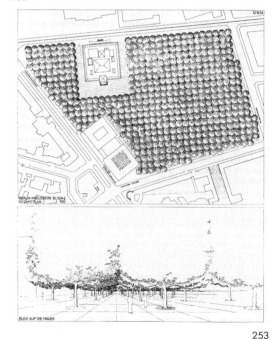

253

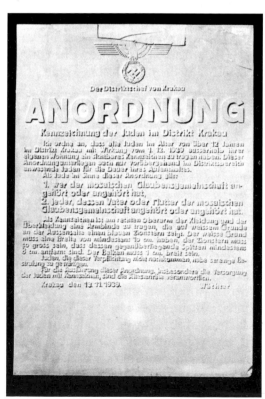

252–254   First prize: draft design by Jürgen Wenzel and Nikolaus Lang, Berlin. Master plan and view upon the Wall (253); model of how to mark the foundations (252); model of one of the projected iron plate markers (254) [Order by the Cracow District Chief, dated Nov. 13, 1939, stipulating that all Jews above the age of 12 must wear a distinguishing patch identifying them as Jews.].

254

Dieter Hoffmann-Axthelm (journalist, historian of architecture)

No memorial was then put there because one wanted to be rid of the site altogether. Now, on the other hand, we have prizewinning entries which, for their part, give the impression as if nothing whatever had been on that site before. 40 years of postwar history mark the place — but what has happened to them? ... That we now ... want to do it differently cannot possibly mean that we should act as if this were once again the Hour Zero and we should start from scratch, making decisions on how to deal with some local heritage left to us by Himmler's terror organization.

Hardt-Waltherr Hämer (architect, member of the Academy of Fine Arts)

We are accustomed to solve problems by creating projects. But this site is a memorial by definition. Memorials have only as much value as is embodied in the lives and thoughts of people ... I do not believe that this site can be turned into something functional, something intended for specific uses our city may require for its daily routine. Nor should it be appropriated by any particular groups, departments, or special interests.

Florian von Buttlar (architect)/Stefanie Endlich (sociologist)

(The contest) is generally considered a failure. This assessment, however, takes the easy way out and does not get to the heart of the matter ... While in regard to the future of the terrain beyond the 750 Year Celebration inofficial discussions are being held about a new contest, among other things a critical assessment of the first major enterprise of this kind is still lacking. Conversely, many important intellectual approaches, bits of information, and forms of participation have materialized, have stimulated successive deliberations, and could contribute to the quest for a suitable solution. To have them get lost in a drawer, as seems about to happen right now, would not merely be a default harmful to the matter at hand, it would also be an insult to the participants in the contest.

Text 86

Appeal by the Society "Aktives Museum Faschismus und Widerstand in Berlin" ["Active Museum of Fascism and Resistance in Berlin"] for a symbolic dig on May 5, 1985

Active Museum of Fascism and Resistance in Berlin, Inc.

1933–1945: LET'S DIG

Operation planned by the Active Museum and the Berlin History Workshop at the *Gestapo* cellars (adjacent to the Gropius-Bau)

The Active Museum of Fascism and Resistance in Berlin, Inc., and the Berlin History Workshop, Inc., will try to draw attention to the history of the terrain at Prinz-Albrecht-Palais at 11 a.m. on Sunday, May 5, 1985. This will be done by means of a commemorative operation on the site, and by a collage of texts by Jürgen Karwelat.

The approach of May 8, the anniversary of liberation from Nazi Fascism, prompts us to commemorate the resistance fighters who at immense sacrifice offered opposition to the Nazi Regime. Many of them were "interrogated" and tortured in the cellars of *Gestapo* headquarters, formerly the School of Industrial Arts and Crafts.

Supported by the anti-Fascist member organizations of Active Museum, we want to take an unequivocal stand on the significance of May 8. Furthermore, we demand that in future days a "site of contemplation" ["*Denk-Stätte*"] be built on the spot where the terror headquarters of German Fascism once stood. This way the experiences and insights gained from history will be passed on so that Fascism and war shall never again spring from German soil.

Support us. Join us!

Sunday, May 5, 1985
at 11 a.m., adjacent to Martin-Gropius-Bau (Stresemannstrasse, S-Bahn Anhalter Bahnhof; U-Bahn Möckernbrücke; B[us] 24, 29)

LET NO GRASS GROW OVER IT!

Active Museum of Fascism and Resistance in Berlin, Inc.   Berlin History Workshop, Inc.

255   View from Gropius-Bau in the direction of Wilhelmstrasse. In the foreground are the excavated remains of the
cellar floor of the *Gestapo* Prison ("*Hausgefängnis*"). On September 1, 1986, wreaths were placed there.

Text 87

Open Letter to the Lord Mayor by "Citizens Concerned with the History and Future of the Gestapo Terrain," December 9, 1985

Citizens Concerned with the History
and Future of the *Gestapo* Terrain
c/o Kunst-am-Bau Kommission Kreuzberg
Mariannenplatz 2
1000 Berlin 36

Berlin, December 9, 1985

The Honorable
Lord Mayor, Mr. Eberhard Diepgen
Rathaus Schöneberg
1000 Berlin 62

Sir:

Dear Lord Mayor:

On December 4 it was one year since you informed the first-prize winner of the contest on how to reconstruct the Prinz-Albrecht-Palais terrain that his draft design would not be realized. Since then, the Senate has not informed the public at all about any possible further steps it plans to take in the matter. The only announcement that was made referred to a provisional renovation of the terrain in time for Berlin's 750-Year-Celebration. A recent debate in Berlin's parliament [*Abgeordneten-haus*] has likewise failed to provide additional information.

There is growing concern that the Senate wants to resolve this vital reponsibility now faced by the city via administrative channels while excluding the public. The question of how to deal with the terrain cannot be resolved without competent deliberation. For here was the command center of the Nazi Regime, where every terror and persecution measure was planned and all murder operations were organized — both for Germany proper and for all countries which she occupied. Berlin's reputation at home and abroad may well be hurt by the manner in which this matter is presently being handled.

It is for exactly this reason that we have founded a group of concerned citizens [*Initiativgruppe*] to emphasize our joint demands more forcefully.

It is one thing for the Senate to ignore the decisions of an international jury which it had appointed itself and which even included two senators. But it cannot very well negate the international significance of the site. It [the Senate] was, and still is, obligated to make known the results of any new deliberations and to include the public in all subsequent planning procedures. What is required here is an international site of contemplation [*Denkstätte*] on a European scale, including a center with documents and exhibits (an Active Museum). All this will have to be discussed. Neither politicians, special administrative bodies, nor single individuals are competent by themselves to determine the terrain's future appearance, or to safeguard the still remaining traces of the state's former terror headquarters. This is simply not possible after a process of repression that has lasted forty years. This task can only be accomplished by a committee of Berliners and persons from outside the city whose members must combine varied expertise in the subject with genuine personal concern. It must be given an opportunity to investigate at home and abroad how similar sites have been dealt with elsewhere — thereby rectifying an omission of the previous contest — and step by step, in an ongoing process that includes dialogues with the public, to develop a solution to the problem. A public debate in the Academy of Fine Arts scheduled for early next year might well lead to the first steps of our work. We are inviting you right now to attend. Meanwhile we turn to you with the urgent request to see to it that the work presently done on the terrain be stopped at once. There have been numerous inquiries from various quarters on whether there were still remnants of walls that were part of the former SS and *Gestapo* building. The responses made by Senate officials have been demonstrably incorrect. As a result there is now the danger that these responses, based though they are on ignorance, will now belatedly come true, and the last remaining traces be totally eliminated.

In view of the significance and urgency of the matter, we beg your understanding of the fact that we are treating this communication as an Open Letter and are sending it, in two-day intervals, to the president of the *Abgeordnetenhaus*, the party delegations, and the media.

With kind regards,

Prof. Ottomar Gottschalk
Deutscher Werkbund Berlin, Inc.

Prof. Hardt-Waltherr Hämer
Akademie der Künste

Dr. Franz Freiherr von Hammerstein
Evangelische Akademie

Michael Pagels
Deutscher Gewerkschaftsbund Berlin

256 During the process of excavation prior to laying the foundation for the provisional exhibition building, the remnants of former cellars were unearthed in early March of 1987. According to inquiries made so far, they were part of a makeshift kitchen and supply building that was put up in 1943/1944 by the *Gestapo* or the SS, immediately adjacent to the courtyard of the *Gestapo* Prison ("*Hausgefängnis*"). The exhibition building was then placed on top of the excavated cellars, although with a different layout.

Ulrich Roloff-Momin
Hochschule der Künste Berlin

Prof. Walter Rossow
Deputy Chairman of the Jury

Prof. Dr. Eberhard Roters
Chairman of the Jury

Gerhard Schoenberner
Aktives Museum, Inc.

Krista Tebbe
Kunst-am-Bau Kommission Kreuzberg

P.S. While this letter was being written, we learned that you intend to have a discussion on the history and future of the *Gestapo* terrain at the beginning of January. In view of the significance and urgency of the problem, however, we decided to send to you our views on the matter in this official form.

Excavations and work for the preservation of traces were carried out on the terrain between July 23 and September 15, 1986. The work was initiated by the Senator of Cultural Affairs, was part of the concept of "provisional restoration" arrived at in 1987, and was carried out under the direction of architect Dieter Robert Frank. By the middle of August, the upper edges of the walls still intact were uncovered along Niederkirchnerstrasse, and thereafter also the basement walls along Wilhelmstrasse to corner Anhalter Strasse, including the remaining foundations of the Prinz-Albrecht-Palais. The most important find were the remnants of an addition built on top of the former *Gestapo* headquarters' lower basement floor [*Sockelgeschoß*]. The last layer of mortar, partly obliterated but still discernable, revealed the layout of some of the former cells of the "*Gestapo* Prison" that was established here in 1933.

5.5. The Interim Solution

In connection with Berlin's 750 Year Celebration in 1987, an interim solution was arrived at. The history of the SS and police in the former "Administrative Center of the SS State" was to be shown as "Topography of Terror," but without anticipating in any way future decisions that might yet be taken with respect to the terrain's use and design.

In response to pressures from citizens' action committees and political organizations, excavations and efforts to safeguard traces were made in the summer of 1986. Beneath the earth and rubble dumped there in the postwar period, fragments of building foundations, boundary walls and cellars emerged. They had escaped the "cleanup" of the terrain in the fifties and sixties. Among them was the floor of several cells in the lower basement of the "*Gestapo* Prison."

While clearing and "provisionally restoring" the entire terrain — roughly 62,000 square meters are involved — attempts were made to accentuate its special historic significance, but without eliminating the traces of the postwar history with its efforts to render invisible and to repress. Emphasis was placed on the character of the terror terrain as an "open wound" of the city, but also on the fact that it is a special place of commemoration and reflection about the origins and consequences of National Socialist domination.

Right at the spot, numerous informative signboards supply knowledge about the individual buildings and their functions during the "Third Reich." An observation platform on top of one of the remaining hills of rubble enables visitors in addition to gain an overview of the terrain as a whole and to place it in relation to Berlin's city structure. A special exhibit hall has been built next to the constructional fragments of prison cells to house the historical documentation. In the spring of 1987, the basement rooms of a former building that housed a canteen and kitchen facilities belonging to Prinz-Albrecht-Strasse 8 were discovered. They were put up, but also destroyed again, during wartime. To this spot the exhibit hall will be moved in order to point out the direct relationship that exists between the terrain and the historical documentation.

The interim solution, originally planned for only a few months, has meanwhile been indefinitely extended on account of strong public interest and the great number of visitors. During the first year alone more than 300,000 people of all age groups visited "Topography of Terror," among them many foreigners.

The debate on the entire terrain's future use and shape is being continued.

257 View across the northeastern part of the terrain, fall of 1987.   At the left, the "House of Ministries", at the center the television tower on Alexanderplatz.

258   Footpath through the terrain, fall of 1987. On the left is
the exhibition hall next to the Martin-Gropius-Bau.

259   A signboard with information relating to the terrain
stands in front of what remains of a former wall that belonged
to Prinz-Albrecht-Strasse 8; fall of 1987.

260   A hill built of rubble, with an observation platform over-
looking the terrain; summer of 1987.

261   The temporary exhibition building and the roofed over cell floors of the *Gestapo* Prison ("*Hausgefängnis*"), summer of 1987.

262   Visitors in the exhibition hall, summer of 1987.

263   View of both floors of the exhibition, summer of 1987.

264   Supports and walls of basement rooms belonging to an auxiliary building adjoining Prinz-Albrecht-Strasse 8. They were discovered in the spring of 1987 and utilized for the exhibition; summer of 1987.

6. Appendix

6.1. Abstracts of Selected Documents

Abstract 1 of Document in Illustration 57

Facsimile of the "Decree for the Protection of People and State," February 28, 1933

The page from the *Reichsgesetzblatt* in which the government published its laws states that on the basis of Article 48, Par. 2 of the Reich Constitution, the decree has been passed to counter Communist acts of violence. Several articles of the Constitution, i.e. those pertaining to freedom of the press, of movement, of free speech, of assembly as well as the inviolability of private letters, phone conversations, etc. are being suspended "until further notice." The Reich Government may temporarily assume control over any individual member state (*Land*) which fails to enforce the suspension of the civil rights listed above.
The administrations of the *Länder*, communities, etc. must carry out all directives issued under this decree by the Reich Government. Whoever puts a human life at risk because the decree was disregarded will be imprisoned in a penitentiary or, under extenuating circumstances, will be put in jail.
The death sentence will be imposed for high-treason, poisoning of public facilities, sabotage, arson and other major crimes. Anybody trying to assassinate the head of state, a member of the Reich Government or of a state (*Länder*) government will be sentenced to death, or receive a life sentence in a penitentiary, or will serve at least 15 years in a penitentiary. Similar penalties will be enforced against anybody who may start an armed insurrection or who deprives somebody of his liberty by holding him hostage during a political conflict. The decree becomes effective on the day of its announcement (Berlin, February 28, 1933).
Signed by
Reich President von Hindenburg, Reich Chancellor Adolf Hitler, Reich Minister of the Interior, Frick, and Reich Minister of Justice, Dr. Gürtner.

Abstract 2 of Document in Illustration 58

Facsimile of a Nazi newspaper report of a police raid on a left-wing artists' colony on Laubenheimer Platz, Berlin.

Under the heading "Now it's over," the article from *Illustrierter Beobachter* (Illustrated Observer) reports with undisguised sarcasm on the arrest of "Communist" artists in Berlin on March 15, 1933. According to the paper, Germany had not lost all its colonies by the Treaty of Versailles. Under the protection of Marxist "cultural politics" one of the most valuable colonies, the so-called "Berlin Artists' Colony," was founded in the Wilmersdorf district of the capital. But the barbaric and unintellectual new regime sent a police detachment to the colony on March 15 in order to surround the colony and to search it. Indeed, the boots of the policemen trampled upon the hallowed spirit of the "grand experiment of Bolshevism," to quote Thomas Mann. Where will the spirit henceforth find its home? It is an open secret, after all, that the left-wing Jewish intellectuals were Germany's only trump card it could play in the international battle of the intellects. And now German literature will lie fallow. Let's just look at the intellectual mugs of the "poets and thinkers" from this "artists' colony" which has been so suddenly raided, and it becomes obvious that they have no equals anywhere.

Abstract 3 of Document in Illustration 68

Facsimile of the front page of *Der Angriff*, June 30, 1934, on the so-called "Röhm *Putsch* (rebellion)" of that date.

Headline: "Hitler tears off the mutineers' rank insignia."
Subheading, left: "The activities of the conspirators were stopped with iron determination."
The article relates Hitler's secret preparations for dealing with the alleged Stormtroopers' (S.A.) plot and the way in which he concealed his own moves in order to mislead the "mutineers." It goes on to describe the nocturnal flight of Hitler and his entourage from the Rhineland to Munich where the Bavarian Minister of the Interior had already deprived two leading Stormtrooper commanders of their functions and had ordered all Stormtrooper units previously called out to go home again. Once Hitler arrived in Munich he witnessed the arrest of the two Stormtrooper commanders and personally stripped them of their rank insignia. Then he proceeded to Bad Wiessee where Stormtrooper Chief of Staff, Ernst Röhm, stayed with his companions. Hitler had him and other high ranking Stormtroopers arrested; there was no resistance. Returning to Munich, Hitler addressed a group of Stormtrooper commanders assembled at Bavaria's Ministry of the Interior and

came away with the conviction that only a handful of Stormtrooper leaders were participants in the plot; the bulk of the Stormtroopers, the article stated, stood solidly behind their Führer.

The article on the right is headlined: "Luxury will be eliminated. Higher penalties for SA-leaders than for non-National Socialists," is followed by the subheading: "[Hitler's] Charge to the new Chief of Staff." The article reports Hitler's set of instructions to Victor Lutze, Röhm's successor. Hitler demands blind obedience from every Stormtrooper and expects all SA-leaders to set a sterling example. Any leader who misbehaves in public will be expelled at once. Furthermore, frugality and modesty rather than conspicuous display shall henceforth govern the behavior of all leaders; thus, no gaudy parties, no luxury limousines. Anybody violating these instructions, whether leader or ordinary SA-man, is to be expelled at once from the SA. Conversely, all leaders will be expected to maintain and strenghten the spirit and good behavior of the units under their command, and to make sure that parents will not hesitate to let their sons join the Party, Hitler Youth or the Stormtroopers from fear that they be morally corrupted. Finally, Hitler calls for obedience, loyalty and comradeship among Stormtrooper units everywhere.
(Signed) Adolf Hitler

Abstract 4 of Document in Illustration 71

Facsimile of a notification about a summary execution on July 1, 1934.

The communication from the office of the "Political Police Commander of the Individual Member States" (*Länder*) informs one Frau Häbich in Stuttgart on January 18, 1935, in response to an inquiry she had sent on November 19, 1934, about the fate of her son, Walther. Her son had been shot on July 1, 1934, in connection with the Röhm revolt. As his execution took place in defense of the state, no further explanations are required.
Heil Hitler,
signature

Abstract 5 of Document in Illustration 77

Facsimile of a decree by Prussia's Minister President Göring of November 20, 1934, extending Himmler's authority as Director of the Secret State Police Office.

The decree is prefaced by a note from the Chief of the Secret State Police Office (Himmler), who draws the attention of all departments "in the house" to its contents and urges them to take notice. Göring's decree states that for technical reasons he has deputized the *Reichsführer-SS*, Himmler, to handle all affairs of the Prussian Secret State Police without further participation of the Prussian State Ministry. Himmler will be completely in charge and responsible only to Göring directly. All correspondence will go under the heading: "Prussian Secret State Police. The Deputy Head and Inspector" and will henceforth be directed exclusively to the Secret State Police Office, Berlin SW 11, Prinz-Albrecht-Strasse 8. Signed: Göring.

Abstract 6 of Document in Illustration 80

Facsimile of a notification by Heydrich to all Prussian State Police branches.

The notification, signed by Heydrich in his capacity as Himmler's deputy (Himmler was then Chief of the Secret State Police) went to all chiefs of the regional State Police branches in Prussia. It informs them of an order by Hitler's deputy, Rudolf Hess, issued on June 9, 1934, that as of July, 15, 1934, the Security Service of the *Reichsführer-SS* will be the only intelligence agency of the National Socialist Party. All other intelligence services still operating, whether openly so or clandestinely, must cease operations by that date. Infractions of this order must be reported at once to the Chief of Secret State Police.

Abstract 7 of Documents in Illustration 128 and 129

128: Fascimile of a memorandum by the State Police Office in Düsseldorf that it has placed a young man suspected of homosexuality into protective custody.

The person in question, a nineteen year old blacksmith's apprentice from Krefeld, was placed into protective custody for a period of seven days. The reason given was that he was strongly suspected of having engaged in homosexual acts with members of the Hitler Youth. The State Police requested that the period of imprisonment be extended.

129: Fascimile of an arrest report made by the *Politische Inspektion* Essen of the State Police on April 8, 1936.

The person arrested, a 46 year old chief inspector, was "temporarily" placed into the police prison at Essen, because he had violated Article 175 of the criminal code. (The article pertains to homosexual acts.)

Abstract 8 of Document in Illustration 142

Facsimile of a May 1934 front page of Streicher's anti-Semitic weekly, *Der Stürmer*.

The page carries the headline "Jewish murder plot against non-Jewish humanity revealed." The entire issue is dedicated to the "exposure" of so-called ritual murder perpetrated by Jews. The polemics in the left column deal with the "terrible suspicion" of what the Jews are up to. On the surface they are just usurers and peddlers — and Heinrich Heine is cited as the source for this statement — but in reality they are "devils in human garb." They have been charged with luring non-Jewish children and adults to places where they can be killed and their blood be used for making matzos (unleavened bread). In the process, the victims are being tortured. This, so *Der Stürmer* claims, is being reported about the Jews, not only in Germany but in other countries as well. The sources for these criminal acts, according to the weekly, are reports of witnesses who have passed their "knowledge" on to children and grandchildren and so forth, down to the present day. In short, the weekly carefully alleges the charges of ritual murder by citing oral tradition, hearsay, etc., while at the same time conveying (by implication) to the primitive reader that this is a story based on facts. The bottom line in bold print is a quotation from the 19th century Prussian historian Heinrich von Treitschke: "The Jews are our misfortune."

Abstract 9 of Document in Illustration 149

Facsimile of a letter by Heydrich of December 21, 1939, on Eichmann's appointment as Heydrich's "Special Section Manager"

The letter, directed to the responsible commanding officers of the Security Police, Security Service and SS Chiefs in key cities of eastern Germany pertains to the "evacuation (*Räumung*) of Germany's eastern provinces" which will require the active participation of Security Police forces. Heydrich informs the recipients of his letter that he has appointed for this particular task SS Captain Adolf Eichmann as his "Special Section Manager" with the Reich Security Main Office, Department IV. Then follows the address of Eichmann's Berlin office and the injunction to direct all correspondence via the Reich Security Main Office at Prinz-Albrecht-Strasse 8.

Abstract 10 of Document in Illustration 156

Facsimile of German notification of measures of reprisal taken against Poles in 1942.

In retaliation for an act of sabotage directed against a railroad in German occupied Poland, 20 Communists from three different localities were publicly hanged. More severe measures are announced should such an act of sabotage reoccur.

Abstract 11 of Documents in Illustration 232, 233, and 234

232: Facsimile of a letter from the Building Inspection Authority Kreuzberg to the Kreuzberg Office of Reconstruction, February 12, 1948.

The writer requests that the ruined buildings on Wilhelmstrasse 98–107, 118–125 be blown up as they constitute a public hazard.

233: Facsimile of an excerpt of a letter from the Senator for Construction and Housing to the Kreuzberg District Board, August 5, 1958.

In answer to the question of the Kreuzberg District Board whether the demolished Prinz-Albrecht-Palais had contained valuable architectural items, the Senator replied in a cautiously worded affirmative that there may have been indeed such items, including vases, architectural fragments, etc., that are buried now under the debris. Should such items ultimately surface, they should be placed in a warehouse or a museum. The Senator added that the building had been torn down for reasons of safety under the supervision of just said Kreuzberg District Board.

234: Facsimile of a letter by the firm Röhl KG to the Kreuzberg District Board, October 15, 1948.

The drill and blast firm Röhl KG confirms acceptance of the job to demolish the Prinz-Albrecht-Palais on Wilhelmstrasse 102, and refers to the bid the firm made on February 27, 1948, as the contractual basis for the job.

Abstract No. 12 of Document in Illustration 242

The firm Max Matthes Fuchs confirms on September 4, 1958 that it has been commissioned to remove the remains of the buildings at Wilhelmstrasse 102.

Work will begin on September 8, 1958 and will take 120 days.

6.2 Table of Ranks

Army	Police	Waffen-SS/Allg. SS	US/Brit. equivalent
Generalfeldmarschall	Reichsführer-SS und Chef der deutschen Polizei		general of the army
Generaloberst	Generaloberst	Oberstgruppenführer	general
General	General	Obergruppenführer	lieut. general
Generalleutnant	Generalleutnant	Gruppenführer	major general
Generalmajor	Generalmajor	Brigadeführer	brigadier general
no equivalent	no equivalent	Oberführer	no equivalent
Oberst	Oberst	Standartenführer	colonel
Oberstleutnant	Oberstleutnant	Obersturmbannführer	lieutenant colonel
Major	Major	Sturmbannführer	major
Hauptmann	Hauptmann	Hauptsturmführer	captain
Oberleutnant	Oberleutnant	Obersturmführer	1st lieutenant
Leutnant	Leutnant	Untersturmführer	2nd Lieutenant
Hauptfeldwebel	no equivalent	Sturmscharführer	sergeant major
Oberfeldwebel	no equivalent	Hauptscharführer	1st/master sergeant
Feldwebel	Meister	Oberscharführer	sergeant
Unterfeldwebel	Hauptwachtmeister	Scharführer	no equivalent
Unteroffizier	Rev.O. Wachtmeister	Unterscharführer	corporal
Stabsgefreiter	no equivalent	no equivalent	no equivalent
Obergefreiter	Oberwachtmeister	no equivalent	no equivalent
Gefreiter	Wachtmeister	Rottenführer	private first class/lance corporal
Oberschütze	Rottwachtmeister	Sturmmann	no equivalent
Schütze	Unterwachtmeister	SS-Mann/Staffelmann	private

6.3. Bibliography

The following titles do not represent a collection of historical literature that served as a basis for the documentation at the exhibition. Instead, it is a brief selection intended to facilitate further research and/or reading on the themes treated in the documentation. Besides works on the National Socialist era, a number of titles dealing with the history of city districts and individual buildings were included as well.

Adam, Uwe Dietrich. *Judenpolitik im Dritten Reich.* (Düsseldorf, 1979) (1st ed. 1972).

Akademie der Künste, ed. *Diskussion zum Umgang mit dem "Gestapo Gelände." Dokumentation.* (Berlin, 1986).

Aronson, Shlomo. *Reinhard Heydrich und die Frühgeschichte von Gestapo und SD.* (Stuttgart, 1971).

Bekiers, Andreas and Karl Robert Schütze. *Zwischen Leipziger Platz und Wilhelmstrasse. Das ehemalige Kunstgewerbemuseum zu Berlin und die bauliche Entwicklung seiner Umgebung von den Anfängen bis heute.* (Berlin, 1981).

Biller, Thomas und Wolfgang Schäche. "Zur historischen Entwicklung der Südlichen Friedrichstadt." In: *Dokumentation zum Gelände des ehemaligen Prinz-Albrecht-Palais und seiner Umgebung,* ed. Internationale Bauausstellung Berlin. (Berlin, 1983).

Birn, Ruth Bettina. *Die Höheren SS- und Polizeiführer. Himmlers Vertreter im Reich und in den besetzten Gebieten.* (Düsseldorf, 1986).

Boberach, Heinz. *Meldungen aus dem Reich. Die geheimen Lageberichte des Sicherheitsdienstes der SS 1938–1945.* (Herrsching, 1984).

Broszat, Martin. *Nationalsozialistische Polenpolitik 1933–1945.* (Stuttgart, 1965).

Broszat, Martin. "The Concentration Camps 1933–1945." In: Helmut Krausnick, Martin Broszat *et al.,* eds. *Anatomy of the SS State,* II. (New York, 1968).

Buchheim, Hans. "The SS. Instrument of Domination." In: Helmut Krausnick, Martin Broszat *et al.,* eds. *Anatomy of the SS State,* II. (New York, 1968).

Eiber, Ludwig, ed. *Verfolgung–Ausbeutung–Vernichtung. Die Lebens- und Arbeitsbedingungen der Häftlinge in deutschen Konzentrationslagern 1933–1945.* (Hanover, 1985).

Friedrich, Jörg. *Die kalte Amnestie. NS-Täter in der Bundesrepublik.* (Frankfurt am Main, 1984).

Giersch, Ulrich. "6 Stationen und ihr historischer Unterbau." In: Internationales Design Zentrum Berlin, ed. *Im Gehen Preussen verstehen. Ein Kulturlehrpfad der historischen Imagination.* (Berlin, 1981).

Graf, Christoph. *Politische Polizei zwischen Demokratie und Diktatur. Die Entwicklung der preussischen politischen Polizei vom Staatsschutzkorps der Weimarer Republik zur Geheimen Staatspolizei des Dritten Reiches.* (Berlin, 1983).

Hilberg, Raul. *The Destruction of the European Jews.* 3 vols. Revised and definitive edition. (New York-London, 1985).

Höhne, Heinz. *The Order of the Death's Head: The Story of Hitler's SS.* (New York, 1969).

Hoffmann, Peter. *Widerstand, Staatsstreich, Attentat. Der Kampf der Opposition gegen Hitler.* 4th rev. ed. (Munich, 1985) (1st ed. 1969).

Hohmann, Joachim S. *Geschichte der Zigeunerverfolgung in Deutschland.* (Frankfurt am Main, 1981).

Internationale Bauausstellung Berlin, ed. *Dokumentation: Offener Wettbewerb Berlin, Südliche Friedrichstadt. Gestaltung des Geländes des ehemaligen Prinz-Albrecht-Palais.* (Berlin, 1985).

Jäckel, Eberhard and Jürgen Rohwer, eds. *Der Mord an den Juden im Zweiten Weltkrieg. Entschlußbildung und Verwirklichung.* (Stuttgart, 1985).

Kempner, Robert M.W. *SS im Kreuzverhör. Die Elite, die Europa in Scherben schlug.* New enlarged ed. (Nördlingen, 1987) (1st ed. 1964).

Kenrick, Donald and Gratton Puxon. *The Destiny of Europe's Gypsies.* (London 1972).

Kogon, Eugen. *The Theory and Practice of Hell: The German Concentration Camps and the System behind them.* (New York, 1950).

Kogon, Eugen *et. al.,* eds. *Nationalsozialistische Massentötungen durch Giftgas. Eine Dokumentation.* (Frankfurt am Main, 1983).

Krausnick, Helmut and Hans-Heinrich Wilhelm. *Die Truppe des Weltanschauungskrieges. Die Einsatzgruppen der Sicherheitspolizei und des SD 1938–1942.* (Stuttgart, 1981).

Langbein, Hermann. *Menschen in Auschwitz.* (Vienna, 1972).

Pätzold, Kurt, ed. *Verfolgung, Vertreibung, Vernichtung. Dokumente des faschistischen Antisemitismus 1933 bis 1942.* (Leipzig, 1984).

Pingel, Falk. *Häftlinge unter SS-Herrschaft. Widerstand, Selbstbehauptung und Vernichtung im Konzentrationslager.* (Hamburg, 1978).

Projektgruppe für die vergessenen Opfer des NS-Regimes, eds. *Verachtet-verfolgt-vernichtet. Zu den 'vergessenen' Opfern des NS-Regimes.* (Hamburg, 1986).

Ramme, Alwin. *Der Sicherheitsdienst der SS. Zu seiner Funktion im faschistischen Machtapparat und im Besatzungsregime des sogenannten Generalgouvernements.* (Berlin, 1970).

Roon, Ger van. *Widerstand im Dritten Reich. Ein Überblick.* 4th rev. ed. (Munich, 1987) (1st ed. 1979).

Rückerl, Adalbert. *NS-Verbrechen vor Gericht. Versuch einer Vergangenheitsbewältigung.* 2nd. rev. ed. (Heidelberg, 1984) (1st ed. 1982).

Rückerl, Adalbert. *NS-Vernichtungslager im Spiegel deutscher Strafprozesse.* 3rd ed., (Munich, 1979) (1st ed. 1977).

Scheffler, Wolfgang. *Judenverfolgung im Dritten Reich 1933–1945.* (Berlin, 1987) (1st ed. 1960; engl. special ed. 1961).

Schmädecke, Jürgen and Peter Steinbach, eds. *Der Widerstand gegen den Nationalsozialismus. Die deutsche Gesellschaft und der Widerstand gegen Hitler.* (Munich, 1985).

Schoenberner, Gerhard. *Der gelbe Stern. Die Judenverfolgung in Europa 1933–1945.* (Frankfurt am Main, 1982) (first ed. 1960; rev. ed. 1978).

Sievers, Johannes. *Bauten für die Prinzen August, Friedrich und Albrecht von Preußen. Ein Beitrag zur Geschichte der Wilhelmstrasse in Berlin (Karl Friedrich Schinkel Lebenswerk).* (Berlin, 1954).

Studien zur Geschichte der Konzentrationslager. (Stuttgart, 1970).

Tuchel, Johannes and Reinold Schattenfroh. *Zentrale des Terrors. Prinz-Albrecht-Strasse 8: Das Hauptquartier der Gestapo.* (Berlin, 1987).

Wegner, Bernd. *Hitlers politische Soldaten: Die Waffen-SS 1933–1945.* 2nd ed. (Paderborn, 1983) (1st ed. 1982).

Zipfel, Friedrich. *Gestapo und Sicherheitsdienst.* (Berlin, 1960).

Zülch, Tilman, ed. *In Auschwitz vergast – bis heute verfolgt. Zur Situation der Roma (Zigeuner) in Deutschland und Europa.* (Reinbek, 1979).

6.4. Abbreviations

AR — Amtsrat [approx. Administrative Councilor]

AVS — Arbeitsgemeinschaft verfolgter Sozialdemokraten [Study Group of Persecuted Social Democrats]

BA — Bundesarchiv [Federal Archive]

BdS — Befehlshaber der Sicherheitspolizei und des Sicherheitsdienstes [Chief of Security Police and Security Service]

Begl. — Beglaubigt [witnessed, certified]

Brif. — Brigadeführer [Brigadier General]

CdS — Chef der Sicherheitspolizei [Chief of Security Police]

CDU — Christlich Demokratische Union [Christian Democratic Union]

CSU — Christlich Soziale Union [Christian Social Union]

DAF — Deutsche Arbeitsfront [German Labor Front]

DDP — Deutsche Demokratische Partei [German Democratic Party]

dergl. — dergleichen [such]

ders. — derselbe [the same]

EK — Einsatzkommando [Special Unit]

FDJ — Freie Deutsche Jugend [Free German Youth]

FS — Fernschreiben [telegram; telex]

geb. — geboren [born]

Gestapa — Geheimes Staatspolizeiamt [Secret State Police Office]

Gestapo — Geheime Staatspolizei [Secret State Police]

gez. — gezeichnet [signed]

GmbH — Gesellschaft mit beschränkter Haftung [Corporation or Association with limited liability]

g.Rs. — Geheime Reichssache [Top Secret]

Hauptstuf, HStuf — Hauptsturmführer [SS Captain]

Hg., hg. — Herausgeber, herausgegeben [editor, edited]

HKL — Hauptkampflinie [main line of resistance]

IBA — Internationale Bauausstellung Berlin [International Architectural Exhibition, Berlin]

KD — Kriminaldirektor [Director of Criminal Investigation Department]

Kdo — Kommando [Command; Commando]

KDS, KdS — Kommandeur der Sicherheitspolizei und des Sicherheitsdienstes [Commander of Security Police and Security Service]

KJVD — Kommunistischer Jugendverband [Communist Youth Association]

KK — Kriminalkommissar [Chief Inspector in the Criminal Investigation Department]

KL — Konzentrationslager [concentration camp]

KPdSU — Kommunistische Partei der Sowjetunion [Communist Party of the USSR]

Komintern — Kommunistische Internationale [Communist International]

Komm. — kommunistisch [Communist]

KPD — Kommunistische Partei Deutschlands [German Communist Party]

KR — Kriminalrat [Chief Inspector Superintendent in the Criminal Investigation Department]

Kripo — Kriminalpolizei [Criminal Police]

KZ — Konzentrationslager [concentration camp]

lfd. — laufend [current; consecutive]

lit. — litauisch [Lithuanian]

MG — Maschinengewehr [machine-gun]

MP — Maschinenpistole [submachine gun]

NS — Nationalsozialismus, nationalsozialistisch [National Socialism, National Socialist]

NSDAP — Nationalsozialistische Deutsche Arbeiterpartei [National Socialist German Workers' Party]

Ober-Gr.F. — Obergruppenführer [SS Lieutenant General]

Oberscharf. — Oberscharführer [SS Sergeant]

Oberstuf — see OStuf

OKH — Oberkommando des Heeres [Army High Command]

OKW — Oberkommando der Wehrmacht [High Command of the Armed Forces]

ORR — Oberregierungsrat [Senior Executive Officer]

OStubaf — Obersturmbannführer [SS Lieutenant Colonel]

OStuf — Obersturmführer [SS First Lieutenant]

PR — Polizeirat [Police Councilor]

RA — Regierungsassessor [Assessor working for the government]

RdErl. — Runderlass [circular letter containing orders or regulations]

R.Deutscher — Reichsdeutscher [Citizen of the German Reich — 1937 borders]

Ref. — Referat; Referendar [lecture or report; candidate for higher civil service]

Reg.-Ass. — see RA

RFSS — Reichsführer-SS [Head of the SS, i.e. Heinrich Himmler]

RFSSuChdDt-Pol i.RMdI — Reichsführer-SS und Chef der Deutschen Polizei im Reichsministerium des Innern [Head of the SS and German Police in the Reich Ministry of the Interior]

RGBl. — Reichsgesetzblatt [National Register of Published Laws]

RKPA — Reichskriminalpolizeiamt [Headquarters of the Reich Criminal Police]

RM — Reichsmark [Reichsmark: German currency until 1948]

RNSt — Reichsnährstand [Agency representing farmers, agricultural laborers and crop gardeners]

RR — Regierungsrat [Administrative Councilor]

RSHA — Reichssicherheitshauptamt [Reich Security Main Office]

RSMO — Reich Security Main Office [see also RSHA]

russ. — russisch [Russian]

SA — Sturmabteilung [Stormtroopers]

SAJ — Sozialistische Arbeiterjugend [Socialist Working Class Youth]

SAP — Sozialistische Arbeiterpartei [Socialist Workers Party]

Schupo — Schutzpolizei [Municipal Police]

SD — Sicherheitsdienst [Security Service]

SED — Sozialistische Einheitspartei Deutschlands [German Socialist Unity Party]

SichPoludSD — Sicherheitspolizei und des SD (Kommandeur, Befehlshaber usw. der ...)

	[... Security Police and Security Service (Head, Commander etc. of ...)]
Sipo	Sicherheitspolizei [Security Police]
SJVD	Sozialistischer Jugend-verband Deutschlands [German Socialist Youth Association]
SPD	Sozialdemokratische Partei Deutschlands [German Social Dem-ocratic Party]
SS	Schutzstaffel [lit.: Protec-tion Squadron]
Staf	Standartenführer [SS Colonel]
Stalag	Stammlager (Kriegsge-fangenenlager) [prisoner of war camp]
Stapo	Staatspolizei [State Police]
StPO	Strafprozessordnung [code of criminal proce-dure]
Stubaf	Sturmbannführer [SS Major]
Unterscharf.	Unterscharführer [SS Corporal]
Unterstuf.	see UStuf.
USPD	Unabhängige Sozialde-mokratische Partei Deutschlands [German Independent Social Democratic Party]
UStuf	Untersturmführer [SS Lieutenant]
VO	Verordnung [decree; ordinance; order]
VVN	Vereinigung der Verfolg-ten des Nazi-Regimes [Association of Persons Persecuted by the Na-tional Socialist Regime]
Wachtmstr.	Wachtmeister [Private First Class; Lance Corpo-ral]
W.V. Haupt-amt	Wirtschafts-Verwal-tungs-Hauptamt [Main Office of Economy and Administration]
ZK	Zentralkomitee [Central Committee]

6.5. Sources of Texts

Text 1	Armin G. Kuckhoff, ed. *Hans Otto. Gedenkbuch für einen Schauspieler.* (Berlin, 1948), p. 83.
Text 2	*Reichsgesetzblatt* (RGBI) Part 1, 1934, No. 71, p. 529.
Text 3	*Preußische Gesetzsamm-lung,* 1933, No. 29, p. 122.
Text 4	*Preußische Gesetzsamm-lung,* 1933, No. 74, p. 413.
Text 5	*Preußische Gesetzsamm-lung,* 1936, No. 5, pp. 21–22.
Text 6	*Reichsgesetzblatt* (RGBI), Part 1, 1936, No. 55, p. 487.
Texts 7–8	BA, Koblenz, R. 58/239.
Text 9	Heinz Boberach, ed. *Meldungen aus dem Reich 1938–1945. Die Geheimen Lageberichte des Sicherheitsdienstes der SS,* vols. 12 and 13. (Herrsching, 1985).
Text 10	BA, Koblenz, R 58/245.
Text 11	Johannes Tuchel and Reinold Schattenfroh. *Zentrale des Terrors. Prinz-Albrecht-Strasse 8: Hauptquartier der Gestapo.* (Berlin, 1987), pp. 167–169.
Text 12	Johannes Tuchel (see Text 11), pp. 190–191.
Text 13	Institut für Marxismus-Le-ninismus beim Zentralko-mitee der Sozialistischen Einheitspartei Deutsch-lands, ed. *Ernst Thäl-mann. Eine Biographie,* 5th ed. (Berlin, 1985), pp. 674–675.
Text 14	Erich Honecker. *Aus mei-nem Leben.* (Berlin, 1982), pp. 128–129.
Text 15	Heinz Schröder. *"Olle Icke" erzählt. Über Wi-derstand, Strafdivision und Wiederaufbau.* (Berlin, 1986), pp. 49–51.
Text 16	Johannes Tuchel (see Text 11), p. 223.
Texts 17–18	BA, Koblenz, R 58/242.
Text 19	BA, Koblenz, R 58/241.
Texts 20–21	BA, Koblenz, R 58/1027.
Text 22	BA, Koblenz, R 58/272.
Text 23	BA, Koblenz, R 58/1027.
Text 24	BA, Koblenz, NS 17, LSSAH/57.

Text 25	*Reichsgesetzblatt* (RGBI), Part 1, 1935, No. 100, pp. 1146–1147.
Text 26	Reimund Schnabel. *Macht ohne Moral. Eine Dokumentation über die SS,* 2nd ed. (Frankfurt am Main, 1959), pp. 78–79.
Text 27	*Reichsgesetzblatt* (RGBI), Part 1, 1938, No. 189, p. 1579.
Text 28	Wolfgang Scheffler. *Ju-denverfolgung im Dritten Reich 1933–45.* (Frank-furt am Main-Vienna, Zu-rich, n.d.), pp. 163–164.
Text 29	Internationaler Militär-gerichtshof. *Der Prozeß gegen die Hauptkriegs-verbrecher.* (Nuremberg, 1947–1949), vol. XXXIII, pp. 534–536.
Text 30	N. Blumental, ed. *Doku-menty i Matrialy z cza-sow okupacji niemieckie w Polsce,* vol. III. (Łodz, 1946), pp. 203–206.
Text 31	*Reichsgesetzblatt* (RGBI), 1941, No. 133, pp. 722ff.
Texts 32–33	H.G. Adler. *Die verheim-lichte Wahrheit. There-sienstädter Dokumente.* (Tübingen, 1958).
Text 34	privately owned by Wolfgang Scheffler.
Text 35	Wolfgang Scheffler, *Judenverfolgung im Dritten Reich 1933–1945.* (Berlin, 1964), p. 80.
Texts 36–40	BA, Koblenz, RD 19/28–15.
Text 41	T. Berenstein, A. Eisen-bach, A. Rutkowski, eds. *Faschismus, Ghetto, Massenmord. Dokumen-tation über Ausrottung und Widerstand der Juden in Polen während des Zweiten Welt-krieges,* publ. by the Jewish Historical Insti-tute at Warsaw, 2nd ed. (Berlin, 1961), pp. 37.
Text 42	BA, Koblenz, R 58/242.
Text 43	*Faschismus, Ghetto, Massenmord* (see Text 40), pp. 42–43.
Text 44	Hauptabteilung I des Stabshauptamtes des Reichskommissars für die Festigung deutschen Volkstums, ed. *Der Men-scheneinsatz. Grund-sätze, Anordnungen, Richtlinien* (Berlin, 1940).

Text 45 privately owned by Wolfgang Scheffler.

Text 46 Internationaler Militärgerichtshof (see Text 28). Document PS-3363.

Text 47 *Das Schwarze Korps,* August 20, 1942.

Text 48 *Faschismus, Ghetto, Massenmord* (see Text 40), p. 303.

Text 49 privately owned by Wolfgang Scheffler.

Text 50 BA, Koblenz, R 58/241.

Text 51 BA, Koblenz, R 58/240.

Text 52 privately owned by Wolfgang Scheffler.

Text 53 Irene Sagel-Grande, H.H. Fuchs and C.F. Rüter, eds. *Justiz und NS-Verbrechen. Sammlung deutscher Strafurteile wegen nationalsozialistischer Tötungsverbrechen 1945–1966,* vol. XIX, No. 552/31. (Amsterdam, 1978).

Text 54 privately owned by Gerhard Schoenberner.

Text 55 privately owned by Wolfgang Scheffler.

Text 56 *Justiz und NS-Verbrechen* (see Text 52), 552/1.

Text 57 privately owned by Gerhard Schoenberner.

Text 58 Politisches Archiv des Auswärtigen Amtes (Political Archive of the Foreign Office), Bonn/Inland II g 177.

Texts 59–62 privately owned by Wolfgang Scheffler.

Text 63 Randolph L. Braham. *The Destruction of the Hungarian Jews. A Documentary Account.* (New York, 1963).

Text 64 privately owned by Wolfgang Scheffler.

Text 65 Alfred Konieczny and Herbert Szurgacz, eds. *Documenta occupationis,* vol. X.. (Poznan, 1976), p. 17.

Text 66 Horst Eberhard Richter. *Flüchten oder Standhalten.* Reinbek, 1976.

Text 67 Karl Heinz Biernat and Luise Kraushaar. *Die Schulze-Boysen/Harnack-Organisation im antifaschistischen Kampf.* (Berlin, 1972), p. 157.

Text 68 Günter Weisenborn. *Memorial.* (Berlin, 1948).

Text 69 Robert Havemann. *Ein deutscher Kommunist. Rückblicke und Perspektiven aus der Isolation.* (Reinbek, 1978), p. 54.

Text 70 Fabian von Schlabrendorff. *Offiziere gegen Hitler.* (Berlin, 1984), pp. 138–139.

Text 71 Josef Müller. *Bis zur letzten Konsequenz. Ein Leben für Frieden und Freiheit.* (Munich, 1975), pp. 220–221.

Text 72 Georg Thomas. "Gedanken und Ereignisse," *Schweizer Monatshefte* 25 (1946), No. 9, pp. 550–551.

Text 73 Franz Lange. Interview, Radio DDR, 1966 (copy of a tape).

Text 74 Hans Speidel. *Aus unserer Zeit. Erinnerungen.* (Berlin, 1977), pp. 222–223.

Text 75 Heinz Hentschke. "Die letzten Stunden in der Reichskanzlei," *Tägliche Rundschau,* May 8, 1946.

Text 76 Wassilij Tschuikow. *Das Ende des Dritten Reiches.* (Munich, 1966).

Text 77 privately owned by Bernhard Horstmann, Nuremberg.

Text 78 Internationaler Militärgerichtshof. *Der Prozeß gegen die Hauptkriegsverbrecher.* (Nuremberg, 1947–1949), vol. XX, pp. 139–140.

Text 79 Adalbert Rückerl. *NS-Verbrechen vor Gericht.* (Heidelberg, 1982), pp. 137–138.

Text 80 Günther Weisenborn. *Der gespaltene Horizont. Niederschriften eines Außenseiters.* (Munich-Vienna-Basel, 1964), pp. 160–161.

Texts 81–82 privately owned by Sabine Weißler, Berlin.

Texts 83–85 Internationale Bauausstellung Berlin GmbH, ed. *Dokumentation Offener Wettbewerb Südliche Friedrichstadt. Gestaltung des Geländes des ehemaligen Prinz-Albrecht-Palais.* (Berlin, 1985).

Texts 86–87 privately owned by Sabine Weißler, Berlin.

6.6. Sources of Illustrations

The numbers given refer to the illustrations, not to the pages.

Berlin, Amerika-Gedenkbibliothek (Collection of Postal Cards): 30, 35.

–, Berlin Document Center: 83–89, 91, 92.

–, Bezirksamt Kreuzberg, Stadtplanungsamt: 232–234, 238.

–, Bildarchiv Preußischer Kulturbesitz: 2, 4, 23–24, 41, 52, 55, 60, 64, 69, 76, 79, 111, 114, 131, 133, 136, 138, 139, 141–144, 148, 154, 165, 168, 186, 188–191, 193–197, 198–201, 204, 219, 226.

–, Thomas Friedrich: 20, 21, 25.

–, Gedenkstätte Deutscher Widerstand: 122.

–, Willi Gleitze: 105.

–, Brigitte Häntsch/Peter Arnke: 99–101.

–, Falk Harnack: 103, 173.

–, Brunhild Hesse: 123.

–, Walther Höppner (†): 107.

–, Kupferstichkabinett SMPK (Jörg P. Anders): 16–19.

–, Landesarchiv Berlin: 27, 42, 43, 97, 217, 242.

–, Landesbildstelle: 1, 10, 12, 28, 29, 32, 33, 213, 215, 218, 224, 231, 247, 249.

–, N. Leonhard: 95, 214.

–, Margret Nissen: 255–264.

–, Marianne Reiff-Hundt: 182.

–, Wolfgang Scheffler: 166.

–, Gerhard Schoenberner: 132, 134, 138, 140, 150, 153, 155–157, 159.

–, Heinz Schröder: 120, 121.

–, Senator für Bau- und Wohnungswesen: 211, 239, 251.

–, Gerhard Ullmann: 250.

–, Ullstein Bilderdienst: 8, 36, 37, 47, 49, 54, 59, 67, 74, 78, 90, 93–94, 106, 108, 113, 117, 118, 119, 124, 137, 145, 160, 161, 163, 175, 178, 179, 181, 202, 203, 208, 210, 220–222, 227, 228, 236, 240, 241, 243, 244.

–, Edith Walz: 104.

–, Marion Gräfin Yorck von Wartenburg: 192

–, Willy Zahlbaum: 209.

Bonn, Archiv der sozialen Demokratie: 110, 112, 115, 127, 170.

Dachau, KZ-Gedenkstätte Dachau: 71.

Düsseldorf, Nordrhein-Westfälisches Hauptstaatsarchiv: 128, 129

Frankfurt am Main, Albrecht Pünder: 116.

Heidelberg, Zentralrat deutscher Sinti und Roma: 147.

Koblenz, Bundesarchiv/Bildarchiv: 65, 73, 77, 80–82, 98, 102, 113, 149, 185, 187, 216.

Mannheim, Jan Foitzik: 171.

Marbach a.N., Schiller-Nationalmuseum/Deutsches Literaturarchiv: 230.

Munich, Bilderdienst Süddeutscher Verlag: 6, 38, 44, 46, 48, 60, 62, 63, 72, 109, 126, 146, 158, 162, 205, 206.

Warsaw, Glwna Komisja Badania Zbrodni Hitlerowskich w Polsce: 130.

Publications:

Amt für Stadtplanung [im Bezirksamt Kreuzberg], ed. *Wir bauen die neue Stadt. Die städtebauliche Neugestaltung der Luisenstadt im Bezirk Kreuzberg.* (Berlin, n.d. [1956]): 236.

Architekten- und Ingenieurverein zu Berlin, ed. *Berlin und seine Bauten,* part VIII, *Bauten für Handel und Gewerbe,* vol. B, *Gastgewerbe.* (Berlin-Munich-Düsseldorf, 1980): 147.

Max Arendt and Paul Torge, *Berlin. Einst und jetzt,* 2nd ed. (Berlin, 1934): 11.

Auschwitz. Camp hitlérien d'extermination. (Varsovie, 1986): 163.

Baugewerkszeitung, 1881: 26.

Internationale Bauausstellung Berlin, ed. *Dokumentation zum Gelände des ehemaligen Prinz-Albrecht-Palais und seiner Umgebung.* (Berlin, 1983): 15.

Internationale Bauausstellung Berlin, ed. *Dokumentation Offener Wettbewerb Berlin, Südliche Friedrichstadt. Gestaltung des Geländes des ehemaligen Prinz-Albrecht-Palais.* (Berlin, 1985): 243–245.

Andreas Bekiers and Karl-Robert Schütze. *Zwischen Leipziger Platz und Wilhelmstrasse. Das ehemalige Kunstgewerbemuseum zu Berlin und die bauliche Entwicklung seiner Umgebung von den Anfängen bis heute.* (Berlin, 1981): 39, 96.

Heinz Bergschicker. *Berlin. Brennpunkt deutscher Geschichte.* (Berlin, 1965): 237.

Berliner Architekturwelt, 1909/1910: 31.
Berlin. Planungsgrundlagen für den städtebaulichen Ideenwettbewerb "Hauptstadt Berlin". (Bonn-Berlin, 1957): 237.

Karl-Heinz Biernat und Luise Kraushaar. *Die Schulze-Boysen/Harnack-Organisation im antifaschistischen Kampf.* (Berlin, 1970): 168, 176.

Berta Braune. *Hoffnung gegen die Not.* (Wuppertal, 1982): 165.

Martin Broszat. *Nationalsozialistische Polenpolitik 1939–1945.* (Schriftenreihe der VfZ, Stuttgart 1961): 152

Deutsche Bauzeitung, 1913: 34.

Deutsche Illustrierte Zeitung, 1933: 69.

Deutsche Widerstandskämpfer 1933–1945, vol. 2 (Berlin, 1970): 65, 228.

Anne Freyer and Jean-Claude Pressac, eds. *L'album d'Auschwitz.* (New York, Toronto, 1981): 160.

Harri Günther. *Peter Joseph Lenné. Gärten, Parke, Landschaften.* (Berlin, 1985): 22.

Wolfgang Haney. *Berlin gestern, heute, morgen.* (Berlin, 1950): 203.

Heute. Eine illustrierte Zeitschrift, 1947: 170.
Werner Hilgemann. *Atlas zur deutschen Zeitgeschichte 1918–1968.* (Munich, Zurich, 1984): 50.

Heinz Höhne. *Der Orden unter dem Totenkopf. Die Geschichte der SS.* (Gütersloh, 1967): 51 (simplified reproduction).

Illustrierter Beobachter, 1932: 45.

Illustrierter Beobachter, 1933: 57.

Information Services Division. Office of the US High Commissioner for Germany, ed. *Landsberg. Ein dokumentarischer Bericht.* (Munich, 1951): 220.

Kartenwerk des Hauptvermessungsamtes Berlin, 1935–1941: 3, 5, 7, 9 (with additional entries).

Neue Berliner Illustrierte, 1946: 214.

Neue Gesellschaft für bildende Kunst, ed. *Der umschwiegene Ort.* (Berlin, 1986) 173.

Der Prozeß gegen die Hauptkriegsverbrecher vor dem Internationalen Militärgerichtshof Nürnberg, 14. November 1945 bis 1. Oktober 1946, vol. XXXVI. (Nuremberg, 1949): 52.

Schäfer. *Konzentrationslager Oranienburg.* (Berlin, n.d. [1934]: 134.

Gerhard Schoenberner. *Der gelbe Stern. Die Judenverfolgung in Europa 1933 bis 1945.* (Gütersloh, 1960): 131.

Johannes Sievers. *Bauten für die Prinzen August, Friedrich und Albrecht von Preußen. Ein Beitrag zur Geschichte der Wilhelmstrasse in Berlin [Karl Friedrich Schinkel Lebenswerk].* (Berlin, 1954): 235.

Stimme des Freidenkers, 1983: 180.

Georg Thomas. *Geschichte der deutschen Wehr- und Rüstungswirtschaft (1918–1943/45).* (Boppard a.Rh., 1966): 199.

Hansgeorg Trurnit, ed. *Das neue Berlin. Stadt der Olympischen Spiele.* (Berlin, n.d. [1936]): 13.

Wasmuths Monatshefte für Baukunst, 24: 40.

6.7. Index of Names